D0319784

SPORTS STAMPS

CARL-OLOF ENHAGEN

SPORTS STAMPS

★

STANLEY PAUL
London

STANLEY PAUL & CO. LTD
178–202 Great Portland Street, London, W.1

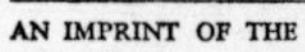

AN IMPRINT OF THE HUTCHINSON GROUP

London Melbourne Sydney
Auckland Bombay Toronto
Johannesburg New York

First published 1961

This book has been set in Times New Roman type face. It has been printed in Great Britain by The Anchor Press, Ltd., in Tiptree, Essex, on Antique Wove paper and bound by Taylor Garnett Evans & Co., Ltd., in Watford, Herts

Contents

CONTENTS

APPENDIX

Illustrations

BETWEEN PAGES 128 AND 129

Introduction

Philately—also called 'the king of hobbies and the hobby of kings'—is perhaps the oldest and most wide-spread of hobbies, and one of its liveliest and popular branches is the collecting of stamps with sports motifs. Sports philately is a comparatively new hobby, but has enjoyed a rapid rise to popularity in recent years. Nowadays, specialization is the key-word in all walks of life, and this also goes for philately. Nothing could be more natural to the sports-minded youth of today than to collect sports stamps.

Besides uniting interest in sport with that of philately, this field of collecting offers the advantage of gathering together a good collection without prohibitive cost, something which hardly applies to other special collections. It is, however, difficult and hazardous to start a new form of collection, and from the beginning there is a great need for guidance, and catalogues; at least that was my own experience.

When I started there were, however, no such catalogues available, and up to the present there is still no complete work in English on this subject. As interest in sports philately seems to be high in the English-speaking countries, judging by letters received since I started my sports stamps articles in *World Sports* ten years ago, an English handbook and catalogue is justified—and indeed necessary.

Many articles on this subject have appeared in the philatelic press and ideas on how to collect sports stamps have been many, various—and contradictory! It has therefore been my aim to collect these ideas together to present them as fairly as possible, together with advice and information. In order to meet every taste I have listed the sports stamps in the following three ways: design (sports), alphabetically (nations) and chronologically (series).

If this book is able to help the sports philatelist in the arrangement of his collection, or to give him information about the various stamps and sports, thus saving him time and perhaps money, I will have succeeded in my aim. This little manual is therefore warmly dedicated to all collectors of sports stamps.

Part One

SCOPE AND DESIGN

1. SPORTS PHILATELY

Development and Future

Sports philately is a comparatively new hobby. The information that the oldest sports stamps are more than sixty years old may therefore come as a surprise to many people. It was—fairly enough—Greece, the home of the Ancient Olympic Games, who pioneered the issuing of sports stamps, the earliest appearing in connection with the first Olympic Games of the modern era held at Athens in 1896. This start could certainly not be called a modest one, as the series contained no less than twelve stamps, all with classical designs.

There was, however, no rapid development in the issue of sports stamps, and Greece still retained her position as the only sports stamps nation in 1906, when a new series of fourteen stamps appeared to honour the tenth-anniversary Olympic Games, also in Athens. Even these stamps had ancient Olympic motifs. Except for one single Peruvian stamp of 1907, showing a hippodrome, there appeared no sports stamps until 1920 when Belgium issued three stamps to commemorate the Olympic Games of Antwerp. Classical designs were also used here, as well as on the Olympic stamps of 1924 issued by France, Uruguay and Costa Rica.

In 1925 something new happened to sports philately. Hungary issued the first sports series ever with modern designs. Furthermore, the stamps were not issued in connection with any special event, as previously, but solely for the benefit of sport, this being accomplished by means of a special surcharge of 100 per cent. Today these stamps may look a little old-fashioned, but no doubt they must have caused a small revolution in the world of stamps at the time.

Strangely enough, Hungary's example was not followed immediately, and sports stamps appeared only sporadically in the 1920's. It was, instead, the 1930's that saw the birth of real sports philately.

Every year produced its crop of sports stamps, with 1935 and 1939 as the best years, fifty-eight and fifty-four stamps then being issued, respectively.

The first half of the 1940's marked quite naturally a decline, because of the war, but the total of this decade is about the same as that of the preceding one, due to the last two years. The Olympic year of 1948 was a milestone in the issue of sports stamps, as the curve of output began to climb rapidly. In the 1950's more than 100 different stamps were issued each year, and in 1960 a new record was established with over 300 new sports issues. The postal authorities in many countries have noticed the great interest in sports philately and they have accordingly started to issue sports stamps, often depicting well-known sportsmen, in many cases with the sole purpose, unfortunately, of enriching their treasuries.

This does, however, mean that those who have chosen sports stamps collecting as their hobby will have no 'spare time' problems.

Not only has the number of sports stamps rapidly increased during the past ten years, but this period has also seen an immense growth in the number of collectors, and many of them have even become organized. In this way thematic collecting—of which our hobby is a branch—has been given a firmer basis by the international association F.I.P.C.O. (Fédération Internationale de la Philatélie Constructive), which has made rules for the judging of thematic collections in exhibitions.

Furthermore, four big international sport exhibitions have now been held; the first in Rome in 1952 being a turning point in sport philately, as it gave rise to an international sports stamps paper—the *Sport-Phila*, issued in Rome in five languages—and a yearly medal—the Bonacossa Medal—for the Best Sports Stamp of the Year. This medal is named after Count Alberto Bonacossa, famous Italian figure-skating champion and member of the International Olympic Committee. Bonacossa, who died in 1952, was probably the world's first and greatest sports stamps collector and sponsored the first exhibition. An international jury consisting of twenty-three members decides, according to technique, appearance, design, printing and so on, what stamp should be awarded the medal. The first medal went to Luxemburg in 1952 for a stamp showing hurdlers. In conjunction with this yearly award there are also extra prizes for various sports.

Another very vigorous branch of sports philately is the collecting of special sports cancellations, which are far more frequent than the stamps themselves and have increased tremendously in numbers during the past years. There were forty-seven and fifty-two different cancellations for the Cortina and the Melbourne Olympics, respectively!

Sports propaganda labels to be used on mail in connection with sports events are also rousing the interest of many sports philatelists.

Arrangement of Collection

The sports collector here faces one of his biggest problems. How is the collection to be arranged? Much has been written on this topic and from the ideas put forward three main principles can be deduced, viz. collecting country by country in alphabetical order, collecting the various series in chronological order of issue and collecting stamps according to the sports depicted in the designs. Within the framework of these principles individual taste may flourish and several combinations are possible. In the following some advantages and disadvantages of the different systems will be considered.

The usual method of stamp collecting—under countries in alphabetical order—might seem the most natural one to many collectors. This system gives you a comprehensive view of the sports stamps of the various countries, and series are kept together unbroken. The chronological system shares the latter advantage and gives you also an interesting survey of the development of sports stamps over more than half a century. A strictly followed chronological method is, however, harder to achieve because of the risks of overlooking some series.

The two basic plans mentioned above have, however, one disadvantage in common, and that is a big one. The real object of collecting—the design—is swamped in the many large series. The usual orthodox way of collecting that has helped millions is thus an obstacle when collecting thematic stamps. It is the design that has attracted you to collect sports stamps—therefore it should be the centre of your interest, and be the foundation upon which the collection is based.

This method is also the most interesting one, giving you opportunity to study and collect your favourite sports and see how they have appeared on stamps from many parts of the world. It is also the most trying and risky one, demanding a great deal of knowledge from its practitioner. But as the desire for knowledge is one of the factors that influence you in taking up a hobby this ought not to be a disadvantage. There is, however, one drawback—the fact that the series have to be split up into their various sports. This you have to face in order to build up a thematic sports collection. It must be mentioned here that F.I.P.C.O. gives recognition only to collections built up in this way, as far as exhibitions are concerned.

Most sports stamps do not present any problems as to the distribution among the different events, which suitably could be placed in alphabetical order. In a few cases, however, there could be some debate about which sport the designer meant to picture, and these will be dealt with later on. When there are two or more sports pictured on one stamp the dominating one has the precedence, i.e. diver (Hungary 1925), runner (France 1937), shot-putter (Albania 1946) and so on.

Many sports stamps have no specific sports design, and for these we have to find a formula. There are many solutions, but here is one that still functions satisfactorily: four groups (or sections)—roughly called 'Sports Events', 'Sports Grounds', 'Sports Parades' and 'Sports Propaganda'—that gather the remaining stamps in a series.

Under 'Sports Events' are placed stamps bearing no specific sporting design issued in connection with a special event. No explanation is needed for the second and third groups, the latter being more or less reserved for the Eastern European countries. 'Sports Propaganda' contains those stamps which have nothing to do with any special event or topic.

Some of the different events can be grouped together under general headings such as athletics, ski-ing, equestrian sports, flying and aquatic sports. In order not to split the beautiful and interesting Olympic issues I suggest a special 'Olympic Games' section, which means that one stamp may appear twice in a complete collection, once under 'Olympic Games' and once under the specific event depicted.

What has been said above about the arrangement of a sports collection should be regarded as a guide for the new collector. The collector who has already devised his special system, and likes it, should keep on that way; it is the individual touch which gives a collection its real pleasure—and attractiveness.

2. THE SCOPE OF THE COLLECTION

What Constitutes a Sports Stamp?

Here is another question at least as hard to answer as that in the preceding chapter. There are and always will be different opinions as to what should be regarded as sports. Nor will any attempt be made to answer this question here—it would be impossible anyway!

One of the reasons for the different views on 'what is sport?' is the value this particular word has in different languages. In English it is often used in a wider sense, embracing outdoor life and pastimes, whereas the same word in other European languages is very often restricted to competitive sports. This difference in interpretation may explain the English, or rather American, inclination towards a wider form of sports stamps collecting.

In an American stamp magazine some years ago it was even suggested that stamps picturing fish (like cod, herring, salmon, etc.) could be introduced to a sports collection, as they could be fished. The same went for all kinds of animals that could be hunted. This is, I think, going a little too far. In order to solve this problem another American sports collector differentiated between 'sports stamps', meaning competitive ones, and 'sporting stamps', which covered everything else remotely connected with sport, from the animal stamps mentioned above to Queen Elizabeth and President Roosevelt (who are and were interested in horse-racing and sailing, respectively!).

Let us start with the assumption that all competitive sports should be included. To this group belong most sports stamps, so this will cause no trouble. Difficulty begins with the sports that are not definitely competitive in character, such as mountaineering, long-distance flights, parachuting, flying model aircraft, gymnastics in general and so on. A general rule could be applied here, saying that if a stamp is issued for sporting reasons it may be included. The Roumanian and Russian mountaineering stamps both formed part of a sports series and are thus included, whereas an Italian alpinist stamp of 1934 shows mountain-climbing as a military necessity. This also applies to hand-grenade throwing (Russia 1940) and parachuting—a popular sport in Eastern Europe—when regarded as sports but not as military exercises. Military ski patrols, when not issued in connection with sport, are similarly excluded.

All forms of gymnastics, on the other hand, should be included, though lacking competitive character.

Now for the really borderline cases. Should scouting be included? It is true that certain sports issues, like those of Hungary in 1925 and Nicaragua in 1949, have had scouting designs, but this great movement should be regarded as something independent, fully deserving to be the subject of a collection of its own. Consequently, I have not included scouting in the main part of the book.

Another controversial case is that of air pioneers and long-distance flyers. Should they be included as prominent sportsmen, or would it not be better to regard them as discoverers of a new era? The latter is perhaps to be preferred, so avoiding the field of collecting becoming too large and unwieldy.

Many collectors include designs showing children playing under the heading 'Play and Pastimes'. It may often be hard to decide whether a stamp depicts play or sport (cf. Netherlands 1949), and a few of these cases are dealt with in the chapter 'The Fringes of Sports Philately' (p. 220). Chess also belongs to this group. Sticking to the general rule these designs should not form a part of a sports collection as they do not represent competitive sports.

Sports stamps with personal motifs deserve special mention. If you keep strictly to the principle that persons who are known chiefly for their sports activity should be included in a sports collection, you will have no difficulties whatsoever. Using this principle, Baron Pierre de Coubertin (founder of the Olympic Games), P. H. Ling (founder of Swedish Gymnastics) and M. Tyrš (founder of the Czech Sokol Movement) are safe for a place; whereas King Albert I of Belgium and Pope Pius XI (mountaineering), King Gustav V of Sweden (tennis), King Olav V of Norway (yachting) and Nansen (ski-ing) are open to question, though sometimes suggested in philatelic papers.

In this connection the question of provisional stamps must also be dealt with. Many sports stamps have been issued with surcharges for changed denomination. Since this does not mean a new sports stamp a place in the collection is not necessary, provided the surcharge has nothing to do with a special sports event or the like. The same goes for the overprinting of country names, e.g. the Aegean Islands on Italian football stamps 1934 and the British on the Olympic series 1948.

Reasons for Sports Stamp Issues

The first sports stamps were inspired by the Olympic Games, and many still are. Every Olympic year means a greater output of sports stamps, the number of Olympic stamps now exceeding 500. Many of them have been issued to collect funds for the expensive Olympic teams. Since 1920 all Summer Olympics have been commemorated with stamps, and Winter Olympics are represented since 1932.

Speaking about Olympics, it must also be stated that the word 'Olympic' has been misused on stamps, especially on those from Latin America (cf. Costa Rica 1924, Dominican Republic 1937, Nicaragua 1937 and Ecuador 1939), against the decrees of Baron de Coubertin but in accordance with modern advertising.

Big sporting events being the chief reason for the issue of stamps, there are, apart from the Olympics, stamps to commemorate—and advertise—world championships in different sports and national and international games. The Balkan Games are very popular with the stamp designers and the World Football Championships have all been honoured on stamps, with the exception of the first one.

The Japanese Sports Games appeared on stamps for the first time in 1947, and have been marked in this way regularly every year since. The same applies to the so-called Peace Cycle Race which passes through Poland, Czechoslovakia and East Germany. The first stamp to celebrate this event was issued in 1948. The Monte Carlo Rally results in a new stamp each year, picturing the different routes to Monte Carlo, and this will no doubt go on for several years.

Most of these stamps have been issued to celebrate a particular event, but others have been produced for purely financial reasons with surcharges for different sports purposes. The money raised in this way has gone to the Olympic team or to the building of stadiums or just simply to 'funds'. The first examples of this were the Portuguese Olympic stamps of 1928, which were issued to finance Portugal's team to go to Amsterdam. The income from the giant issue of Nicaragua in 1949 went to a newly built stadium, and the German equestrian stamps before the war kept horse-breeding going as well as Hitler's cultural fund.

The postal authorities of less scrupulous 'stamp' nations, noticing the big interest in sports stamps and their unmistakable financial importance, have started to issue big sports series, often depicting well-known sportsmen. The best examples of this are the five latest issues of the Dominican Republic picturing Olympic winners. In order to enrich her treasury further, the republic produced her stamps in special sheets and with several variations.

Another reason for sports issues is sports propaganda itself. Typical examples are the Soviet issues—quite naturally as the U.S.S.R. often uses stamps in education. Another good example is the big Chinese radio-gymnastics series, with forty different stamps issued to instruct the people in various gymnastic movements.

On the other hand there are many stamps with sporting designs which form part of ordinary issues having no direct connection with sports. Many of these designs have been chosen to show the importance of sport in daily life (e.g. yachting). Anniversaries of persons or sports federations have also contributed to the increasing output of sports stamps.

Sports Stamps Countries

That sport nowadays belongs to everyone and is world-wide is a well-known fact which is reflected in the world of stamps. About 100 different countries from all parts of the world have paid their tribute to sport on stamps. There are not many nations left now which are unrepresented, and it is far easier to mention the few exceptions than those which are included in this book.

Only one country remains unrepresented in Europe at the time of writing, Andorra. In America only Chile is left, but since the World Football Championships will be held there in 1962 this will probably not be the case for long.

In Africa there are a larger number of countries as yet unrepresented, like South Africa, Ethiopia and some of the new states. Ghana, Morocco, Togo, Guinea, Malagasy and Tunisia have all joined in the sports 'stampede' in 1960. Especially strange is the fact that the 'Springboks', always keen on sports and with good Olympic records, have not been commemorated on any issue of sports stamps.

Asia is also well represented with a few South-East Asian and Arab nations left outside.

As for the fifth continent, Australia, as well as New Zealand and even Fiji, has got a place in sports philately.

Where do most sports stamps originate? A careful analysis shows that the East European countries are dominant. This is no surprise, since these nations are not only among the most industrious in issuing all kinds of stamps but also take great interest in sports, an interest which has resulted not only in sports stamps but also in many victories and records.

Russia comes first with more than 130 stamps, followed by Roumania and Germany (totals for the two parts being combined as in the Olympics) with over 100 each. Then come all the East European nations, like Hungary, Bulgaria, Poland, Czechoslovakia and Yugoslavia, with between 80 and 100 each. China (thanks to her gymnastics stamps) is next; followed by 'stamp' nations like the Dominican Republic, San Marino, Monaco and some Central American countries, together with Japan, Greece and Italy. Great Britain, the 'home of sport'—and its successor, the United States—are far behind.

3. THE DESIGN

The Choice of Design

The most interesting thing about a sports stamp is the design itself. More than seventy different sports and sporting events are represented on stamps. Not surprisingly, the most popular sports like athletics and football also predominate among sports stamps.

Starting with athletics, it is obvious that discus-throwing is one of the favourite events depicted, thanks chiefly to the popular 'Discobolus' statue by Myron. The track events are quite naturally popular, steeplechasing being the last and smallest member of the family, with only two stamps. Among the field events the throws dominate with jumps well behind. Only in recent years have the jumping events come into their own. Of the field events, hammer-throwing (4) and hop, step and jump (1) have the smallest number of stamps.

There is an astoundingly big output of female athletic stamps, representing all the ladies' events, even the Swedish *slungboll*, now obsolete in the championships.

Walking—eight stamps—is less well represented than might be expected, while the rather odd (to put it mildly!) sport of hand-grenade throwing has one representative.

Football (soccer) is the dominating ball game, both in reality and on stamps, but other ball games, like basketball and baseball, are also well represented. Tennis, which then follows, is not so popular among stamp designers nowadays as it once was, but its younger brother, table tennis, is rapidly gaining ground. Ice hockey is also amongst the most popular games on stamps. Rugby and volley ball are represented too, and in recent years hockey, pelota, handball and badminton have appeared. More unusual games like hurling—predecessor to hockey—roller hockey and softball—a variant of baseball—are also pictured, whereas popular sports like cricket, bowling and golf have not yet appeared.

Other sports with a great output of stamps are competitive gymnastics, in which all the events have been depicted, and equestrian sports. Of the latter, horse-racing, trotting, riding (show-jumping and three-day event) and polo are represented, with the dressage event still missing.

One remarkable thing shown by the statistics is the great frequency of winter-sports stamps, especially ski-ing in all its branches. Despite the fact that ski-ing is limited by natural reasons in space and time, it takes an advanced position in sports philately. Also represented are most other winter sports, like speed- and figure-skating, ice yachting, bobsleigh-tobogganing (even from Togo!) and ice hockey, already mentioned above. The only winter sports still missing are curling, skating with sails, and bandy, the latter very popular in Northern Europe and Russia.

Among water sports yachting takes pride of place, chiefly due to its appearance in many non-sports series. Rowing is also popular, with all classes represented, though canoeing has only recently attained any interest. Swimming and diving are also old favourites and water polo is becoming more and more popular.

Motor sports, especially motor-cycling, have a good position, with the exception of motor-boating, which has only two representatives—from Russia (!) and Roumania. Cycling is one of the foremost sports depicted on stamps, with regular issues each year, thanks chiefly to the Peace Cycle Race in Poland.

The 'fighting' and 'power' sports are well in evidence, with fencing, wrestling, boxing and weight-lifting. Judo is also seen on two Japanese stamps. Flying present a rich variety of designs, from balloon-sailing to parachuting.

Archery and shooting occur less often on stamps, though the latter is represented by rifle-, pistol- and clay-pigeon-shooting. Even the modern pentathlon has one stamp to itself.

Finally, some national sports are pictured, like the Afghan *buzcashi*, Malayan *bersilat*, Burmese *chinlon*, Icelandic *glima*, Swiss *hornussen* and so on.

Well-known Sportsmen on Stamps

Pictures of well-known scientists, artists, authors and politicians of bygone days have been seen on stamps for the past seventy-five years, but to see your own favourite sportsman—still living and mentioned by name—on your mail would have been more or less incredible only a few years ago. It all started after the Melbourne Olympics, when the Dominican Republic began to issue a series depicting famous Olympic champions through the ages, and followed this by four others picturing Olympic victors of 1956.

Depicting famous sportsmen on stamps is not, however, a new idea. If you look at the stamps close enough you will find that designers and engravers have often found their inspiration in the world around them, basing their designs on actual photographs. One of the oldest examples of this you will find on a Colombian stamp of 1935, where you can see the famous duel in the 5,000 m. in the 1912 Olympics between H. Kolehmainen, Finland, and J. Bouin of France, who in 1960 was commemorated on a French stamp.

A photograph of the American discus-thrower and Olympic champion of 1936, Carpenter, inspired no less than three stamps—France 1937, Finland 1940 (not issued) and Japan 1947. The design of one Turkish stamp of 1940 was based on a picture of Meadows, the Olympic pole-vault champion. The copy is exact except for a piece of plaster on his left leg.

Two hurdlers—the Frenchman J. Arifon and the American women's champion N. Cowperthwaite—were both within a few months reproduced on stamps from Monaco and Yugoslavia. The American badge on the girl's suit has been changed to the Yugoslavian one.

Other examples of the 'foreign loans' are the women's downhill champion of 1936, Christl Cranz, Germany, on an Austrian stamp in 1936; the Soviet women's discus world-record holder, Nina Dumbadze, on a Czech stamp in 1951; and the Oxford University rowing eight on a Monaco stamp in 1948. The same University's rugby team was also honoured on a Japanese stamp in 1953.

The latest examples of 'photographic' stamps are the 1960 football stamps of Costa Rica, which show various teams, Hungary and Sweden among them. The same Viennese printing firm were also responsible for the Haitian Olympic set, for which the Austrian Olympic team provided the basis for one of the designs.

Sportsmen of the stamp designers' own home country have naturally inspired them more frequently, though—often because of rules against depicting living persons on stamps—they have refrained from making the likeness too exact. Thus the model for the U.S. Olympic stamp of 1932, showing a sprinter at his starting blocks, was a Californian student athlete J. A. Le Coney, his face being made unrecognizable. Finnish sports stars—Nurmi, Järvinen, Heikinnen (ski-ing), Saarvala (gymnastics) and wrestler Friman—are reproduced in a series of 1945. In a French sport series of 1953, honouring her Olympic victories of the previous year, you can easily trace Mimoun and the two cousins d'Oriola (fencing and show-jumping).

Emil Zatopek and his wife Dana Zatopkova can be seen on Czech stamps in 1955 and 1954 respectively, while Sweden's famous ace skier, Nils Karlsson, was no doubt used as the model for the design of the World Ski Championship stamp of 1954.

On four Turkish stamps of 1949, marking the European Wrestling Championship in Ankara, actual photographs of Turks and Swedes in action are used. Here you will find famous wrestlers like Dogu and Akar of Turkey, and Grönberg and Pettersén of Sweden.

Joaquin Blume, the Spanish gymnast and European champion, was killed in an aeroplane crash in 1959 and commemorated on two stamps in 1960.

The famous Dynamo eleven was honoured on Russian stamps on two different occasions in 1948 and 1949.

The South American women's sprinting champion of 1938, Carola Castro of Ecuador, is honoured on a stamp her country issued the year after.

A Japanese women's skating champion—Estu Ibaraki—can be seen on a beautiful stamp of 1949.

Soviet sports stars from Melbourne were honoured in 1957 with action pictures very much resembling those taken at the Olympic Games. They show Vladimir Kuts, gymnast Victor Chukarin and women's javelin-thrower Irene Jaunzeme.

The Polish women's long-jump gold-medallist and world-record holder (6·35 m.), Elzbieta Krzesinska, was also commemorated on a special stamp after the Melbourne Games. In the Polish 1960 Olympic set seven Polish medal-winners from four different Games—including Krzesinska—were honoured.

Also depicted on the stamps of their home countries in 1959 and 1960 were the high-jumpers Iolanda Balas (Roumania) and Lansky (Czechoslovakia).

But not only recent Olympic champions are pictured on stamps. Some of the most famous sportsmen from the Ancient Games in Olympia have also appeared; like Milon from Kroton, who was considered the best athlete in five Games between 540 and 516 B.C. He is pictured on one French Olympic stamp of 1924 breaking up a tree-trunk, an allusion to his disastrous death. Milon, the strongest man of his time, according to a legend tested his strength on a tree-trunk split by wedges. He became trapped however when the halves closed in, and fell a victim to wild animals.

Another ancient Olympic hero—Diagoras from Rhodes, and champion in boxing 464 B.C.—is pictured on a Greek stamp in 1937 in his most glorious hour, being carried by his two sons Akusitaos, champion boxer, and Damagetos, pancration (mixture of boxing and wrestling) champion, at the 83rd Olympic Games in 448 B.C.

The link between the ancient and the modern Olympic Games was the French Baron de Coubertin, who founded the International Olympic Games Committee in 1894. He was honoured by three stamps issued by Haiti (!) in 1939, but not until 1956 was his picture used on the stamps of his own country.

Among other sports leaders to figure on stamps: the respective founders of Swedish Gymnastics, P. H. Ling; the Czech Sokol Movement, M. Tyrš; and the German Turnen, F. L. Jahn.

Until recently the active sportsmen had appeared more or less anonymously on stamps, but after the Central American initiative—provided by Guatemala (two national soccer heroes), the Dominican Republic (five Olympic sets) and Haiti (Silvio Cator, Haitian world-record holder in broad jump—7·93—thirty years ago)—you can expect almost anything in the way of sports favourites on stamps.

The Dominican list of Olympic heroes so far contains the following names: Fanny Blankers-Koen, Jesse Owens, Kitei Son, Lord Burghley, Bob Mathias, Paavo Nurmi, Ugo Frigerio and Mildred Didrickson (all athletics) of earlier Olympic Games. The 1956 Olympic champions pictured are Lars Hall (modern pentathlon), Betty Cuthbert, Eigil Danielsen, Alain Mimoun, Norman Read, Robert Morrow, Chris Brasher and A. Ferreira da Silva (all athletics) in the first series; and Gerald Ouellette (shooting), Ron Delany (athletics), Tenley Albright (figure-skating), Joaquin Capilla (diving), Ercole Baldini (cycling), Hans Winkler (riding), Alfred Oertler and Shirley Strickland (athletics) in the second triangular-shaped series; the third series was devoted to Gillian Sheen (fencing), Milton Campbell (athletics), Shozo Sasahara (wrestling), Madeleine Berthod (downhill ski-ing), Murray Rose (swimming), Charles Jenkins and Tom Courtney (relay race), the Indian hockey team and the Swedish yachting team, respectively. Her latest set honours Gholam Takhti (wrestling), Mauru Furukawa (swimming), Mildren McDaniel (athletics), Terry Spinks (boxing), Carlo Pavesi (fencing), Pat McCormick (diving), Mithat Bayrak (wrestling) and Ursula Happe (swimming).

Sports Stamps Aesthetics

After having dealt with the reasons for issuing and the choice of designs, we have not far to look for the ways the designers have chosen for solving their problems. Sports philately shows a plentiful variety of ideas, ranging from brave but unsuccessful attempts to real beauties.

On one side one must consider composition, printing and choice of colour, and on the other style.

Most sports stamps, like the majority of modern stamps, are recess printed with photogravure predominant. It is here, quite naturally, that most of the loveliest stamps are to be found, and the rich possibilities for shades of colours that go with this form of printing have been successfully exploited. The best are those from the Swiss printing firm, Courvoisier, which has received two Bonacossa Medals (e.g. stamps from Switzerland, Liechtenstein and Luxemburg, 1952; the Turkish wrestlers of 1949).

Other beautiful productions are the Japanese regular sports issues, the Austrian ski-ing stamps of 1933 and 1936, Italy's soccer stamps of 1934 and the San Marino issue of 1955.

Among steel-engraved stamps, the Olympic issues from Greece 1906, Germany 1936 and Monaco 1948 offer good examples. Austria (1946 and 1948), some Swedish stamps and the excellent Belgian issue of 1950 also deserve mention.

Lithographed stamps have not got the same chances in this 'good looks' contest, and, indeed, the category contains some of the worst examples, like Costa Rica 1929, Yugoslavia's rowing stamps in 1932 and the big sports series of Colombia in 1935. The Dutch Olympic issue of 1928 and the Balkan Games issues of Bulgaria 1931–3 also belong to this group, being produced by off-set printing.

Some old sports stamps sets were produced by letterpress, a little-used process today. To this group belong the Olympic series of Greece 1896 and France 1924. A stylish Swiss gliding stamp—awarded first prize in an English contest for the most beautiful stamp of 1949—was printed in both photogravure and letterpress.

Many interesting observations can be made if you start looking at the styles of the designs. As mentioned above, many designers have copied actual photographs to be on the safe side. Some of them, however, have used their own imaginations and knowledge with more or less success. Among the best results here you will find the Japanese and Hungarian stamps, just to mention a few. Many of them have been less successful, though. A 'classical' example offers the frightful 'ski-jumper' of U.S.A. 1932. The downhill skier of Hungary 1925 is not much better, though the position of the skis is correct.

Other examples of badly drawn stamps are the Dutch runner (1928), Roumanian diver (1945) and hurdlers (1946), Nicaraguan pole-vaulter (1949) and Polish runners (1952) and figure-skater (1953).

In general, however, the designs are attractive and stylish, making it more and more difficult to single out particular stamps as either very good or very bad.

4. THE ECONOMICS OF SPORTS PHILATELY

An aspect not unimportant to the collector is the economic one. Every beginner will no doubt want to know something about the cost of building a sports collection. Take heart! As I have mentioned above, it will prove less expensive to obtain a complete sports collection than to complete a collection of any of the usual 'stamp countries'.

The prices of the different sports series can be obtained from any of the big stamp catalogues. Because of the rapid expansion of sports philately there is sometimes still a wide gap between supply and demand, which makes many of these prices fictitious. This is also the reason why no prices are given in this book. They would soon become out of date and valueless. The great demand for particular sports stamps has also unfortunately led to speculation.

The most expensive sports series of today are naturally to be found among the older issues. Colombia's 1935 series is still at the top, followed by Tripolitania 1934, the Bulgarian 1931 and 1933 issues, and the two oldest Olympic issues from Greece in 1896 and 1906. As always, it is the highest denominations that have created these prices.

It is not necessary, however, to get these expensive series at once. Since the highest denominations often lack a real 'sports design', you could well build a representative collection without these costly stamps.

A difficulty which every thematic collector has to tackle is procuring at reasonable prices individual sports stamps which form part of a general 'non-sporting' issue. The whole series has often to be bought in order to obtain one single sports stamp. This unfortunately still goes for sports stamps, but it is to be hoped that these inconveniences will vanish with the increasingly better distribution and service by stamp dealers to the growing number of sports stamp collectors.

Part Two

OLYMPIC STAMPS

THE OLYMPIC GAMES

The original Olympic Games, the most important sports festival of Ancient Greece, were celebrated every fourth year from 776 B.C. to A.D. 393 at Olympia in the Peloponnese. According to some historians they can even be traced as far back as the fifteenth century B.C. The Games were abolished by Emperor Theodosius I in A.D. 394, at which time the extensive sports establishments and temples were destroyed. The Games were revived in Athens in 1859, 1870 and 1875 by the Greek Zappas, with little success, however. The initiative that led to the modern international Olympic Games was taken by the French baron Pierre de Coubertin, who put forward his proposals for the first time in 1892. The first Olympic Games of the modern era was held in Athens in 1896 in honour of Greece, the home of the Ancient Games. An International Olympic Committee (I.O.C.) was formed in 1894 and exercises the ultimate authority over the Olympic Games.

The Olympic Games must be regarded as the foundation on which modern sport is built, and a victory in them is still considered the peak of a sportsman's career. It seems reasonable, therefore, to start with the Olympic Games as pictured on stamps, and make these the subject of a special collection—remembering that the first sports stamps series were Olympic.

Greece 1896. *1st Olympic Games in Athens*

1l. yellow, 2l. rose, 5l. light mauve, 10l. grey green, 20l. red brown, 25l. red, 40l. violet, 60l. grey black, 1d. blue, 2d. olive, 5d. green, 10d. brown.

For this series—the first sports stamps set ever—only classical designs were chosen, alluding to the origin of the Games. The designs were partly taken from the sports of Ancient Greece and partly from Greek mythology. The two lowest denominations (1 and 2l.) show two 'fist fighters', the predecessors to our modern boxers. The 'fist fight' was introduced to the Games as early as 688 B.C. The two following denominations (5 and 10l.) picture the classical 'Discobolus', the discus-thrower, by Myron (450 B.C.), so often used as a symbol of sport. Two stamps (20 and 40l.) show an antique vase—the prize most frequently awarded in the Ancient Games—with a reproduction of the Goddess of War, Pallas Athene. Two other stamps (25 and 60l.) depict a four-horse chariot, a so-called 'quadriga'.

One stamp (1d.) represents the ancient Olympic Stadium of Athens which was restored and became the site of the Olympic Games in 1896 and 1906. In the background is the Acropolis. Two stamps (2 and 5d.) show statues found in Olympia which once embellished the Olympic Arena. The lower denomination pictures the statue by Praxiteles of 'Hermes' (350 B.C.), and the higher Paeonius' statue of the Goddess of Victory (420 B.C.). The last stamp in this series (10d.) shows a view of the Acropolis with the Parthenon.

This series, one of the finest in sports philately, is nowadays rather difficult to obtain. Five denominations of this series were surcharged in 1901 as supplementary stamps to the ordinary issues and, as such, are not necessary in a sports collection.

Greece 1906. *Special Olympic Games in Athens*

1l. brown, 2l. grey black, 3l. orange, 5l. green, 10l. red, 20l. claret, 25l. ultramarine, 30l. purple, 40l. brown, 50l. maroon, 1d. grey black, 2d. rose, 3d. olive yellow, 5d. blue.

For the Greek Special Olympic Games of 1906, celebrating the tenth anniversary of the founding of the modern Olympic Games, stamps were similarly chosen with ancient sports and mythological designs. The two lowest denominations (1 and 2l.) show the discus-throwing Apollo with his attribute, the tripod, in the background. The design is taken from a silver coin from the island of Kos in the fifth century B.C.

The two following denominations (3 and 5l.) picture a long-jumper. In his hands can be seen the 'halters'—weights used to help the jumper reach greater distances.

The 10l. shows the Goddess of Victory holding an aesculapian staff in her hand. At her feet lies an amphora, the victory prize of that time. The whole design is taken from a silver coin from Terracina in Sicily.

Two other stamps (20 and 50l.) depict a scene from Greek mythology, which shows Hercules carrying the canopy of the stars and the moon and the Titan, Atlas, offering him the apples of the Hesperides. The design is taken from a stone bas-relief in the Temple of Zeus at Olympia.

The 25l. stamp also shows Hercules, this time in a more sporting activity. He is fighting with the giant Antaeus, who received his strength by the touch of the ground. Hercules decided the fight to his advantage by squeezing the giant to death in the air. Hercules is on the left, where his symbol—the lion skin—is also hanging.

The 30l. stamp reproduces a well-known Hellenistic statue, now in Florence, of two wrestlers, with the Acropolis in the background. The next denomination (40l.) shows the Daemon of the Games, a winged goddess, either Eos or Nike, with a cock in her hands. Three stamps (1, 2 and 3d.) portray four runners in a race.

The highest denomination of this series (5d.) depicts the Olympic offering ceremony to Zeus, which was always performed at the opening of the Ancient Games. The Goddess of Victory, Nike, carrying in her hands an oblation bandage, is standing with a priest and three athletes round an altar in the centre of the picture.

Belgium 1920. *7th Olympic Games in Antwerp*

5c. green, 10c. red, 15c. brown.

The Olympic Games of Paris in 1900, St. Louis 1904, London 1908 and Stockholm 1912 not having left any philatelic mementoes in the shape of stamps, Belgium became the second country to issue Olympic stamps. As before, only classical designs were used: the 'Discobolus' of Myron, the 'quadriga' and a statue depicting a runner, probably the messenger from Marathon. The stamps were sold with an extra five centimes to aid war invalids. Like the series of 1896 these stamps were later surcharged because of monetary changes.

France 1924. *8th Olympic Games in Paris*

10c. green, 25c. red, 30c. brown and black, 50c. blue.

From the Olympics of 1920 no Olympic Games have passed unnoticed from a philatelic point of view. The designs of the French stamps are partly modern and all allegorical. The lowest denomination (10c.) shows an athlete with laurels giving the Olympic salute in front of the Stade de Colombes in Paris, where the Olympic Games were staged. The 25c. stamps has a symbolic figure carrying a little statue of Victory in her hands. In the background Nôtre-Dame and the Pont Neuf can be seen. The 30c. denomination depicts Milon from Kroton, the foremost athlete of the Ancient Games.

The 50c. stamp shows a laurelled Olympic victor.

In connection with these Olympic Games it was also planned to issue another stamp reproducing the ancient amphitheatre of Nîmes, but the proposition never went further than trial specimens, which now are rather expensive.

The French series was also overprinted for use in Lebanon and Syria, at that time French mandated territories. There were two types of overprint: 'Grand Liban' and 'Syrie'.

A series of three stamps was issued in 1925 by Costa Rica with the inscription 'Juegos Olimpicos'. This series had, however, no connection with the official Olympic Games and is, therefore, dealt with in the chapter 'Sports Events'.

Uruguay 1924. *Olympic Football Victory in Paris*

2c. rose, 5c. purple, 12c. blue.

These stamps, issued to commemorate Uruguay's Olympic football victory of 1924, are dealt with more explicitly in Part Three, under 'Football'.

Czechoslovakia 1925. *8th Olympic Congress in Prague*

50h. green, 100h. red, 200h. blue

The International Olympic Committee held a congress in Prague in 1925. To honour the I.O.C., the Czechoslovakian postal authorities decided to overprint three stamps bearing the picture of President Thomas Masaryk. The overprint contains the following words in a semicircle: 'CONGRESS OLYMP. INTERNAT. PRAHA 1925.' These are among the most expensive of sports stamps.

Netherlands 1928. *9th Olympic Games in Amsterdam*

1½c. green, 2c. purple, 3c. green, 5c. blue, 7½c. orange, 10c. red, 15c. blue, 30c. sepia.

The Dutch postal authorities broke with the old Olympic stamps traditions by choosing modern designs. These were stylized, and did not always do justice to the events pictured, which are: rowing, fencing, football, yachting, shot-putting, running, horse-riding and boxing, respectively. These stamps were sold with a smaller premium for the benefit of the Dutch Olympic Committee.

Portugal 1928. *9th Olympic Games in Amsterdam*

15c. red and black, 30c. red and black (postage due).

These two stamps, the 15c. showing a hurdler, were issued to finance the participation of Portugal in the Olympic Games of 1928. The hurdler stamp was compulsory on all postal matter, in addition to the ordinary rate of postage, for three days (22nd–24th May 1928). Those who did not follow these instructions had the postage-due stamp affixed and had to pay double the amount on delivery. The issue was 1·8 million copies of each stamp. The postage-due stamp was the first ever to picture the Olympic rings, and was also inscribed 'AMSTERDAO'.

Uruguay 1928. *Olympic Football Victory in Amsterdam*

2c. purple, 5c. red, 8c. blue.

Uruguay also won the football tournament in the 1928 Games. See chapter on 'Football'.

U.S.A. 1932. *3rd Winter Olympic Games at Lake Placid* (2c. red)
10th Olympic Games in Los Angeles (3c. violet, 5c. blue)

U.S.A. was the first country to issue stamps for the Winter Olympic Games, though these had taken place since 1924. The design, however, is a little confusing, since a downhill skier is pictured, although downhill ski-ing was not then part of the Winter Games.

The Summer Games—the 'Sunshine' Olympics as they were called—were celebrated with two stamps, one showing a sprinter in his 'starting blocks' the other the 'Discobolus' in front of a globe.

Germany 1935. *4th Winter Olympic Games in Garmisch-Partenkirchen.*
6+4pf. green, 12+6pf. red, 25+15pf. blue.

1936. *11th Olympic Games in Berlin*
3+2pf. brown, 4+3pf. blue, 6+4pf. green, 8+4pf. red, 12+6pf. carmine, 15+10pf. claret, 25+15pf. ultramarine, 40+35pf. mauve.

The German Olympic winter stamps were issued in 1935, to publicize the Games. The designs were speed-skating, ski-jumping and bob-sleighing, respectively.

The designs of the Summer Games stamps were gymnastics, diving, football, javelin throwing, torch race, fencing, rowing and riding, respectively. All of these stamps carried a special premium for the benefit of sport. These stamps revolutionized sports philately with their stylish and attractive design. They were also issued in two sheets of four stamps, each with a special frame.

Haiti 1939. *Baron Pierre de Coubertin*
10+10c. red, 60+40c. violet, 1c.25+60c. black.

Although these stamps, of which the two highest denominations were for airmail, were not issued in connection with any Olympic event, they have been put in this group because of the design. The reason for the issue of these stamps was to get money for building a stadium in the capital of Haiti—Port-au-Prince. The design chosen was the picture of *Pierre de Coubertin*, the founder of the modern Olympic Games. His picture is surrounded by the flag of Haiti and the Olympic five-ring flag.

No Olympic Games took place until three years after the end of the Second World War, and no Olympic issues appeared for five years. The Finns who, at short notice, had made excellent preparations for the Games at Helsinki in 1940, had not forgotten the philatelist. An Olympic stamp was printed but never issued.

Switzerland 1944. *50th Anniversary of the founding of the Olympic Games*

10c. black and orange, 20c. black and red, 30c. black and blue.

The Olympic ideal was not quite forgotten, however, in the din of battle, for Switzerland celebrated the 50th Anniversary of the Olympic Games of the modern era by issuing three stamps almost unequalled in beauty of picture and colour composition. The design is of Apollo, from a statue in the temple of Zeus at Olympia of about 460 B.C., and the Olympic rings. The jubilee was celebrated in Lausanne, where an Olympic museum is established and all the Olympic insignia are kept. Pierre de Coubertin is also buried there.

Switzerland 1948. *5th Winter Olympic Games in St. Moritz*

5+5c. brown, yellow and green, 10+10c. blue and brown, 20+10c. claret, yellow and black, 30+10c. black, blue and light blue.

The Swiss were given the task of arranging the 1948 Winter Games—Britain lacking the facilities—and with a compulsory stamp issue they did not fail their proud philatelic traditions. The two lowest denominations show the coat-of-arms of St. Moritz—a sun—and a snow crystal, respectively, both with the Olympic rings. The two higher denominations depict an ice-hockey goalkeeper and a downhill skier.

Austria 1948. *Olympic Games of 1948*

1s.+50g. blue.

The first Olympic Games after the Second World War were held in 1948. The Austrians decided, as the Portuguese had done twenty years previously, to help finance their participation by issuing a stamp with a premium in addition to the postal value. This stamp, showing the sacred Olympic flame, is one of the most beautiful of sports stamps.

Korea 1948. *Olympic Games of 1948*

5w. green, 10w. violet.

Korea joined both the international sports family and the ranks of sports philately by issuing two commemorative stamps for the 14th Olympic Games. The lower denomination has a Korean flag surrounded by laurels and surmounted by the Olympic rings. The 10w. shows a torch-runner. The Koreans celebrated their Olympic début with two bronze medals.

Monaco 1948. *Olympic Games of 1948*

50c. green, 1f. red, 2f. blue, 2.50f. red, 4f. slate, 5+5f. brown, 6+9f. violet, 10+15f. red, 15+25f. blue.

Monaco issued, presumably for purely financial reasons, a beautiful series of nine stamps representing hurdling, running, discus-throwing, basketball, diving, rowing, downhill ski-ing, tennis and yachting, respectively. The opinion that this set was issued for purely pecuniary reasons seems confirmed by the fact that Monaco did not take part in these Olympic Games, or in any previous Games, and that it was only sold in conjunction with another one honouring a sculptor.

This set was only the beginning of a long line of Olympic series issued by countries other than the 'host'.

Great Britain 1948. *14th Olympic Games in London*

2½d. ultramarine, 3d. violet, 6d. purple, 1s. brown.

The first British sports stamps to appear were issued to commemorate the first post-war Olympic Games in 1948. The designs chosen were symbolic ones: the globe surrounded with laurels, a stylized athlete symbolizing speed, the Olympic rings and the Goddess of Victory over the Northern Hemisphere. According to tradition the sovereign—King George VI—was also pictured on the stamps. This series was also used overprinted at British postal agencies outside Great Britain such as Bahrain, Kuwait, Muscat and Dubai, Morocco and Tangier.

Peru 1948. *14th Olympic Games 1952*

1s. blue, 2s. brown, 5s. green, 10c. yellow.

The Peruvians also honoured the British Olympic Games by issuing four stamps. The designs are: a map showing air route from Peru to England, basketball, discus-throwing ('Discobolus') and rifle-shooting, respectively. These stamps were also issued in sheets with a special premium for the benefit of a children's hospital. In 1956 this set returned, overprinted, for the Olympic Games of Melbourne.

Norway 1951. *6th Winter Olympic Games in Oslo 1952*

15+5ö. green, 30+10ö. red, 55+20ö. blue.

The Norwegians, hosts for these Winter Games, took the opportunity to issue sports stamps for the first time. The designs are typically Norwegian: the two most popular Norwegian sports—speed-skating and ski-jumping—together with a beautiful winter landscape.

Finland 1951–2. *15th Olympic Games in Helsinki 1952*

12+2m. red, 15+2m. green, 20+3m. blue, 25+4m. brown.

The Finnish Olympic set came in two parts: the 12 and 20m. denominations in the autumn of 1951 and the rest during the winter 1952. The stamps show: diving, the Olympic stadium at Helsinki, football and a modern sprinter with runners from Ancient Greece in the background.

Austria 1952. *Olympic Games of 1952*

2s.60+40g. green.

As in 1948, the Austrians issued a stamp with a premium to finance their participation in the Olympic Games. The design was again well composed, showing the Olympic rings and a laurel.

Saar 1952. *15th Olympic Games*

15+5f. green, 30+5f. blue.

For the same reason as Austria, Saar issued two Olympic stamps with allegorical designs, picturing an athlete with a torch and a hand holding an olive branch in front of a globe.

Hungary 1952. *15th Olympic Games*

30f. brown, 40f. green, 60f. red, 1fo. blue, 1.70fo. orange, 2fo. bistre.

The Hungarians issued a very beautiful sports-promotion set of big diamond-shaped stamps marking the Olympics. These illustrate some of the most successful Hungarian sports: running, swimming, fencing, gymnastics and hammer-throwing. The set is completed by a picture of the newly built Nép Stadium in Budapest. The stamps are all adorned with the Olympic rings and a peace dove.

Germany (West Berlin) 1952. *Pre-Olympic Games Festival in Berlin*

4pf. brown, 10pf. green, 20pf. red.

These stamps, bearing a torch with the Olympic rings and an olive branch, were issued in connection with the all-German qualifying rounds held in Berlin from 20th June to 6th July 1952.

Yugoslavia 1952. *15th Olympic Games*

5d. chocolate on buff, 10d. yellow on brown, 15d. blue on pink, 28d. light red on chocolate, 50d. dark green on green, 100d. mauve on brown.

A set showing gymnastics, running, swimming, boxing, basketball and football, respectively. The stamps are designed in a very simple but very attractive manner. They were also used for the Yugoslavian zone of Trieste, but in changed colours and with the overprint: 'STT—VUJNA.'

Monaco 1953. *15th Olympic Games 1952*

1f. magenta and violet, 2f. green and blue, 3f. blue and light blue, 5f. brown and green, 8f. lake and red, 15f. brown, green and blue, 40f. black, 50f. violet, 100f. grey green, 200f. red.

Monaco followed the 1948 precedent by issuing a new Olympic set for the Olympic Games of 1952. This time, however, it was very much delayed and did not appear until February 1953. The series was drawn by two different designers—the four highest denominations intended for airmail compare unfavourably with the lower denominations. The diamond-shaped designs are: basketball, football, yachting, cycling, gymnastics, Louis II Stadium in Monaco, the torso of an athlete, epée-fencing, rifle-shooting and an Olympic torch with the Monaco rock as a background.

Australia 1954–5. *16th Olympic Games in Melbourne 1956*
2s. blue (1954), 2s. green (1955).

Two years before the Games the Australians started their Olympic Games publicity with a stamp reproducing the winning design for the Olympic poster competition. The picture shows, besides the compulsory Olympic rings, the coat-of-arms of Melbourne. In 1955 the same stamp was issued once more, this time in a changed colour.

San Marino 1955. *1st Olympic Sports Stamps Exhibition in San Marino*
80l. red, brown and black, 120l. green, brown and black.

The first international Olympic stamps exhibition was held in San Marino in 1955. The stamps issued show hurdling and relay-racing, respectively.

San Marino 1955. *7th Winter Olympic Games in Cortina d'Ampezzo 1956*
1l. olive brown and yellow, 2l. blue and red, 3l. yellow brown and brown, 4l. green and black brown, 5l. red and blue, 10l. ultramarine and light red, 25l. grey black and red, 50l. grey blue and brown, 100l. blue green and black, 200l. orange and black.

For the Winter Games of 1956 San Marino issued as early as December 1955 a beautiful winter-sports set. The 10l. design (girl figure-skating) won first prize in the Bonacossa Medal competition. The stamps depict speed-skating, skating, ski-ing, bobsleigh, downhill ski-ing, figure-skating and ski-jumping, respectively.

Italy 1956. *7th Winter Olympic Games*
10l. green, brown and orange brown, 12l. grey and olive yellow, 25l. grey violet and red orange, 60l. blue and yellow orange.

This Italian Olympic set was immensely popular and had to be reprinted. It pictures the Olympic arenas among the Dolomites in Cortina.

The designs show the jumping hill 'Trampolina Italia', the snow or ski stadium 'Stadio della Neve' or 'dello Sci', the ice rink 'Stadio de Ghiaccio', and the skating track of Misurina.

Monaco 1956. *Olympic Games at Cortina and Melbourne*

15f. green olive brown and red brown, 30f. red orange.

The first design is almost identical with the lowest Italian Olympic denomination, i.e. the ski-jumping hill of Cortina. The stamp, devoted to the Summer Games, depicts both ancient and modern events and in keeping with this the inscription is in both Greek and French.

Sweden 1956. *16th Olympic Equestrian Games in Stockholm*

20ö. red, 25ö. blue, 40ö. green.

Because of the strict Australian quarantine regulations the equestrian events could not be held in Melbourne, and were therefore awarded to Stockholm, where they were held 10–17th June 1956.

The stamps, which were issued in coil form imperforate on two sides, and in booklet form imperforate one side and perforated on the other three, bear the motif of a horseman taken from the Parthenon frieze from the Acropolis.

Czechoslovakia 1956. *16th Olympic Games*

75h. violet brown and yellow, 120h. grey green and orange.

Two stamps with the same design were issued, one in the spring, the other in the autumn, and show a woman discus-thrower, a hurdler and a long-distance runner.

Iran 1956. *10th Anniversary of the Iranian Olympic Committee*

5r. red violet.

The coat-of-arms of Iran and the Olympic rings. The French text on the lower part of the stamp is mis-spelt 'ARNNIVERSAIRE' instead of 'ANNI...'

Germany (West) 1956. *Olympic Year of 1956*

10pf. green.

A plain and stylish stamp on which the currency figures are made from a classical frieze pattern and the outline of a running track.

Saar 1956. *16th Olympic Games*

12+5f. blue green and green, 15+5f. brown and violet brown.

The design is based on the Greek sculpture 'Young man from Benevento' (about 300 B.C.) and the Olympic rings.

Netherlands 1956. *16th Olympic Games*

2+3c. blue and black, 5+3c. yellow and black, 7+5c. red brown and black, 10+5c. grey and black, 25+9c. green and black.

This series was issued with a premium to finance the Dutch Olympic team. As Holland finally did not compete in the Olympic Games the collected funds were given to Hungarian relief. The designs are of yachting, women's sprinting, hockey and water polo. One stamp also shows an antique amphora: a vase filled with oil which was often the prize awarded during the Ancient Olympic Games.

Hungary 1956. *16th Olympic Games*

20f. light green blue and brown, 30f. olive green and brown, 40f. red orange and brown, 60f. grey green and brown, 1fo. red and brown, 1.50fo. blue violet and brown, 2fo. yellow green and brown, 3fo. red lilac and brown.

A beautiful set, showing canoeing, riding, fencing, hurdling (women's), football, weight-lifting, gymnastics (women's) and basketball, respectively.

Germany (East) 1956. *16th Olympic Games*

20pf. red brown, 35pf. grey blue.

These simply drawn stamps show Olympic symbols such as the torch, olive branch, rings and an ancient javelin-thrower.

Bulgaria 1956. *16th Olympic Games*

4s. ultramarine, 12s. red brown, 16s. yellow brown, 44s. dark green, 80s. brown, 1l. dark red.

The designs are: gymnastics (women's), discus-throwing, pole-vaulting, football, basketball and boxing.

Yugoslavia 1956. *Olympic Year of 1956*

10d. red lilac and brown, 15d. dark blue and brown, 20d. ultramarine and brown, 30d. grey green and brown, 35d. dark brown and brown, 50d. dark green and brown, 70d. lilac brown and brown, 100d. red brown and brown.

This set is original not only for its stylized approach but also for the fact that every sports motif is linked with an animal: sprinting—deer; canoeing—swan; downhill ski-ing—bird; swimming—flying-fish; football—panther; water polo—fish; table tennis—butterfly; shooting—falcon.

Roumania 1956. *16th Olympic Games*

20b. red orange, 55b. ultramarine, 1l. lilac red, 1.55l. green, 1.75l. violet.

The designs were: Olympic torch, water polo, gymnastics (women's), canoeing and high-jumping (women's).

Australia 1956. *16th Olympic Games*

4d. carmine, 7½d. blue, 1s. multicoloured, 2s. multicoloured.

The two lowest denominations, which were printed in Australia, show the coat-of-arms of Melbourne beneath the Olympic rings and torch, and the Olympic rings and the Southern Cross respectively. The highest denominations were printed in Europe and reproduce a view from Collins Street in Melbourne, and a view of the city as seen from the River Yarra.

Poland 1956. *16th Olympic Games*

10g. brown and grey, 20g. grey violet and brown, 25g. black and light blue, 40g. red brown and green, 60g. olive brown and rose, 1.55z. brown and violet.

These Polish Olympic stamps depict sabre-fencing, boxing, rowing, steeplechase (the first time ever on stamps), javelin-throwing and women's gymnastics.

Liberia 1956. *16th Olympic Games*

4c. olive green and brown, 6c. green and grey, 8c. red brown and ultramarine, 10c. rose black and grey, 12c. green and blue violet, 20c. and 40c. orange black and ultramarine.

This none too beautiful set shows a laurel with Olympic rings flanked by a kangaroo and an emu, the 'Discobolus' of Myron, the Goddess of Victory with a laurel, an ancient chariot, the Olympic Park at Melbourne and a map of Australia with the Olympic torch. The last design also appears in another denomination (40c.) with the same colour in a special sheet in a rather small issue.

France 1956. *16th Olympic Games* (Pierre de Coubertin)

30f. violet and grey.

The founder of the modern Olympic Games, the French *Baron Pierre de Coubertin* (1863–1937), was honoured on this stamp. In addition to the portrait of *Coubertin*, the stamp shows an athlete and the Olympic flag, which was introduced by Coubertin himself.

Korea (South) 1956. *16th Olympic Games*

20w. orange, 50w. green

Olympic torch, rings and an olive branch.

Turkey 1956. *16th Olympic Games*

40k. yellow green and brown, 65k. grey and red.

The Turks chose wrestling as the motif for their Olympic stamps, presumably as this was the only event in which they obtained any points.

Poland 1956. *16th Olympic Games*

1.55z. red brown and orange.

The Polish woman long-jumper, *E. Krzesinska*, who won her event at the Olympic Games with a new world record (6·35 m.), was honoured on this special stamp.

Peru 1956. *16th Olympic Games*

1s. blue green, 2s. red brown, 5s. green, 10s. yellow.

The Olympic stamps of Peru for 1948 (!) were issued once again in a charity sheet with an overprint 'Melbourne 1956' which does not show any great amount of imagination. These stamps were actually issued in November 1956 but were not allowed to be used on mail until the 15th April 1957 when they were made legal for only one day. The stamps were sold only between the 19th November 1956 and 19th February 1957.

The Dominican Republic 1957. *Well-known Olympic Victors*

1c. red brown and blue, 2c. grey brown blue and red, 3c. violet and red, 5c. orange red and blue, 7c. green blue and red, 11c. yellow blue and red, 16c. red and green, 17c. blue grey and red.

The initiative of the West Indian republic in portraying well-known Olympic heroes was a milestone in sports philately and has already had imitators. In this set Olympic winners are pictured in the Olympic Stadium with their respective national flags in the background. The eight chosen were:

Fanny Blankers-Koen, Netherlands, gold medals 1948 in women's 100 m., 200 m., 80m. hurdles and relay race 4×100 m.

Jesse Owens, U.S.A., gold medals 1936 in 100 m., 200 m., long-jump and relay race 4×100 m.

Kitei Son, Japan, gold medal 1936 in the Marathon.

Lord Burghley, Great Britain, gold medal 1928 in 400 m. hurdles.

Bob Mathias, U.S.A., gold medals 1948 and 1952 in decathlon.

Paavo Nurmi, Finland, gold medals 1920 in 10,000 m. and cross-country (individually and team), 1924 1,500 m., 5,000 m., team race 3,000 m. (individually and team), cross-country race (individually and team), 1928 in 10,000 m.; silver medals 1920 in 5,000 m., 1928 in 5,000 m. and steeplechase.

Ugo Frigerio, Italy, gold medals 1920 in 3,000 m. and 10,000 m. walks, 1924 in 10,000 m. walk; bronze medal 1932 in 50 km walk.

Mildred Didrickson, U.S.A., gold medals 1932 in women's 80 m. hurdles and javelin; silver medal in high-jump.

These stamps were also issued in special sheets and surcharged for the Hungarian Relief.

The Dominican Republic 1957. *Olympic Victors in Melbourne 1956 (I)*

1c. brown blue and yellow, 2c. orange blue and red, 3c. grey blue, blue and red, 5c. olive green, blue and red, 17c. red brown, blue and red, 11c. green blue and red, 16c. light violet, blue and red, 17c. olive brown, green and yellow.

These stamps were decorated with the national flags of the respective athletes, and were of large diamond shape. The eight victorious athletes chosen were:

Lars Hall, Sweden, modern pentathlon.
Betty Cuthbert, Australia, women's 100 m., 200 m., relay 4×100 m.
Eigil Danielsen, Norway, javelin-throwing.
Alain Mimoun, France, marathon.
Norman Read, New Zealand, 50 km. walk.
Robert Morrow, U.S.A., 100 m., 200 m., relay 4×100 m.
Chris Brasher, Great Britain, steeplechase.
A. Ferreira da Silva, Brazil, hop, step and jump.

The three highest denominations were for use on airmail. As previously, this set was also printed in special sheets, this time with three different types of centre: one with an Olympic gold medal, another with the Olympic flag and a third with the Dominican flag. The latter was printed with the colours of the flag upside-down but was immediately withdrawn, and only about 200 copies were issued. These sheets were later overprinted for the Golden Jubilee of the Boy Scouts and so should not be included in a sports stamps collection.

Russia 1957. *16th Olympic Games*

20k. green and violet, 20k. blue and grey, 25k. orange and dark blue, 40k. multicoloured, 40k. violet and grey, 60l. blue violet and brown.

The Russians also honoured their Olympic victors in the 1956 Olympics with the following six stamps:

Running (*V. Kuts*); ladies' javelin (*I. Jaunzeme*); gymnastics (*V. Chukarin*); football; boxing; weight-lifting.

The Dominican Republic 1957. *Olympic Victors 1956 (II)*

1c. light brown red and blue, 2c. brown green and orange, 3c. light violet blue and red, 5c. orange green and red, 7c. grey green, green and red, 11c. light blue black and yellow, 16c. red and blue, 17c. red violet, blue and red.

The Dominican postal authorities could not resist issuing a new Olympic-victor set after the successful results of the earlier ones. This time it also honoured a victor from the Winter Games and one from the equestrian events in Stockholm. The eight victors now chosen were:

Gerald Ouellette, Canada, rifle-shooting, short distance.
Ron Delany, Ireland, 1,500 m.
Tenley Albright, U.S.A., figure-skating.
Joaquin Capilla, Mexico, high-diving.
Ercole Baldini, Italy, road cycle race.
Hans Winkler, Germany, horse-jumping.
Alfred Oerter, U.S.A., discus-throwing.
Shirley Strickland, Australia, women's 80 m. hurdles.

Once more many special sheets were later issued and surcharged for refugee relief. These stamps, and especially the sheets, were not well received by philatelists. Much criticism has been aroused by the methods of the Dominican postal authorities, and sports philatelists have been urged not to collect these sheets, which have been printed in very small quantities.

The Dominican Republic 1958. *Olympic Victors 1956 (III)*

1c. blue grey and rose, 2c. light blue and grey brown, 3c. violet and grey, 5c. blue grey and red brown, 7c. dark blue and light brown, 11c. olive and blue, 16c. orange and green, 17c. blue and red.

The Dominicans continued to try the patience of sports philatelists by issuing a new set of eight Olympic victors, together with their national flags. These were also printed in different special sheets, and with a surcharge for the Geophysical Year. The Olympic winners now chosen were:

Gillian Sheen, Great Britain, women's foil-fencing.
Milton Campbell, U.S.A., decathlon.
Shozo Sasahara, Japan, wrestling, free style, featherweight.
Madeleine Berthod, Switzerland, women's downhill ski-ing.
Murray Rose, Australia, swimming, free style, 400 and 1,500 m.
Charles Jenkins and Tom Courtney, U.S.A., relay race 4×400 m.
Indian Hockey Team.
Swedish Yachting Team.

San Marino 1959. *Famous members of I.O.C.*

2l. orange brown and dark grey, 3l. red violet and dark brown, 5l. blue and dark green, 30l. blue violet and dark grey, 60l. dark green and dark brown, 80l. red and dark green, 120l. light brown.

Issued to commemorate San Marino's joining of the International Olympic Committee, the set depicts some of its most well-known members: *Pierre de Coubertin* (2l and 120l.), *Alberto Bonacossa* (3l.),

Avery Brundage (5l.), *Carlo Montú* (30l.), *J. S. Edström* (60l.), *H. de Baillet-Latour* (80l.).

Italy 1959. *Publicity for the 17th Olympic Games in Rome 1960*

15l. orange and brown, 25l. dark blue, light blue and grey brown, 35l. dark brown and olive yellow, 60l. rose and grey brown, 110l. dark brown and yellow.

Buildings in Rome connected with the Games: Dioscuri Fountain, the Tower of the Capitol, the Baths of Caracalla, the Constantine Arch and the Basilica of Massenzio.

Germany (East) 1960. *Olympic Games of 1960*

5pf. orange brown and brown, 10pf. orange brown and green, 20pf. orange brown and red, 25pf. orange brown and blue.

Boxing, women's sprinting, ski-jumping and yachting.

U.S.A. 1960. *8th Winter Olympic Games in Squaw Valley*

4c. blue.

Olympic rings and a snowflake.

Russia 1960. *8th Winter Olympic Games*

10k., 25k., 40k., 60k. and 1r., all multicoloured.

Ice hockey, speed-skating, downhill ski-ing, figure-skating (women's) and ski-jumping.

Czechoslovakia 1960. *8th Winter Olympic Games*

60h. light blue and dark brown, 1.80k. light green and grey.

Ice hockey and figure-skating (pairs).

Hungary 1960. *8th Winter Olympic Games*

30f. blue and light brown, 40f. green and light brown, 60f. red and light brown, 80f. violet and light brown, 1fo. green blue and light brown, 1.20fo. red brown and light brown, 2+1fo. multicoloured.

Ski-ing, ice hockey, ski-jumping, speed-skating (women's), downhill ski-ing, figure-skating (women's) and the Games' emblem.

Haiti 1960. *8th Winter Olympic Games*

50c. green and multicoloured, 50c. blue green and red brown, 1.00g. red violet and blue green, 1.50g. blue and multicoloured.

Stamps of the 1959 Pan American Games issue overprinted especially for this event.

Paraguay 1960. *17th Olympic Games*

0.30g. red and green, 0.50g. red violet and blue, 0.75g. olive and yellow, 1.50g. violet and green, 12.45g. red and blue grey, 18.15g. brown violet and olive brown, 36g. green and violet red.

In Paraguay's first-ever sports issue the four lower values show football, the three higher (airmail) basketball.

Togo 1960. *Olympic Games of 1960*

0.30f. green blue and red, 0.50f. red and dark brown, 1f. light green and red, 10f. dark green ultramarine and red brown, 15f. green and red brown, 20f. yellow brown green and dark brown, 25f. violet red orange and dark brown.

Three of Togo's first sports stamps commemorated the Winter Games, downhill ski-ing, ice hockey and bobsleigh (!), the remaining four the Rome Games (cycling, discus-throwing, boxing and sprinting).

Bulgaria 1960. *8th Winter Olympic Games*

1l. blue white and red brown (also imperf.)

Skier.

Yugoslavia 1960. *Olympic Games 1960*

15d. violet grey yellow and orange, 20d. blue brown and light violet, 30d. ultramarine and grey, 35d. red violet grey and light brown, 40d. olive green grey and light green, 55d. blue green grey blue and grey brown, 80d. red yellow brown and grey, 100d. violet yellow brown and grey.

In this set one stamp (30d.) marks the Winter Games (skiers) and the others the Summer Games (shot-putting and running, swimming, wrestling, cycling, yachting, riding and fencing).

Belgian Congo 1960. *17th Olympic Games*

50c.+25c. blue and red, 1.50f.+50c. red and green, 2f.+1f. green and red, 3f.+1.25f. red violet and blue, 6.50f.+3.50f. red brown and red.

High-jumping, hurdling, football, javelin- and discus-throwing.

Ruanda Urundi 1960. *17th Olympic Games*

50c.+25c. blue grey and red, 1.50f.+50c. dark red and black, 2f.+1f. grey black and red, 3f.+1.25f. red orange and green, 6.50f.+3.50f. olive green and red.

Same design as for the Belgian Congo with changed colours.

Monaco 1960. *Olympic Games of 1960*

0.05f. dark brown green and red, 0.10f. red brown green and blue, 0.15f. red violet olive brown and red, 0.20f. olive blue and green, 0.25f. dark green, green and violet brown, 0.50f. dark blue, blue green and violet brown.

The two highest values—downhill ski-ing and figure-skating—represented the Squaw Valley Games. The other values depicted riding, swimming, long-jump and javelin-throwing.

San Marino 1960. *17th Olympic Games*

1l. rose and dark violet, 2l. grey and orange brown, 3l. olive brown and dark violet, 4l. red and dark brown, 5l. brown and light blue, 15l. green and violet, 10l. red brown and blue, 20l. light violet and violet, 25l. blue green and orange brown, 40l. yellow brown and red, 60l. grey green and orange brown, 80l. ultramarine and orange, 110l. yellow green red and black, 125l. red and dark brown.

Shot-putting, gymnastics, walking, boxing, fencing, cycling, hockey, basketball, rowing, running, football, swimming, riding and shooting.

This set, which was very popular and rapidly sold out, was reissued later imperforate, in three sheets (grey green, red, and green).

Roumania 1960. *17th Olympic Games (I)*

40b. blue grey and blue, 55b. blue grey and black, 1.20l. blue grey and red, 1.60l. blue grey and yellow, 2.45l. blue grey and green (when imperforated the last denomination is 3.70l.).

Swimming, gymnastics, high-jump, boxing and canoeing. When put together the stamps form the Olympic rings.

Roumania 1960. *17th Olympic Games (II)*

20b. grey, 40b. red brown, 55b. blue, 1l. red, 1.60l. violet red, 2l. violet.

The designs are similar to Series I, with football added.

5l. blue, 6l. red (imperf.) in one sheet each.

These two souvenir sheets show part of a stadium and the Olympic flame.

Iran 1960. *17th Olympic Games*

1r. violet brown, 6r. blue and violet grey.

Traditional Persian sports of polo and archery.

Czechoslovakia 1960. *17th Olympic Games*

1k. orange yellow and grey, 1.80k. light red and grey, 2k. blue and grey.

Running, gymnastics and rowing.

Poland 1960. *17th Olympic Games*

60g. blue, 60g. violet red, 60g. violet, 60g. blue green, 2.50z. ultramarine, 2.50z. red brown, 2.50z. red, 2.50z. green (white figures in embossed printing).

This Olympic set is rather original, being comprised of two sheets of four stamps which, when put together, form a continuous athletics track. The stamps honour former Polish medal-winners in previous Olympics: *Konopacka* (gold 1928), *Kusoczinzki* (gold 1932), *Polish cycle team* (silver 1924), *Polish riding team* (silver 1936), *Turski* (gold 1948), *Chycla* (gold 1952), *Krzesinska* (gold 1956).

Italy 1960. *17th Olympic Games*

5l. yellow brown, 10l. orange and blue grey, 15l. ultramarine, 25l. violet and grey brown, 35l. violet red, 60l. grey green and grey brown, 110l. red violet, 150l. light blue and grey brown, 200l. dark green.

Classical designs and the Olympic arenas in Rome were chosen by the Italians to commemorate their own Olympics—Romulus and Remus, Roman consul going to Games, 'Discobolus', Apollonius' 'Resting Fist Fighter', Lysippos' 'Apoxyomenos', the Olympic Stadium, the Velodrome, the large and small sports arenas.

France 1960. *17th Olympic Games*

0.20f. red violet, dark brown and light blue.

This Olympic stamp also honours the French sports idol Jean Bouin (silver medal 1912).

Germany (West) 1960. *Olympic Year 1960*

7pf. red brown, 10pf. olive green, 20pf. red, 40pf. dark blue.

Olympic rings combined with classical Greek designs: wrestling, running, discus- and javelin-throwing, and chariot-racing.

Russia 1960. *17th Olympic Games*

5k, 10k, 15k, 20k, 25k, 40k, 40k, 40k, 60k, 1r (all multicoloured).

Runners at the tape, wrestling, basketball, weight-lifting, boxing, fencing, gymnastics, diving, canoeing and riding.

Mongolia 1960. *17th Olympic Games*

5m. carmine blue green and grey, 10m. violet yellow and grey, 15m. green red and grey, 20m. brown red, light blue and grey, 30m. olive yellow green and grey, 50m. grey blue green and grey, 70m. yellow green violet and grey, 1t. rose green and grey.

Four rectangular and four large diamond-shaped stamps showing riding, running, swimming, wrestling, hurdling, gymnastics, high-jumping and discus-throwing.

Surinam 1960. *17th Olympic Games*

8+4c. grey red brown and black, 10+5c. orange red brown and black, 15+7c. violet red brown and black, 20+10c. blue red brown and black, 40+20c. green red brown and black.

Shot-putting, basketball, running, swimming and football.

Greece 1960. *17th Olympic Games*

20l., 50l., 70l., 80l., 1d., 1.50d., 2.50d., 4.50d., 5d., 6d., 12.50d. (all multicoloured).

For the first time since 1906, when they were themselves the hosts, the Greeks commemorated the Olympic Games. The set provides a pictorial story of how the Ancient Games at Olympia were organized, the designs being based on old Greek vases and pottery. One of the best-ever sets in sports philately.

Maldives 1960. *17th Olympic Games*

2l. red violet and dark green, 3l. grey green and red violet, 5l. red brown and violet blue, 10l. green and red brown, 15l. dark brown and blue, 25l. red and olive, 50l. yellow orange and violet, 1r. green and red violet.

This island republic in the Indian Ocean made her sports stamps début with a set of eight stamps, five picturing cycling and the higher values basketball.

Ghana 1960. *17th Olympic Games*

3d. light blue, 6d. light green, 1s.3d. light brown, 2s.6d. light red (on all stamps there are also the national colours of Ghana and the Olympic rings).

An Olympic torch with Ghana's flag, a sprinter, Africa and the Olympic rings.

Haiti 1960. *17th Olympic Games (I) and (II)*

10c. yellow and dark brown, 20c. red and dark blue, 50c. yellow brown and dark green, 1g. green blue and dark brown. *Airmail:* 50c. olive brown and red violet, 1.50g. green and red violet, 2.50g. red violet and blue grey.

Four of these stamps show *Baron de Coubertin* and a parade of athletes in the 1896 Olympics, against a background of either a parading team in the Melbourne Olympics or a stadium with the Olympic flame. The other values show 'Discobolus' and the Olympic Stadium and a gymnastics exhibition in the Olympic Stadium in Athens 1906. Four of these stamps—50c., 1g. (ordinary mail) and 50c., 1.50g. (airmail)—were later surcharged twenty-five centimes. A sheet containing two imperforate stamps was also issued.

Hungary 1960. *17th Olympic Games*

10f. light blue and yellow brown, 20f. brown orange and yellow brown, 30f. light violet and brown, 40f. yellow and yellow brown, 50f. light red and yellow brown, 60f. grey green and yellow brown, 1fo. violet brown and yellow brown, 1.40fo. ultramarine and yellow brown, 1.70fo. yellow brown and light brown, 2+1fo. violet red and light brown, 3fo. grey and brown and 10fo. blue and yellow brown (sheet).

Silhouetted figures, based on classical Greek designs, representing rowing, boxing, archery, discus-throwing, ball-playing, running, riding, wrestling, fencing, Romulus and Remus, and the arms of Hungary with the Olympic rings in colour. A special sheet commemorating the Winter as well as the Summer Games reproduced the Romulus and Remus emblem, the Olympic flame and rings in natural colour.

Korea (South) 1960. *17th Olympic Games*

20w., 40w., light blue and red brown (also sheet).

A weight-lifter, and the Northern Gate (Tong Dae Moon) of Seoul.

Sudan 1960. *17th Olympic Games*

15m. ultramarine, 55m. green, 3p. yellow.

Sudanese football player and the Sudan coat-of-arms.

Tunisia 1960. *1st Tunisian participation in the Olympic Games*

5m. olive and violet brown, 10m. blue grey, red violet and green, 15m. red and red violet, 25m. green blue and grey blue, 50m. green and blue.

A cyclist, Olympic symbol, a woman tennis player(!), a runner and a basketball player.

Turkey 1960. *17th Olympic Games*

30k. red violet, 30k. brown grey, 30k. blue grey, 30k. grey green, 30k. light brown.

Hurdling, basketball, wrestling, football and riding.

Bulgaria 1960. *17th Olympic Games*

8s. brown (dark brown), 12s. dark violet (violet), 16s. blue green (red brown), 45s. red violet (dark green), 80s. blue (green blue), 2l. dark green (olive).

Issued both perforated with figures in light rose and imperforate with yellow figures. Designs depict football, wrestling, weight-lifting, gymnastics, canoeing and running.

Liberia 1960. *17th Olympic Games*

5c. green and violet brown, 10c. violet red and violet brown, 15c. orange and violet brown, 25c. violet blue and violet brown and 50c. red violet and violet brown (sheet).

A weight-lifter and a man carrying a basket on his head, a single sculler and three natives in a canoe, a walker and a man carrying a stick with two buckets on his shoulder, a javelin-thrower and a native hunting a leopard with a spear, and a sprinter with the Olympic Stadium in Rome in the background.

The Dominican Republic 1960. *Olympic Victors 1956 (IV)*

1c. grey green and red, 2c. green blue and orange, 3c. red brown and grey blue, 5c. ultramarine and brown, 7c. blue and green, 11c. grey and blue, 16c. red brown and red, 17c. blue and black (also imperf. and in sheets.).

A new series of Melbourne victors appeared four years afterwards portraying: *Gholam Takhti* (Iran), *Mauru Furukawa* (Japan), *Mildred McDaniel* (U.S.A.), *Terry Spinks* (Great Britain), *Carlo Pavesi* (Italy), *Pat McCormick* (U.S.A.), *Mithat Bayrak* (Turkey), *Ursula Happe* (Germany).

Panama 1960. *17th Olympic Games*

3c. violet, 5c. green; *airmail:* 5c. orange, 10c. orange brown, 25c. blue, 50c. brown (the last two also in sheets).

Fencing, football, basketball, cycling, javelin-throwing and runner carrying a torch.

Cuba 1960. *17th Olympic Games*

1c. light violet, 2c. yellow, 8c. blue, 12c. red (also in imperf. blue grey sheet).

Yachting, pistol-shooting, boxing and sprinting.

Guinea 1960. *17th Olympic Games*

50f. red violet and multicoloured, 100f. blue and multicoloured (*ordinary mail*). 100f. red green and blue, 200f. green brown and red violet, 500f. orange blue and green (*airmail*).

Two 1959 sets were reissued with the surcharge 'Jeux Olympiques, Rome 1960' and the Olympic rings. They form the first sports set of this new African state.

Morocco 1960. *17th Olympic Games*

5f. red brown, violet blue and olive green, 10f. brown, blue and orange brown, 15f. orange brown, blue and green, 20f. violet brown, olive and blue, 30f. olive brown, red violet and violet blue, 40f. brown red, violet and light blue, 45f. violet blue, red violet and dark green, 70f. black, blue and dark brown.

Wrestling, gymnastics, cycling, weight-lifting, running, boxing, yachting and fencing.

Somalia 1960. *17th Olympic Games*

0.05S. green blue, 0.10S. yellow blue, 0.45S. violet blue, 1.80S. red blue.

Olympic torch with Somalian flag, relay race and sprinting.

Philippines 1960. *17th Olympic Games*

6c. light green brown, 10c. violet red brown, 30c. orange brown, 70c. light blue brown.

Diamond-shaped stamps depicting basketball, sprinting, rifle-shooting and swimming.

Lebanon 1960. *17th Olympic Games*

2.50+2.50p. blue brown, 5+5p. yellow brown, 7.50+7.50p. violet brown, 15+15p. red brown, 25+25p. green brown, 35+35p. ultramarine brown. The last three also in a sheet.

Diamond-shaped stamps depicting boxing, wrestling, shot-putting, fencing, cycling and swimming.

Costa Rica 1960. *17th Olympic Games*

1c. yellow black, 2c. grey blue black, 3c. red black, 4c. orange yellow black, 5c. yellow green black, 10c. orange red black, 25c. green black, 85c. red violet black, 1s. grey black, 10s. grey violet black, 5s. dark blue, light blue brown gold (in perf. and imperf. sheet).

Diamond-shaped stamps depicting running, swimming, cycling, weight-lifting, tennis(!), boxing, football, basketball, baseball(!), pistol-shooting and the Rome Olympics' official emblem.

Central African Republic, Congo (former French), Gabon, Tchad, 1960. *17th Olympic Games*

250f. red surcharge on 500f. black green black.

Ordinary stamps of French Equatorial Africa depicting birds in a tree, surcharge for the new republics and the Olympic Games.

Yemen 1960. *17th Olympic Games*

2b. rose black, 4b. yellow black, 6b. orange black, 8b. blue green black, 20b. orange ultramarine black. (4b. denomination also in imperf. sheet.)

Olympic torch and rings.

Afghanistan 1960. *17th Olympic Games*

175p. red brown with green surcharge.

Stamp showing the national sport *buzcashi*, surcharged with Olympic rings and text.

U.A.R. (Syria) 1960. *17th Olympic Games*

15p. multicoloured, 20p. blue orange brown, brown, 25p. yellow red violet, 40p. violet red, red violet.

Basketball, swimming, native fencing and horse-jumping.

Part Three

INDIVIDUAL SPORTS AND THEIR STAMPS

1. AQUATIC EVENTS

SWIMMING

Swimming events were known in Ancient Greece, and in Rome, while among the Teutonic peoples, especially the Vikings, competitions were frequent. Competitive swimming was also practised during the Middle Ages in the Scandinavian countries, and at the end of the eighteenth century it was especially popular in Sweden where the world's oldest swimming club (Upsala Simsällskap of 1796) still exists. Modern-style competitive swimming first appeared in the middle of the nineteenth century in England and from there spread all over the world.

It was only recently that swimming became popular on sport stamps. The most popular design shows the start. Free style, butterfly stroke and back stroke have also been depicted, but the breast stroke has not found much favour with the designers.

Swimming designs can also be seen on many other stamps but only those relating to competitive swimming have been included in this section.

Bulgaria 1931–3. *1st Balkan Games in Sofia*
12l. blue and green, 12l. orange (1933).
The start of a race in a swimming pool.

Colombia 1935. *3rd National Games in Barranquilla*
24c. green and ultramarine.
Girl doing the crawl.

Roumania 1937. *25th Anniversary of the Roumanian Athletic Union*
50+50b. brown.
Girl doing the crawl.

Panama 1938. *4th Central American Games in Panama*
7c. grey.
Back-stroke crawl.

Japan 1948. *3rd National Swimming Championships in Yawata*
5.00y. green-blue.
A male swimmer doing the crawl.

Russia 1949. *Sports issue*
30k. violet.
Two girl swimmers at the start of a race.

Japan 1949. *4th National Swimming Championships in Yokohama*
8.00y. grey-blue.
A swimmer ready for the start.

Hungary 1950. *Sports issue*
10f. blue-green.
A beautiful stamp, showing a girl swimmer at the start of a race.

Hungary 1952. *Olympic Games*
40f. green.
A girl swimmer doing the crawl.

Poland 1952. *Sports issue*
30+15g. light blue.
Girl swimmer at the start.

Yugoslavia 1952. *Olympic Games*
15d. rose violet.
Girl swimmer at the start.

The same design was issued with changed colours and overprinted 'STT-VUJNA' for use in the Yugoslav zone of Trieste.

Hungary 1953. *Inauguration of Nép Stadium, Budapest*
30f. green and red brown.
This extremely beautiful stamp, showing a butterfly swimmer, won the Bonacossa Medal of 1953.

France 1953. *French Olympic Successes in 1952*
20f. carmine and brown.
This stamp was probably intended to symbolize the changeover in a relay race. It was issued to honour, among others, the French 400 m. free-style gold medallist *J. Boiteux*; the silver medallist in the 100 m. back stroke, *G. Bozon*; and the French 4 × 200 m. relay team which won the bronze medal.

Czechoslovakia 1954. *Sports issue*
1k. grey and blue.
This stamp, showing a girl swimmer at the start, bears the motto: 'Every Citizen a Swimmer.'

Russia 1954. *Sports issue*
40k. blue and red brown.
No less than six swimmers, with a butterfly swimmer in the foreground.

Philippines 1954. *2nd Asian Games in Manila*
18c. green.
Diving into the pool at the start of a race. The Asian Games' emblem also adorns the stamp.

Liberia 1955. *Sports issue*
12c. blue and dark brown.
A heat of swimmers about to start.

Poland 1955. *2nd World Youth Games in Warsaw*
1.55z. light green.
A swimmer leaving the pool after a race.

Russia 1956. *National Spartacist Games*
25k. blue green.
A swimmer doing the crawl.

Yugoslavia 1956. *Olympic Year*
30d. grey green and brown.
A symbolic design incorporating a swimmer and a flying-fish.

Canada 1957. *Sports and Pastimes issue*
5c. light blue.
A girl doing the crawl.

Uruguay 1958. *14th South American Swimming Championships in Montevideo*
10c. green blue.
A girl swimmer at the start.

Liechtenstein 1958. *Sports issue*
15c. light blue and brown violet.
The start of a women's back-stroke race.

Hungary 1958. *European Swimming Championships in Budapest*
3fo. green.
Swimmer at full stretch.

Bulgaria 1958. *Students Sports Games in Sofia*
16s. dark blue.
Butterfly stroke.

The Dominican Republic 1958. *Olympic Victors 1956 (III)*
7c. dark blue and light brown.
The Olympic 400m. and 1500m. champion *Murray Rose*, Australia.

North Vietnam 1959. *Sports issue*
6x. rose and olive brown.
Swimmers in a river.

Panama 1959. *3rd Pan American Games in Chicago*
3c. light blue and red brown.
Boys doing the crawl.

Yugoslavia 1960. *17th Olympic Games*
30d. grey blue, light violet and brown.
Stylized swimmers doing the crawl.

Monaco 1960. *17th Olympic Games*
0.10f. red brown, blue green and blue.
Woman doing the crawl.

San Marino 1960. *17th Olympic Games*
80l. dark ultramarine and orange, 80l. green and orange brown (imperf. in sheet).
Start of women's race.

Roumania 1960. *17th Olympic Games (I)*
40b. dark grey, blue and yellow (also imperf.).
Swimmer at start of race.

Roumania 1960. *17th Olympic Games (II)*
20b. blue grey.
As above.

U.A.R. 1960. *8th Anniversary of the Revolution*
35m. dark blue.
Man and woman swimmers.

Surinam 1960. *17th Olympic Games*
20+10c. blue and orange brown.
The crawl.

Mongolia 1960. *17th Olympic Games*
15m. green grey olive and red.
Swimmer at the start.

The Dominican Republic 1960. *Olympic Victors 1956 (IV)*
2c. green blue and orange, 17c. blue and black.
Breast stroke champions *Mauru Furukawa*, Japan, and *Ursula Happe*, Germany.

North Korea 1960. *15th Anniversary of the Republic*
10w. dark green, orange brown, black.
The crawl.

Philippines 1960. *17th Olympic Games*
70c. light blue, brown.
The crawl—women.

Lebanon 1960. *17th Olympic Games*
35+35p. ultramarine, violet brown.
The crawl.

Costa Rica 1960. *17th Olympic Games*
2c. grey blue, black.
Woman swimmer about to start.

U.A.R. (Syria) 1960. *17th Olympic Games*
20p. blue, orange brown, brown.
Breast stroke.

DIVING

High diving has an ancient pedigree and was practised several thousand years B.C. Springboard diving was originally a purely German event and was popular there as early as the end of the eighteenth century. The sport spread at the start of this century to the U.S.A. which has dominated it ever since.

Diving has been a popular subject among stamp designers. The high swallow dive is the most favoured design, only a few stamps being devoted to other variations. Diving also formed part of the design of a Finnish stamp of 1956 (described under 'Gymnastics').

Hungary 1925. *Sports issue*
400k. blue green and green.
This stamp shows no less than three different events—diving, swimming and rowing—but as diving forms the main motif it has been included in this section. The dive is hardly a good one.

Russia 1935. *World Spartacist Games in Moscow*
2k. blue and black.
This large diamond-shaped stamp shows women diving.

Germany 1936. *11th Olympic Games in Berlin*
4+3pf. blue grey.
A straight high dive.

Lithuania 1938. *National Sports Festival in Kaunas*
30+10c. blue.
This stylized design depicts a woman diving with a yacht in the background.

Russia 1938. *Sports issue.*
5k. red.
A woman diver on the springboard just before the jump.

Ecuador 1939. *Victory in the 1st Bolivar Games in Bogotá, Colombia, 1938*
2s. olive.
A stylish high dive by one of the few male divers pictured on stamps.

Slovakia 1944. *Sports issue*
1.30+1.30k. blue green.
A diving tower, a male diver and the Slovakian flag.

Roumania 1945. *Sports issue*
16+184l. light violet, 16+184l. brown (imperf.).
An unattractive picture of a man performing a high dive.

Roumania 1946. *Sports issue*
20l. orange red.
A head dive with a somersault.

Japan 1947. *2nd National Sports Games in Kanazawa*
1.20y. red violet.
A stylish straight-forward dive.

Monaco 1948. *Olympic Games*
4f. grey.
The start of a springboard dive.

Russia 1948. *Sports issue*
50k. blue.
A swimming stadium adorned with flags provides the frame and background to this stamp. The diver—in rather too small a scale—is diving from the highest platform.

Nicaragua 1949. *10th World Amateur Baseball Championships in Managua 1948*
4c. brown violet, 75c. rose (*airmail*).
A beautifully stylish dive.

Guatemala 1950. *6th Central American and Caribbean Games*
35c. blue and grey.

Bolivia 1951. *5th South American Championships in La Paz 1948*
1b. red violet and black.
A straight header.

Finland 1951. *15th Olympic Games in Helsinki 1952*
12+2m. rose.
A back dive.

Trieste Zone B 1952. *Sports issue*
100d. black blue.
A back dive.

Iceland 1955-57. *Sports issue*
1.25k. blue, 1.75k. blue (1957).
A swallow dive. This design was reissued two years later.

Russia 1956. *National Spartacist Games*
40k. blue.
A swallow dive, with yachts in the background.

Cuba 1957. *Sports and Youth issue*
24c. dark blue, light blue and brown violet.
A piked dive.

The Dominican Republic 1957. *Olympic Victors 1956 (II)*
5c. orange green and red.
Joaquin Capilla of Mexico performing a back dive in the Melbourne Olympics.

Uruguay 1958. *14th South American Swimming Championships in Montevideo*
5c. green.
Piked dive.

Japan 1958. *3rd Asian Games in Tokyo*
24c. dark blue, rose and yellow.
Back dive.

Hungary 1958. *European Swimming Championships in Budapest*
2.50fo. red brown and yellow.
Back dive.

Yugoslavia 1959. *The Partisan Games*
80d. grey blue and olive.
Swallow-divers.

Argentine 1959. *3rd Pan American Games in Chicago*
3+1.50p. olive and black.
Swallow dive.

China (Communist) 1959. *1st National Games in Peking*
8d. green, brown and black.
Straight header.

Russia 1960. *17th Olympic Games*
40k. violet blue and olive brown.
Forward and backward dives.

The Dominican Republic 1960. *Olympic Victors 1956 (IV)*
11c. grey and blue.
High and springboard champion, *Pat McCormick*, U.S.A.

Formosa 1960. *15th National Taiwan Games*
$0.50 blue, deep blue, red orange and yellow.
Straight header.

WATER-POLO

Water-polo originated in England at the end of the nineteenth century. The first rules were devised in 1876, after which the game spread rapidly to the Continent, where the Middle European countries now dominate the sport. The first water-polo stamp did not appear until 1952.

Luxemburg 1952. *World Cycle Championships and Olympic Games 1952*
3f. olive grey.
A beautiful design depicting water-polo players.

Hungary 1953. *Inauguration of Nép Stadium in Budapest*
80f. green and red brown.
Second place in the 1953 Bonacossa Competition rewarded this extremely beautiful design, showing a forward about to shoot in front of the goal.

Netherlands 1956. *16th Olympic Games in Melbourne*
25+8c. light green and black.
The Dutch have always been well to the fore in this sport which was therefore represented in the set issued to benefit their Olympic team, which unfortunately finally did not go to Melbourne.

Yugoslavia 1956. *Olympic Year*
50d. dark green and brown.
A stylized design incorporating a water-polo player and a fish.

Roumania 1956. *16th Olympic Games in Melbourne*
55b. ultramarine.
Another stylized design.

Hungary 1958. *European Swimming Championships in Budapest*
1fo. light blue.
A water-polo player on the attack.

Russia 1959. *2nd National Spartacist Games.*
60k. blue and orange.
Fighting for the ball.

2. ARCHERY

The origin of archery is prehistoric, for Stone Age cave paintings of archers have been found. Archery was practised in Egypt and Asia, and was carried on as a sport up to the middle of the nineteenth century by the Turks. During the latter part of the Middle Ages archery was also practised as a sport in England, France and Belgium. Thus an archery tradition exists in many countries, but it was not until the 1920's that an international association was established.

Many collectors have asked if archery can be justifiably included in a sports stamps collection, and certainly stamps which show archery in an otherwise non-sporting design should not qualify. Many stamps depict natives with bows and arrows, but these designs must be classified as illustrating a profession—hunting or fishing—and not a sport. The first modern archery design did not appear until 1954; the first sets therefore show native or ancient forms of competitive archery.

Tannu Tuva (North Mongolia) 1936. *15th Anniversary of Republic*
70k. brown lilac.
A sports festival. In the foreground are competitive archers, while in the background there are wrestlers, riders and spectators.

Lithuania 1938. *National Sports Festival in Kaunas*
5+5c. green.
A kneeling archer, symbolizing sport.

Iran 1953. *Ancient Persian Sports*
2.50r. blue, 10r. violet.
A kneeling archer and a picture showing King Darius hunting lions on horseback.

Japan 1954. *9th National Sports Games in Sapporo*
5y. grey brown.
Modern archer with target in the background.

Czechoslovakia 1957. *World Archery Championships in Prague*
60h. grey green.
A woman archer.

France 1958. *French Sports*
18f. blue green and light brown.
In this set, commemorating old French sports, one stamp depicts an archer to honour the Medieval Archery Guilds still in existence.

Somalia 1958. *Sports issue*
0.10s. orange.
Native archer.

Brazil 1958. *10th Spring Games*
2.50c. brown orange.
Women archers in action.

Poland 1959. *Sports issue*
60g. orange and brown violet.
Woman archer.

Mongolia 1959. *National Sports issue*
20m., 30m. (multicoloured).
Mongolian archers.

Thailand 1959. *S.E.A.P. Games in Bangkok*
1.25b. green.
Native archer.

Iran 1960. *17th Olympic Games*
6r. blue and violet grey.
Ancient Persian archer.

Hungary 1960. *17th Olympic Games*
30f. light violet and brown.
Ancient Greek archer.

North Korea 1960. *Sports and Pastime issue*
5w. orange, yellow, black, blue and red
Native archer.

3. ATHLETICS

SPRINTING

Primitive competitions in short-distance running are among the oldest known forms of sporting events, and sprinting has existed through all the various phases in the development of athletics.

Short-distance running has been a rather popular subject with the sports stamps designers. No less than fifty-three different stamps from thirty-seven countries have depicted this event.

U.S.A. 1932. *10th Olympic Games in Los Angeles*
3c. violet.
This stamp, showing a runner at his starting position, was well drawn, and had the American schools champion, *J. A. Le Coney* from Lafayette College, as a model. As the American law forbids the reproduction of living persons on stamps the face of the runner has been changed.

Russia 1935. *World Spartacist Games in Moscow*
1k. blue and orange.
The design looks a little grotesque and has more to say about the futuristic Russian art of the 'thirties than about sport.

Roumania 1937. *8th Balkan Games in Bucharest*

1+1l. violet, 6+1l. brown.

Sprinter breasting the tape.

Yugoslavia 1938. *9th Balkan Games in Belgrade*

50+50p. orange.

Sprinter at the tape.

Greece 1939. *10th Balkan Games in Athens*

50l. dark green.

An ancient design used in a modern way. The stamp shows a man wearing a helmet and a shield. He is taking part in an arms-carrying race (*hoplitodromia*), a very popular event during the Ancient Olympic Games.

Slovakia 1944. *Sports issue*

2+2k. light brown.

Two runners at the start of a sprint. One of the runners has been given a baton by the designer—presumably for ornamental reasons since both runners are starting together and this would be impossible in an ordinary relay race.

Roumania 1946. *Sports issue*

50l. violet.

Starting sprinter.

Monaco 1948. *Olympic Games 1948*

1f. red.

A runner breaking the tape. The model is said to be the German sprinter *Borchmeyer*.

Japan 1948. *3rd National Sports Games in Fukuoka*

5y. green.

A very stylish and attractive stamp showing a starting sprinter.

Guatemala 1950. *6th Central American and Caribbean Games*

3c. red and black.

Two runners at the finish before the tape.

Switzerland 1950. *Swiss Confederation Festival*

30+10c. purple.

Three sprinters at the gun.

Belgium 1950. *4th European Athletics Championships in Brussels*

8+4f. green.

Two sprinters at the finish. Like the rest of the stamps of this set the athletes are wearing their national insignia. In this case, an Italian is beating a Swede.

Israel 1950. *3rd Maccabiah Games in Tel Aviv*

80p. olive and black.

Starting sprinter and stylized race track.

Finland 1952. *15th Olympic Games in Helsinki*

25+4m. brown.

Starting sprinter with symbolic Ancient Greek runners in the background.

Hungary 1952. *15th Olympic Games*

30f. brown.

Sprinter at the tape.

Poland 1952. *Sports issue*

1.15z. light green.

A very badly drawn stamp showing sprinters at the tape.

Yugoslavia 1952. *15th Olympic Games*

10d. yellow and brown.

Starting sprinter. The same stamp was issued in different colours and with the overprint 'STT–VUJNA' for the Yugoslavian zone (B) of Trieste.

Spanish Sahara 1954. *Children's Charity issue*

10+5c. violet, 60c. brown.

In this charity set for children one design is said to be of running, but closely resembles a long-jumper's take-off.

Liberia 1955. *Sports issue*

25c. rose and green.

Considering the curves in the track this seems to be a quarter-mile race. It also appeared, with different colours, in a special sheet with a boxing stamp—in a small issue of only 5,000 stamps.

Brazil 1955. *5th National Children's Games in Rio de Janeiro*

60c. brown.

Each autumn (i.e. spring with us) special games are held with different kinds of events for children between six and fifteen years. This design shows boys at the start of a race.

Liechtenstein 1956. *Sports issue*
1f. red orange and grey brown.
Starting sprinters.

Yugoslavia 1956. *Olympic Year 1956*
10d. red lilac and brown.
Starting sprinter and deer.

China (Communist) 1957. *1st Chinese Workers' Games 1955*
8d. dark green, light brown, red and green.
Starting sprinter. Like the other stamps in the series this is adorned with a red flower.

The Dominican Republic 1957. *Olympic Victors 1956 (I)*
11c. grey green, red and blue.
Robert Morrow, U.S.A.

Lebanon 1957. *2nd Pan Arabian Games in Beirut*
2p. 50c. dark brown.
The emblem of the Games, with a picture of two runners.

Spanish Guinea 1958. *Sports issue*
80c. grey green, 3p. blue.
Sprinter at the tape.

Somalia 1958. *Sports issue*
2c. light violet.

Japan 1958. *3rd Asian Games in Tokyo*
14y. red yellow blue and black.
A sprinter at the finishing line.

The Dominican Republic 1958. *Olympic Victors 1956 (III)*
2c. light blue and grey brown.
Decathlon champion, *Milton Campbell*, U.S.A.

Austria 1959. *Austrian Workers' Sports Festival in Linz*
1s. red violet.

Argentina 1959. *3rd Pan American Games in Chicago*
20+10c. green and black.
Starting sprinter.

Togo 1960. *17th Olympic Games*
25f. violet red, orange and dark brown.
Starting sprinter.

San Marino 1960. *17th Olympic Games*
40l. yellow brown and red, 40l. red brown (imperf. in sheet).
At the tape.

Czechoslovakia 1960. *17th Olympic Games*
1k. orange yellow and grey.
Starting sprinters with Roman buildings in the background.

Roumania 1960. *Ordinary mail*
1.60l. violet blue.
Sprinter on the blocks.

Germany (West) 1960. *Olympic Year 1960*
10pf. olive green.
Ancient Greek sprinters from a vase (550 B.C.).

Russia 1960. *17th Olympic Games*
5k. multicoloured.
At the tape.

Mongolia 1960. *17th Olympic Games*
10m. violet, yellow and grey.
At the tape.

Surinam 1960. *17th Olympic Games*
15+7c. violet, red brown and black.
At the tape.

Greece 1960. *17th Olympic Games*
4.50d. multicoloured.
Ancient Greek runners.

Ghana 1960. *17th Olympic Games*
1s.3d. light brown, 2s.6d. light red (both also contain green, yellow and red).
Starting sprinters and map of Africa.

Bulgaria 1960. *17th Olympic Games in Rome*
2l. dark green and light rose, 2l. olive and light green (imperf.).
Sprinter.

Hungary 1960. *17th Olympic Games*
60f. grey green and yellow brown.
Ancient Greek race with arms.

Liberia 1960. *17th Olympic Games*
50c. red violet and violet brown (imperf. in a sheet).
Sprinter and Olympic Stadium of Rome.

Cuba 1960. *17th Olympic Games*
12c. red, 12c. grey blue (imperf. in sheet).
Stylized starting sprinter.

Somalia 1960. *17th Olympic Games*
0.45S. violet blue, 1.80S. red blue.
Running sprinters.

Philippines 1960. *17th Olympic Games*
10c. violet, red brown.
Starting sprinter.

Formosa (Nationalist China) 1960. *15th National Sports Games of Taiwan*
$3.20 yellow, orange and red.
Starting sprinter.

Riu Kiu Islands 1960. *8th National Games of Kyushu and Okinawa*
8c. grey and brown.
Starting sprinters.

MIDDLE- AND LONG-DISTANCE RUNNING

In the Ancient Olympic Games there was a race of four stadium lengths (about 800 yards) called *hippios*. During the Middle Ages, middle-distance races were arranged in England, but it was not until the nineteenth century that they were at all common. The mile race soon became the high spot in amateur competitions. Races from half to one-and-a-half miles are regarded as middle-distance running.

There also existed in the original Olympics a long-distance race, *dolichos* (twenty-four stadium lengths or about three miles). The distance could, however, be varied from between seven to twenty-four stadium lengths. During the Middle Ages long-distance running hardly existed, but from the end of the seventeenth century races were often held in England and she became the leading country at this kind of race.

In the following, no distinction has been drawn between middle- and long-distance running because of the difficulty of distinguishing one from the other on the various stamps.

Greece 1906. *Special Olympic Games in Athens*

1d. black, 2d. rose, 3d. yellow.

The same classical design on these Greek stamps shows four runners who, judging by style and arm movements, are competing in a long-distance race. On the left of the stamp is the pole that was the turning point of the track.

Belgium 1920. *7th Olympic Games in Antwerp*

15c. brown.

Probably inspired by the runner who brought news of the victory at Marathon to Athens in 490 B.C. The Marathon race is a modern event, however, introduced in the modern Olympic Games in 1896 on the initiative of the French historian, Bréal, who first drew attention to the myth about this messenger.

Netherlands 1928. *9th Olympic Games in Amsterdam*

10c. red.

Stylized long-distance runner.

Colombia 1935. *3rd National Games in Barranquilla*

7c. red.

This design is based on the duel between the Finn *Kolehmainen* and the Frenchman *Bouin* in the 5,000 m. race in the Olympic Games at Stockholm 1912.

Salvador 1935. *3rd Central American Games in San Salvador*

15c. red, 25c. violet, 30c. brown, 55c. blue, 1co. black.

A runner breaking the tape forms the design of this airmail set.

Colombia 1937. *4th National Games in Manizales*

1p. black.

Runner with an old-fashioned, artificial style.

France 1937. *Postal Workers' Sports Fund*

40+10c. lake.

Athletics on a sports ground with both runners and a discus-thrower in action. As the runners dominate the design it has been placed in this group.

Roumania 1937. *8th Balkan Games in Bucharest*

6+1l. brown.

A runner—probably middle-distance—breaking the tape.

Ecuador 1939. *Victory in the First Bolivar Games 1938*

10c. blue.

A long-distance runner—probably in a Marathon race.

Turkey 1940. *11th Balkan Games in Ankara*

3k. olive.

A long-distance runner with a perfect style, probably based on an action photograph of a Finn, *G. Höckert*, Olympic winner of the 5,000 m. in 1936.

Finland 1945. *Sports issue*

3.50+1.75m. violet.

A runner, no doubt inspired by Paavo Nurmi.

Roumania 1948. *Balkan Games in Sofia, Bulgaria, 1947*

2+2l. claret.

A runner within a laurel wreath.

Russia 1948. *Sports issue*

15k. violet.

Based on a photograph showing the start of a road race.

Roumania 1948. *Sports issue*

5+5l. green, 5+5l. brown (imperf.).

Three long-distance runners.

Bulgaria 1950. *Sports issue*
4l. green.
Two long-distance runners.

Roumania 1950. *Sports issue—Sport and Work—(G.M.A.)*
11l. green.
A rather badly composed design showing a number of runners unaccountably placed in the middle of the track.

Monaco 1953. *15th Olympic Games of 1952*
40f. black grey.
This badly drawn stamp baffles any attempt at analysis; it could even represent walking.

San Marino 1953. *Sports issue*
3l. blue green and black.
A runner near the tape; triangular-shaped stamp.

France 1953. *French Olympic successes in 1952*
25f. dark green and grey brown.
French-Algerian long-distance runner *Alain Mimoun O'Kacha.*

Formosa (Nationalist China) 1954. *Youth Day*
40c. blue, $5.00 red.
A long-distance runner with a national emblem and a Chinese temple in the background.

Czechoslovakia 1954. Sports issue
30h. sepia.
This stamp portrays, unmistakably, the great runner and the world-record holder, *Emil Zatopek*, followed by another runner.

Russia 1954. *Sports issue*
40k. brown and red brown.
Road race.

Japan 1955. *10th National Games in Kanagawa*
5y. blue grey.
Road race; according to official statements a 20 km. event.

Korea (South) 1955. *36th National Sports Games—80th Birthday of Syngman Rhee*
20w. brown violet, 55w. dark green.
Middle-distance runner rounding a bend.

Czechoslovakia 1956. *Kosice Marathon Race*
80h. red violet and light blue.
Five Marathon runners in the famous Kosice Race. Judging by the style, the second runner from the left seems to have entered the wrong race.

The Dominican Republic 1957. *Well-known Olympic Victors*
3c. violet and red, 11c. yellow blue and red.
Kitei Son, Japan, and *Paavo Nurmi*, Finland.

The Dominican Republic 1957. *Olympic Victors at Melbourne 1956 (I)*
5c. olive green, blue and red.
Mimoun, the Marathon winner.

Russia 1957. *16th Olympic Games 1956*
20k. red violet and green.
Vladimir Kuts, winner of the 5,000 and 10,000 m.

Roumania 1957. *10th International Athletic Championships in Bucharest*
1.75l. red white and black.
A runner with a deer in the background.

The Dominican Republic 1957. *Olympic Victors 1956 (II)*
2c. grey brown, green and orange.
This triangular-shaped stamp depicts *Ron Delany*, winner of the 1,500 m.

Somalia 1958. *Sports issue*
60c. light brown.
A native runner.

Roumania 1958. *3rd Youth Spartacist Games in Bucharest*
1l. brown.
Middle-distance runner.

The Dominican Republic 1959. *3rd Pan American Games in Chicago*
3c. violet and red, 11c. yellow blue and red.
Imperforate stamps (*Son* and *Nurmi*) of the Olympic issue of 1957, with a special surcharge.

Roumania 1959. *8th Balkan Games in Bucharest*
1l. brown and silver.
1958 issue with a special surcharge in silver.

Albania 1959. *1st National Spartacist Games*
5l. dark red.
Albanian middle-distance runner.

Yugoslavia 1960. *17th Olympic Games*
15d. violet grey, yellow and orange.
Stylized runner and shot-putter.

Poland 1960. *17th Olympic Games*
60g. violet red and white.
Figure representing *J. Kusoczinski*, who won the gold medal in the Olympic 10,000 m. 1932.

France 1960. *17th Olympic Games*
0.20f. red violet, dark brown and light blue.
Jean Bouin, the French running ace of the years before World War I (*see* Colombia 1935).

Tunisia 1960. *1st Tunisian participation in the Olympic Games*
25m. green blue.
Tunisian runner.

Morocco 1960. *17th Olympic Games*
30f. olive brown, red violet and violet blue.
Runner.

Spain 1960. *Sports issue*
25c. blue violet and red brown, 1.50p. dark green and grey brown.
Runner.

Costa Rica 1960. *17th Olympic Games*
1c. yellow black.
Runner at the tape.

RELAY-RUNNING

A predecessor to the modern relay-race was the ancient torch race which was originally a religious custom but later assumed the character of a sports event. Modern relay-racing was first introduced into American university sports about 1890. Relay-races are also run as publicity events over very long distances.

Under this heading, therefore, can be included the Olympic-torch relay which has been a part of all the Olympic Games since 1936.

Germany 1936. *11th Olympic Games in Berlin*
12+6pf. red.
For the first time the Olympic flame was carried from Olympia in Greece, where it had been kindled by the sun's rays, through seven countries and over a distance of more than 1,800 miles to Berlin, where it arrived twelve days later. Each runner had to cover a kilometre in about five minutes.

Lithuania 1938. *National Sports Festival at Kaunas*
60+15c. dark brown.
Stylized relay-runner breaking the tape.

Yugoslavia 1938. *Charity Series for Railway Officials*
2+2d. mauve.
Torch runner with a peculiar style.

Russia 1940. *Physical Culture Day*
15k. red.
The stamp shows a photograph of a relay-racer at full speed in a stadium packed with spectators.

Korea 1948. *14th Olympic Games in London*
10w. violet.
Torch runner in front of the Olympic rings.

Japan 1949. *4th National Games in Tokyo*
8y. brown.
Handing over the baton.

Belgium 1950. *4th European Athletic Championships in Brussels*
1.75f.+25c. red.
This stamp, showing a British relay team changing the baton, appeared later in a special sheet with a premium for the benefit of sport.

Bolivia 1951. *5th South American Championships in La Paz 1948*
3.00 sepia and black.
Handing over the baton.

Czechoslovakia 1952. *United Czechoslovakian Sports issue*
1.50k. sepia.
Baton-changing between two Czech runners.

Hungary 1953. *Inauguration of Nép Stadium in Budapest*
3fo. red and brown.
Hungarian relay team.

Greece 1954. *5th Anniversary NATO issue*
1200d. orange yellow.
A stylized Ancient Greek torch runner.

Poland 1954. *2nd National Spartacist Games in Warsaw*
1z. dark blue.
Baton-changing.

San Marino 1955. *1st Olympic Sports Stamps Exhibition in San Marino*
120l. green red and brown.
Runner handing over the baton. This stamp was awarded third place in the Bonacossa Competition, 1955.

Russia 1956. *National Spartacist Games*
10k. rose.
Handing over the baton.

The Dominican Republic 1958. *Olympic Victors of 1956 (III)*
11c. olive and blue.
Charles Jenkins and *Tom Courtney* baton-changing (in the winning) U.S.A., 4 × 400 m. team.

U.S.A. 1959. *3rd Pan American Games in Chicago*
3c. red and blue.
Runner with a torch.

Korea (South) 1959. *40th National Games*
40w. light blue and red brown (also imperf. in sheet).
Changing baton.

Panama 1960. *17th Olympic Games*
50c. brown (also imperf. in sheet).
Runner with torch.

Somalia 1960. *17th Olympic Games*
0.10S. yellow and blue.
Handing over the baton.

HURDLING

Modern hurdle-racing originated in England and by 1864 the 120 yards hurdle race was already popular. The longer distance (440 yards) was introduced much later.

Hurdle-racing is one of the most popular sports subjects on stamps. This can be explained by the obvious beauty of the movements involved, which lend themselves to graceful reproduction. You will find some of the most attractive of sports stamps among those depicting hurdling.

Hungary 1925. *Sports issue*
2,500k. sepia.
Hungary was the first country to issue sports stamps having no connection with any particular event. In this set you will find a stamp with a hurdler.

Portugal 1928. *9th Olympic Games in Amsterdam*
15c. red and black.
A hurdler with the national emblem and a sixteenth-century ship.

Cuba 1930. *2nd Central American Games in Havana*
1c. green, 2c. red, 5c. blue, 10c. light brown, 20c. purple.
The design shows a hurdler rounding a bend of the track, suggesting that this is a longer distance race.

Colombia 1935. *3rd National Games in Barranquilla*
10c. blue and brown.
A rather unattractive stamp with a bad design and ugly colours.

Russia 1935. *World Spartacist Games in Moscow*
3k. brown and blue.
This diamond-shaped stamp pictures two hurdlers, shoulder to shoulder.

Roumania 1937. *8th Balkan Games in Bucharest*
4+1l. red.
A hurdler striding over the obstacles.

Yugoslavia 1938. *9th Balkan Games in Belgrade*
1+1d. green.
Three hurdlers.

Turkey 1940. *11th Balkan Games in Ankara*
8k. brown.
Turkey continued the tradition of depicting hurdling in the Balkan Games series with a forceful stamp.

Roumania 1946. *Youth Movement Propaganda*
10+200l. purple and blue.
Two hurdlers whose style leaves a lot to be desired.

Japan 1947. *2nd National Sports Games in Kanazawa*
1y. 20s. magenta.
Two hurdlers.

Monaco 1948. *Olympic Games*
50c. green.
From a picture of the French hurdler *Arifon.*

Bulgaria 1949. *Physical Culture Campaign*
9l. olive.
This design shows unmistakably the present place of sport in the plans of the totalitarian powers. Its relation to military service is shown by providing the hurdler with a 'shadow'—a soldier in full equipment leaping the same obstacle—but in his case the peaceful hurdle has changed into a barbed-wire fence.

Belgium 1950. *4th European Athletic Championships in Brussels*
20+5c. green.
A Belgian hurdler, also the poster of the Championships.

Bolivia 1951. *5th South American Championships in La Paz 1948*
1b. brown and black.
Hurdle race; probably the quarter-mile distance.

Luxemburg 1952. *Sports issue*

1f. green.

This stamp, produced by the well-known printing firm of Courvoisier in Switzerland, received the first prize in the competition for the Bonacossa Medal, 1952, the first time it was conferred.

Spanish Sahara 1953. *Children's Charity issue*

5+5c. chestnut, 15c. green.

These stamps, said to picture a hurdle race, show two burnous-clad men jumping over a lath.

San Marino 1955. *1st Olympic Sports Stamps Exhibition in San Marino*

80l. red, red brown and black.

Hurdlers in action.

Liechtenstein 1956. *Sports issue*

20c. yellow olive and violet brown.

An attractive design showing the hurdler in his take-off stride.

The Dominican Republic 1957. *Well-known Olympic Victors*

5c. orange red and blue.

Lord Burghley, winner of the Olympic 400 m. hurdle race in Amsterdam in 1928.

Bulgaria 1958. *Balkan Games in Sofia*

80s. green.

A simple but attractive impression of a hurdler striding over the hurdle.

Czechoslovakia 1959. *Sports issue*

1k. olive yellow and red violet.

Hurdler in action.

The Dominican Republic 1959. *3rd Pan American Games in Chicago*

5c. orange red and blue.

Imperforate stamp (*Burghley*) of 1957 Olympic issue (I) with special surcharge.

Panama 1959. *3rd Pan American Games in Chicago*

20c. green and red brown.

Hurdler jumping low hurdles.

Belgian Congo 1960. *17th Olympic Games*

1.50f.+50c. red and green.

Two hurdlers.

Ruanda Urundi 1960. *17th Olympic Games*
1.50f.+50c. dark red and black.
As Belgian Congo.

Mongolia 1960. *17th Olympic Games*
30m. olive yellow, green and grey.
Two hurdlers and Olympic emblem.

Turkey 1960. *17th Olympic Games*
30k. red violet.
Turkish hurdler.

Formosa (Nationalist China) 1960. *15th National Sports Games of Taiwan*
$3.00 grey brown, beige and dark brown.
Chinese hurdler.

STEEPLECHASING

Like hurdling, this form of running originated in English public schools during the first part of the nineteenth century. The steeplechase has been on the English championships schedule since 1879. It was not until the 1920's, however, that the event reached the Continent and it did not become really popular until after the Second World War.

Poland 1956. *16th Olympic Games in Melbourne*
40g. red brown and green.
As the world record at the time of the issue was held by the Pole, *Chromik*, it was natural for the Poles to choose this event for a stamp design.

The Dominican Republic 1957. *Olympic Victors in Melbourne 1956 (I)*
16c. light violet blue, blue and red.
Chris Brasher, Great Britain, just passing the water jump.

THROWING THE DISCUS

Discus-throwing originated in Ancient Greece, not as a separate event but forming a part of the pentathlon. Discus-throwing was also performed in Imperial Rome but was never popular. During the Middle Ages, and indeed to the end of the nineteenth century, the event was completely neglected. Modern discus-throwing started simultaneously in Germany and Greece about 1870.

Discus-throwing is a popular sports subject in the world of stamps. Frequently the well-known 'Discobolus' by Myron has been used as the basis for the design. This statue embodies, with its beautiful lines, the classical sports ideal and more than half the designs reproduced have been inspired by it.

Greece 1896. *1st Olympic Games in Athens*
5l. mauve, 10l. grey.
The first time that 'Discobolus' appeared on a stamp.

Greece 1906. *Special Olympic Games in Athens*
1l. brown, 2l. black.
Apollo making the preliminary swing before throwing, ancient style.

Belgium 1920. *7th Olympic Games in Antwerp*
5c. green.
'Discobolus.'

Costa Rica 1924. *National Games in San José*
5c. green.
This badly drawn stamp is in complete contrast to the Belgian issue. The statue is quite unproportional.

U.S.A. 1932. *10th Olympic Games in Los Angeles*
5c. blue.
'Discobolus' again, this time in front of a globe.

Colombia 1935. *3rd National Games in Barranquilla*
4c. green.
'Discobolus.'

Salvador 1935. *3rd Central American Games in San Salvador*
5c. red, 8c. blue, 10c. orange, 15c. brown, 37c. green.
This design pictures the classical style as portrayed by Myron, but probably for reasons of decency the designer has given the thrower sports wear.

Colombia 1937. *4th National Games in Manizales*
10c. red.
This small-sized stamp was the first to show the modern discus-thrower.

The Dominican Republic 1937. *1st National Games in Ciudad Trujillo*
1c. green, 3c. violet, 7c. blue.
'Discobolus'; in the background the blue-white-red Dominican flag.

Russia 1938. *Sports issue*
10k. black.
Final phase of the throw.

Bulgaria 1939. *9th National Gymnastics and Sports Festival in Sofia*
4l. brown.
'Discobolus' against a background of white pillars and ruins.

Greece 1939. *10th Balkan Games in Athens*
6d. red brown.
An Ancient Greek thrower at the start of the swing.

Turkey 1940. *11th Balkan Games in Ankara*
10k. dark blue.
A modern design picturing the start of the swing.

Japan 1947. *2nd National Sports Games in Kanazawa*
1.20y. magenta.
The designer was inspired by a photograph of the Berlin gold-medal winner, *K. Carpenter*, U.S.A.

Monaco 1948. *14th Olympic Games*
2f. blue green.
'Discobolus' brought up to date.

Peru 1948. *14th Olympic Games*
5so. green.
'Discobolus' in a beautiful classical frame, with the Olympic rings.

Panama 1950. *Physical Culture Fund*
0.01b. violet and black.
'Discobolus.'

San Marino 1953. *Sports issue*
1l. brown and black.
'Discobolus' against a background of the San Marino Hills; triangular in shape.

Hungary 1953. *Inauguration of the Nép Stadium in Budapest*
50f. brown and olive.
Hungarian discus-thrower in the swing, watched by a team-mate.

Philippines 1954. *2nd Asian Games in Manila*
5c. blue.
Start of the swing.

Bulgaria 1956. *16th Olympic Games*
12s. red brown.
Start of the swing.

Liberia 1956. *16th Olympic Games*
6c. green grey.
'Discobolus.'

Peru 1956. *16th Olympic Games*
5s. green.
The 'Discobolus' from the Olympic set of 1948 overprinted 'Melbourne 1956'.

The Dominican Republic 1957. *Well-known Olympic Victors*
7c. green, blue and red.
The double decathlon champion of 1948 and 1952, *Bob Mathias*, U.S.A., throwing the discus.

The Dominican Republic 1957. *Olympic Victors 1956 (II)*
15c. red and blue.
Winner in Melbourne, *Alfred Oerter*, U.S.A.

Somalia 1958. *Sports issue*
0.05S. red orange.
A native discus-thrower.

Haiti 1959. *3rd Pan American Games in Chicago*
50c. green and red violet, 1.50g. blue and grey brown.
'Discobolus' and Haitian flag.

San Marino 1959. *World University Games in Turin*
30l. orange.
As San Marino 1953.

The Dominican Republic 1959. *3rd Pan American Games in Chicago*
7c. green, blue and red.
Imperforate stamp (*Mathias*) of 1957 Olympic issue (I) with special surcharge.

Lebanon 1959. *3rd Mediterranean Games in Beirut*
15p. green grey.
'Discobolus'.

Haiti 1959. *Sports issue*
50c. green and red violet, 1.50g. blue and grey brown.
Stamps of the Pan American Games issue with special surcharge: 'Pour le sport+0.75 centimes.'

Haiti 1960. *8th Winter Olympic Games*
50c. green and red violet, 1.50g. blue and grey brown.
Pan American Games issue with special Olympic surcharge.

Togo 1960. *17th Olympic Games*
15f. green and red brown.
Discus-thrower.

Belgian Congo 1960. *17th Olympic Games*
6.50f.+3.50f. red brown and red.
The swing.

Ruanda Urundi 1960. *17th Olympic Games*
6.50f.+3.50f. olive green and red.
As Belgian Congo.

Italy 1960. *17th Olympic Games*
35l. violet red.
'Discobolus.'

Germany (West) 1960. *Olympic Year 1960*
20pf. red.
Ancient Greek discus- and javelin-throwers.

Greece 1960. *17th Olympic Games*
2.50d. light blue, red brown and black.
Ancient Greek discus-thrower.

Haiti 1960. *17th Olympic Games (I) and (II)*
20c. red and dark blue, 1.50g. green and red violet.
'Discobolus' and the Rome Olympic Stadium. The high value reappeared a few weeks later surcharged 25c.

Hungary 1960. *17th Olympic Games*
40f. yellow and yellow brown.
'Discobolus.'

Formosa (Nationalist China) 1960. *15th National Taiwan Games*
$0.80 light red violet, red violet and yellow.
The swing.

THROWING THE JAVELIN

Javelin-throwing is one of the earliest of known sports. It formed a part of the pentathlon of the Ancient Games, where target- as well as length-throwing was practised. In the Middle Ages javelin-throwing was one of the 'gallant sports', and formed part of the education of a knight.

Javelin-throwing is one of the most graceful of sports events and consequently has interested many stamp designers.

Germany 1936. *11th Olympic Games*
12+6pf. red.
A javelin-thrower with the Olympic rings on his breast. The Germans regarded this as a good omen because the German *Stöck* was, quite unexpectedly, the winner of this event during the Games that followed.

Roumania 1937. *25th Anniversary of the Roumanian Sports Union*
1+0.50l. violet.
Thrower pictured from the rear.

Roumania 1937. *8th Balkan Games in Bucharest*
2+1l. green.
The Roumanians issued, strangely enough, two javelin stamps in the same year, with only a few months' interval. The style of this stamp leaves much to be desired.

Greece 1939. *10th Balkan Games in Athens*
3d. red.
The Greeks followed the Roumanian example by issuing two javelin stamps within a year. The javelin-thrower here is shown against a background of a round disc symbolizing the bowls on which such designs

were painted in ancient times. On this stamp you can see how a good throw was performed during the Ancient Olympic Games. When throwing, a leather sling was used at the javelin's centre of gravity to make the throw longer by rotation. This leather sling can be seen on the stamp.

Greece 1940. *National Youth Movement Issue*
15d. black and green.
Javelin-thrower wearing the Movement's emblem. During the short Greek occupation of Albania, in 1941, this stamp was overprinted for use there.

Mexico 1941. *National Revolution Games in Mexico City*
10c. green.
A forceful javelin design with the Revolutionary Monument of Mexico City in the background, together with Mexican flags.

Finland 1945. *Sports issue*
7+3.50m. light brown.
This stamp was inspired by a picture of the former world-record holder *M. Järvinen.*

Bulgaria 1949. *Sports issue*
4l. red.
As on the hurdler stamp in the same set, the military importance of sport is shown here by a military 'shadow' figure. The javelin-thrower has a hand-grenade-throwing soldier behind him.

Japan 1949. *4th National Sports Games in Tokyo*
8y. brown.
An excellent study of a javelin-thrower.

Belgium 1950. *4th European Athletic Championships in Brussels*
90+10c. purple.
Finnish javelin-thrower demonstrating a model throw.

Hungary 1950. *Sports issue*
40f. blue and olive.
A very attractive javelin design.

Bolivia 1951. *5th South American Championships in La Paz 1948*
2.50b. orange and black.
Javelin-thrower.

Poland 1954. *2nd National Spartacist Games in Warsaw*
60g. orange brown, 1.55z. blue grey.
A stylized design showing man and woman javelin-throwers.

San Marino 1954. *Sports issue*
8l. red violet and violet.
Javelin-thrower.

Liechtenstein 1956. *Sports issue*
10c. orange brown and grey green.
A beautifully composed stamp both in style and colour.

Germany (East) 1956. *2nd National Sports and Gymnastic Festival in Leipzig*
10pf. black blue.
Javelin-thrower just before release.

Germany (East) 1956. *16th Olympic Games*
35pf. grey blue.
An Ancient Greek javelin-thrower from 525 B.C.

Poland 1956. *16th Olympic Games*
60g. olive brown and rose.
The man who inspired this beautiful design was *Sidlo*, who was favourite in Melbourne but finished as runner-up.

The Dominican Republic 1957. *Olympic Winners in Melbourne 1956 (I)*
3c. grey blue, blue and red.
The man who beat *Sidlo* was the Norwegian, *E. Danielsen*. The stamp is the first to show the follow-through.

Russia 1957. *3rd World Youth Games in Moscow*
60k. grey brown and blue.
A forceful picture of a Russian javelin-thrower.

Roumania 1957. *10th International Athletic Championships in Bucharest*
55b. yellow, black and white.
A javelin-thrower with a buffalo in the background.

Spanish Guinea 1957. *30th Flight Anniversary Issue*
25p. olive.
This stamp was issued to celebrate the Squadron Flight between Melilla in Spanish Morocco and Fernando Poo in 1927. The arm of a javelin-thrower was chosen for the design.

Ifni 1959. *Sports issue*
50+20c. brown grey.
Javelin-thrower.

Belgian Congo 1960. *17th Olympic Games*
3f.+1.25f. red violet and blue.
The throw.

Ruanda Urundi 1960. *17th Olympic Games*
3f.+1.25f. red orange and green.
As Belgian Congo.

Germany (West) 1960. *Olympic Year 1960*
20pf. red.
Ancient Greek javelin-thrower (cf. discus throwing).

Greece 1960. *17th Olympic Games*
5d. green blue, red brown and black.
Ancient Greek javelin-thrower.

Liberia 1960. *17th Olympic Games*
25c. violet blue and violet brown.
Javelin-thrower and native hunter.

Panama 1960. *17th Olympic Games*
25c. light blue.
The throw.

PUTTING THE SHOT

Shot-putting is a modern sports event based on the ancient stone-putting. Stone-putting is the oldest form of throwing event and existed in the Ancient Olympic Games.

Of the designs, only one stamp depicts the throw itself; the remainder all show the 'wind-up'.

Netherlands 1928. *9th Olympic Games*
$7\frac{1}{2}+2\frac{1}{2}$c. orange.
Stylized picture of a shot-putter.

Switzerland 1932. *Children's Charity issue*
10c. orange.
A man putting a big stone—one of the national sports of Switzerland.

Yugoslavia 1938. *9th Balkan Games in Belgrade*
2+2d. blue.
This is one of the few throwing stamps in which you can see the object thrown actually leaving the hand.

Albania 1946. *12th Balkan Games in Tirana*
1q. black lilac, 2q. light green, 5q. brown, 10q. red, 20q. blue, 40q. lilac, 1f. orange.
Well-drawn stamps in beautiful colours. In the background a soldier throwing a hand grenade can be seen.

Yugoslavia 1948. *14th Balkan Games in Belgrade*
2+1d. green.
A shot-putter in the national sports colours.

Switzerland 1950. *Swiss Confederation Festival issue*
10+10c. green.
Stone-putting.

Bulgaria 1950. *Sports issue*
20l. blue.
Perhaps the most stylish shot-putting stamp yet issued.

Japan 1951. *6th National Games in Hiroshima*
2y. brown.
Shot-putter at the start of the throw.

Bulgaria 1958. *Balkan Games in Sofia*
4l. red violet.
Shot-putter.

Yugoslavia 1960. *17th Olympic Games*
15d. violet grey, yellow and orange.
Stylized shot-putter and runner.

San Marino 1960. *17th Olympic Games*
1l. rose and dark violet, 1l. green and red brown (imperf. in sheet).
Shot-putter.

Belgium 1960. *Independence of Belgian Congo*
2.50f. light blue.
Four native shot-putters in training.

Surinam 1960. *17th Olympic Games*
8+4c. grey, red brown and black.
Shot-putter.

Lebanon 1960. *17th Olympic Games*
7.50+7.50p. violet brown.
Shot-putter.

HAMMER-THROWING

Hammer-throwing, originally using an ordinary blacksmith's hammer, was a Celtic sport, introduced into Scotland about A.D. 300, from where it spread to England, eventually reaching court circles—Henry VIII, among others, distinguished himself at this sport. In Scotland and in Ireland the sport has continued in its original form until the present day, but it fell from favour in England and did not reappear until 1866 when it was recognized in the championships schedule as a modern sport. Only comparatively recently has the event been recognized by stamp designers.

Hungary 1952. *15th Olympic Games*
1.70fo. orange.
The Hungarians won gold medals in the event both in London and Helsinki.

Poland 1955. *2nd World Youth Games in Warsaw*
40g. wine red.
Hammer-thrower in the swing.

Israel 1958. *5th Maccabiah Games*
500p. olive yellow and red violet.
A beautifully designed stamp showing a forceful hammer-throw.

Japan 1959. *14th National Games*
5y. blue grey.

LONG-JUMP

In the Ancient Olympic Games the long-jump did not exist as a special event but formed part of the pentathlon and was often practised in the gymnasiums. Long-jumping was also very popular in the medieval folk festivals, and especially in England such competitions were arranged in the fifteenth and sixteenth centuries.

The earliest of these stamps had classical designs, the first modern ones surprisingly not appearing until 1956.

Greece 1906. *Special Olympic Games in Athens*

3l. orange, 5l. green.

An Ancient Greek long-jumper.

Greece 1939. *10th Balkan Games in Athens*

8d. blue on grey.

This stamp also has a classical design. The athlete is here pictured jumping with 'halters' in his hands.

Japan 1956. *11th National Sports Games in Hyogo*

5y. grey violet.

Long-jumper in the air.

The Dominican Republic 1957. *Well-known Olympic Victors*

2c. grey brown, blue and red.

Jesse Owens, U.S.A., pictured in a long-jump during the Olympic Games in Berlin 1936.

Roumania 1957. *10th International Athletic Championships in Bucharest*

20d. blue, white and black.

A stylized long-jumper with a bird in the background.

Spanish Guinea 1958. *Sports issue*

15c. yellow brown, 2.30c. light violet.

A coloured long-jumper just before landing.

Haiti 1958. *30th Anniversary of Silvio Cator's long-jump world record in 1928*

5c. olive green, 10c. yellow brown, 20c. red violet, 50c. light violet, 50c. light green, 1g. orange brown, 5g. blue grey.

Haiti could not resist following the example set by her neighbour, the

Dominican Republic, of issuing stamps depicting well-known athletes. The set issued contained no less than seven stamps, the three highest denominations being for airmail. The designs portrayed Haiti's one and only well-known athlete, *Silvio Cator*, who won the Olympic silver medal in 1928 for the long-jump and a few weeks later set a new world record in Paris with 7.93 m.

The Dominican Republic 1959. *3rd Pan American Games in Chicago*

2c. grey brown, blue and red.

Imperforate stamp (*Owens*) of 1957 Olympic issue (I) with special surcharge.

Monaco 1960. *17th Olympic Games*

0.15f. red violet, olive brown and red.

Jumper in action.

Greece 1960. *17th Olympic Games*

1.50d. yellow orange, red brown and black.

Ancient Greek long-jumper from about 500 B.C.

HIGH-JUMP

The high-jump never formed part of the Ancient Games. During the Middle Ages it is said to have been arranged as a test of skill and may also have been practised by the Vikings. As a modern competitive sport, high-jumping originated in Scotland.

Roumania 1937. *8th Balkan Games in Bucharest*

10+1l. blue.

'Scissors' style.

Japan 1948. *3rd National Sports Games in Fukuoka*

5y. green.

'Scissors' style.

Russia 1949. *Sports issue*

2r. black.

Strangely, a picture of the Californian style—the so-called 'Western roll'!

Brazil 1958. *8th Children's Games*

2.50c. rose.

A boy using the 'scissors' style.

Bulgaria 1958. *Balkan Games*
60s. blue.
A simply but beautifully drawn stamp depicting diving style.

Czechoslovakia 1959. *Sports issue*
2k. light ultramarine and brown.
Czech high-jumper (probably *Lansky*) jumping 2·10 m. (6 ft. 10⅔ in.).

Yugoslavia 1959. *Partisan Games*
15d. violet blue and brown.
Stylized high-jumper and runners.

Germany (East) 1959. *3rd Gymnastics and Sports Festival in Leipzig*
10+5pf. dark green.
Jumper passing over the bar in diving style.

Belgian Congo 1960. *17th Olympic Games*
50c.+25c. blue and red.
High-jumper, 'scissors' style.

Ruanda Urundi 1960. *17th Olympic Games*
50c.+25c. blue grey and red.
As Belgian Congo.

Mongolia 1960. *17th Olympic Games*
70m. yellow green, violet and grey.
High-jumper, diving style.

HOP, STEP AND JUMP

The hop, step and jump is an old Irish event that spread to other countries relatively late and which, up to the 1910's, was dominated by the Irish.

The Dominican Republic 1957. *Olympic Victors in Melbourne 1956 (I)*
17c. light brown, blue green, green, yellow and blue.
The Olympic winner, *A. Ferreira da Silva*, Brazil.

POLE-VAULT

Pole-vault was probably practised in the later part of the Middle Ages, and even earlier still on the East Coast, where the peasants used long poles to jump over ditches, canals and brooks. Primitive events in long-jumping with a pole were arranged but high-jumping using a pole probably did not exist until the seventeenth century. Firmer rules were drafted in the nineteenth century, and the event spread to U.S.A., which has dominated in competitions for more than half a century.

Bulgaria 1935. *8th Gymnastic Games in Sofia*
7l. blue.
Probably an unsuccessful attempt.

Yugoslavia 1938. *9th Balkan Games in Belgrade*
1.50+1.50d. red violet.
The jumper has already passed the crossbar and is just leaving the pole.

Turkey 1940. *11th Balkan Games in Ankara*
6k. red.
The Olympic victor in Berlin 1936, *Earle Meadows*, U.S.A.

Yugoslavia 1948. *14th Balkan Games in Belgrade*
5+2d. grey blue.
A Yugoslav vaulter passing the crossbar.

Nicaragua 1949. *10th World Amateur Baseball Championships in Managua 1948*
3c. green, 1cor. blue (*airmail*).
Pole vaulter in a style which leaves a lot to be desired.

Guatemala 1950. *6th Central American and Caribbean Games*
4c. brown and black.
An attractive stamp showing the crossing of the bar.

Belgium 1950. *4th European Athletics Championships in Brussels*
4+2f. light blue.
A stylish design with Brussels' modern Heysel Stadium in the background.

Japan 1950. *5th National Sports Games in Nagoya*
8y. brown.
Pole-vaulting.

Liechtenstein 1956. *Sports issue*
40c. light blue and red brown.
A very beautiful design depicting the 'bow'.

Bulgaria 1956. *16th Olympic Games*
16s. yellow brown.
Same design as above.

WOMEN'S ATHLETICS

Women's athletics have existed since ancient times. After the First World War women's athletics expanded rapidly, and in 1921 the International Female Athletic Union was formed on the initiative of Alice Milliat. Women's athletic events were introduced to the Olympic Games in 1928 at Amsterdam.

As will be seen, women's athletics is a very popular subject on stamps and has therefore its own section in which the various sports events have been collected together.

Lithuania 1938. *National Sports Festival in Kaunas*
15+5c. red.
This is the first stamp to picture women's sports. Javelin-throwing was chosen for the stylized design.

Russia 1938. *Sports issue*
4k. green.
Two women sprinters at the tape.

Ecuador 1939. *Victory at the First Bolivar Games 1938*
10c. orange.
The victorious sprinter *Carola Castro* from Ecuador.

Germany 1939. *German Postal Employees' Fund*
15+10pf. claret.
The recreations of postal workers—a girl throwing a javelin in the foreground; in the background girls performing gymnastic exercises.

Roumania 1945. *Sports Propaganda and Charity issue*
12+188l. olive green, 12+188l. orange red (imperf.).
A woman discus-thrower in modified, 'Discobolus' style.

Yugoslavia 1947. *Federal Sports Festival in Belgrade*
2d. 50p. red.
A girl runner.

Roumania 1948. *13th Balkan Games in Sofia, Bulgaria, 1947*
1+1l. grey brown.
Discus-throwing girl within a laurel.

Yugoslavia 1948. *17th Balkan Games in Belgrade*
3+1d. red.
As mentioned earlier, the designer was inspired by a photograph of the American hurdling champion *Nancy Cowperthwaite*, Yugoslav colours being substituted for American. The Games were boycotted by the other Balkan nations, for political reasons, and were cancelled.

Czechoslovakia 1951. *9th Sokol Congress and Games in Prague*
1k. 50h. red brown.
The Soviet world-record discus-thrower, *Nina Dumbadze*.

Sweden 1953. *50th Anniversary Swedish Sports Federation*
40ö blue.
One value in this anniversary set depicts the national women's event, *slungboll* (sling ball).

Czechoslovakia 1953. *Sports issue*
60h. purple.
Dana Zatopkova, wife of *E. Zatopek*, making her winning Olympic throw, 1952.

Russia 1954. *Sports issue*
40k. black and chestnut.
A heat in the women's 80 m. hurdles.

Brazil 1956. *6th Children's Games*
2.50c. blue.
Two girls handing over the baton in a relay race.

Germany (East) 1956. *2nd National Sports and Gymnastic Festival in Leipzig 1956*

15pf. red violet.

This stamp, showing a girl hurdling, is a so-called 'blocked' denomination of which only comparatively small numbers were issued. It may therefore be hard to obtain.

NOTE: *Iron Curtain countries tend to issue sets which include one value which is controlled and achieves a scarcity value out of proportion with others in the set.*

Netherlands 1956. *16th Olympic Games in Melbourne*

5+3c. yellow and black.

Woman sprinter.

Brazil 1956. *8th Spring Games in Rio de Janeiro*

2.50c. brown red.

Girl hurdling.

Hungary 1956. *16th Olympic Games*

60f. grey green and brown.

Hurdling race.

Roumania 1956. *16th Olympic Games*

1.75l. violet.

High-jump.

Poland 1956. *16th Olympic Games*

1.55z. red brown and orange.

This has the same frame as the earlier Olympic series, and appeared after the Games to commemorate the sole Polish gold-medal winner—long-jumper *Elzbieta Krzesinska.*

The Dominican Republic 1957. *Well-known Olympic Victors*

1c. red brown and blue, 17c. blue grey and red.

Fanny Blankers-Koen, Netherlands, winning the 200 m. in the 1948 Olympic Games at London and *Mildred Didrickson*, U.S.A., the 80 m. hurdles at the 1932 Olympic Games in Los Angeles.

China 1957. *1st Chinese Workers' Games 1955*

4d. violet red, brown, red and green.

A woman shot-putter.

Russia 1957. *16th Olympic Games*
20k. grey blue.
The Olympic women's champion, *I. Jaunzeme*, who won the javelin-throwing event.

The Dominican Republic 1957. *Olympic Victors in Melbourne 1956 (I)*
2c. orange, dark blue and red.
Betty Cuthbert, Australia.

The Dominican Republic 1957. *Olympic Victors 1956 (II)*
17c. red violet, dark blue and red.
Another Australian woman athlete—*Shirley Strickland.*

Bulgaria 1958. *Balkan Games in Sofia*
16s. red brown, 44s. olive green.
A woman sprinter at the tape and a javelin-thrower, both simply yet beautifully drawn.

Czechoslovakia 1959. *Sports issue*
30h. orange brown.
Javelin-throwing.

Russia 1959. *2nd National Spartacist Games*
25k. yellow green and red brown.
Sprinting, with sling-ball, javelin-throwing and hurdling in background.

The Dominican Republic 1959. *3rd Pan American Games in Chicago*
1c. red brown and blue, 17c. blue grey and red.
Imperforate (*Blankers-Koen* and *Didrickson*) of 1957 Olympic issue (I), special surcharge.

Brazil 1959. *11th Spring Games*
2.50c. violet red.
Shot-putting.

China (Communist) 1959. *1st National Games in Peking*
8d. yellow, red brown and black, 8d. light blue, red brown and black.
Sprinting and high-jump.

Germany (East) 1960. *17th Olympic Games*
10pf. orange brown and green.
Sprinting.

Roumania 1960. *17th Olympic Games (I)*

1.20l. grey, red and green (also imperf.).

Iolanda Balas, the Roumanian high-jump phenomenon, no doubt inspired the designer.

Roumania 1960. *17th Olympic Games (II)*

55b. blue.

As above.

Poland 1960. *17th Olympic Games*

60g. blue, 2.50z. green.

Figures in relief representing *H. Konopacka*, discus-throwing and *E. Krzesinska*, long-jumping.

The Dominican Republic 1960. *Olympic Victors 1956 (IV)*

3c. red brown and grey blue.

Mildred McDaniel, U.S.A., high-jumping.

North Korea 1960. *15th Anniversary of the Republic*

5w. yellow, green, orange, blue and black.

Woman runner at the tape.

WALKING

The oldest known walking competitions took place in England at the end of the seventeenth century. Not until the end of the nineteenth century were the present rules introduced, and walking formed a part of the British championship programme for the first time in 1866. About the turn of the century the sport spread to the Continent, particularly Germany and France. Walking has been featured at all the Olympic Games since 1906 with the exception of 1928.

San Marino 1954. *Sports issue*

1l. rose and blue, 80l. green and blue.

A walker with a somewhat artificial style.

The Dominican Republic 1957. *Well-known Olympic Victors*

16c. red and green.

The Italian walker, *Ugo Frigerio*, who dominated the walking events of the 1920's.

The Dominican Republic 1957. *Olympic Victors in Melbourne 1956 (I)*
7c. red brown, dark blue and red.
The victor of the 50 km. walk, *Norman Read*, New Zealand.

The Dominican Republic 1959. *3rd Pan American Games in Chicago*
16c. red and green.
Imperforate stamp (*Frigerio*) of 1957 Olympic issue (I) with special surcharge.

San Marino 1960. *17th Olympic Games*
3l. olive brown and dark violet, 3l. green and red brown (imperf. in sheet).
Walker.

Liberia 1960. *17th Olympic Games*
15c. orange and violet brown.
A walker and a native carrying buckets on a stick.

HAND-GRENADE THROWING

Hand-grenade throwing (not 'live'!) has become a regular event in athletic competitions in Russia and several other countries. Victory is determined by length of throw.

Russia 1940. *2nd Day of Physical Culture*
1r. olive grey.
A Moscow athlete throwing a hand grenade in a stadium.

4. BADMINTON

Badminton was introduced to Great Britain in the beginning of the 1870's by British officers from India, where it had been played for centuries. It was officially demonstrated for the first time in 1873, under the name 'Poona', at Badminton in Gloucestershire, hence its present name. New rules were laid down in 1887 and the game spread in the 1920's to the Dominions and other countries. Denmark and U.S.A. were the leading exponents in the 1940's, but the game is now dominated by the countries of South-East Asia.

Indonesia 1958. *Victory in the Thomas Cup Tournament 1958*
25s. light red, 50s. yellow, 1r. light brown.
Indonesia won the Thomas Cup in 1958, beating Malaya. To commemorate this a set of three values was issued, depicting the Thomas Cup with the Indonesian flag in the background.

Japan 1958. *13th National Games in Toyama*
5y. red violet.
A woman badminton player smashing.

5. BASEBALL

Baseball originated from a game called 'town ball' played in U.S.A. about 1800. Modern baseball began in 1839 when a young engineer, Abner Doubleday from Cooperstown, evolved it from 'town ball' and drew up a set of rules. The game spread rapidly and is now regarded as the national sport of U.S.A.

Though more or less unknown to the European public, baseball is the most popular ball game in the New World. Not surprisingly, the stamps depicting the game have all been issued by non-European countries.

Philippines 1934. *10th Far Eastern Games in Manila*
2c. light brown.
Catcher and batter in full action.

Colombia 1935. *3rd National Games in Barranquilla*
18c. violet and yellow.
A baseman trying to stop the runner reaching base.

Nicaragua 1937. *Sports issue*
1c. yellow, red, blue and green.
Stamps issued to finance the participation of Nicaragua in the Central American Games in Panama the following year. Showing a batter in action, they all have the same denomination and were also issued in a special sheet.

Panama 1938. *7th Central American Games in Panama*
2c. green.
Batter after making a hit.

U.S.A. 1939. *Centennial of Baseball*

3c. violet.

U.S.A. commemorated the centenary of the game with a special stamp. This shows boys playing baseball on an open piece of ground.

Venezuela 1944. *7th World Amateur Baseball Championships in Caracas*

0.05b. brown, 0.10b. dark green, 0.20b. blue, 0.30b. rose, 0.45b. violet, 0.90b. red orange, 1b. grey, 1.20b. yellow green, 1.80b. yellow brown.

This great baseball event was celebrated with a large set all with the same design: a batter and a catcher.

Japan 1948. *3rd National Sports Games in Fukuoka*

5.00y. grey green.

This is one of the most beautiful of baseball designs, showing a desperate race to reach base.

Nicaragua 1949. *10th World Amateur Baseball Championships in Managua 1948*

1c. orange brown, 15c. lilac red; 30c. red brown, 5co. light green (*airmail*).

The 1c. and 5co. values depict softball and the 15c. and 30c. baseball. The latter design illustrates a typical race for home base, with the umpire watching closely. The 30c. and 5co. were airmail stamps, square in shape. Softball is a simpler and milder form of baseball. By making the playing area smaller, and the ball softer than in baseball, it is very well suited to women. The 1c. and 5co. stamps show a woman catching the ball.

Liberia 1955. *Sports issue*

10c. blue and rose.

As Liberia was founded by negroes returning from the U.S.A. one might expect baseball to be the national game of Liberia. This stamp shows home base, with batter, catcher and umpire in action.

Cuba 1957. *Sports and Youth issue*

8c. olive green and light green.

Batter waiting for the pitch.

Panama 1959. *3rd Pan American Games in Chicago*

10c. grey and red brown.

Batter in action.

Costa Rica 1960. *17th Olympic Games*

1s. grey black.

Batter.

6. BASKETBALL

Basketball is of North American origin. The game was invented in 1891 by Dr. James A. Naismith of Springfield, Mass. The game spread rapidly over the whole of U.S.A., where there are at present more than ten million players. Basketball is played all over the world and is the sport with the greatest number of participants.

Philippines 1934. *10th Far Eastern Games in Manila*

16c. violet.

Two players fighting for the ball.

Panama 1938. *7th Central American Games in Panama*

1c. red.

A player throwing for goal.

Ecuador 1939. *Victory in the 1st Bolivar Games 1938*

50c. olive grey.

Open play, probably the 'throw' at the start of the game.

Lithuania 1939. *3rd European Basketball Championship in Kaunas*

15+10c. red brown, 30+15c. dark green, 60+40c. blue black.

Lithuania was the first European country to illustrate basketball. The designs of the low values show a goal being scored and two players fighting for the ball. The highest value has the basket and a hand throwing the ball in one corner, surrounded by the flags of the seventeen participating nations.

Bulgaria 1947. *13th Balkan Games in Sofia*

4l. green.

A goal throw.

Monaco 1948. *14th Olympic Games*

2f. 50c. red.

A game in progress.

Peru 1948. *14th Olympic Games in London*

2s. brown.

A rather ornate design with its old-fashioned frame of pillars, and shows players fighting for the ball in front of the basket. The stamp reappeared overprinted in 1956.

Nicaragua 1949. *10th World Amateur Baseball Championships in Managua 1948*

15c. green, 35c. olive green (*air mail*).

Basketball player preparing to make a goal throw.

Hungary 1950. *Sports issue*

1.70fo. red violet and brown.

For the first time women players are shown in action.

Bolivia 1951. *2nd National Sports Congress 1948*

0.30b. red violet and black.

A game in progress.

Monaco 1953. *15th Olympic Games in Helsinki 1952*

1f. red and black violet.

A diamond-shaped stamp illustrating a goal throw.

Russia 1954. *Sports issue*

1r. red brown and brown.

An incident in front of the basket. It was later overprinted in 1959 after the 1958 world championships in Chile.

Brazil 1954. *2nd World Basketball Championship in Rio de Janeiro*

1.40c. red brown.

Symbolic design showing a goal throw, the ball representing a globe of the world.

Poland 1955. *2nd World Youth Games in Warsaw*

1z. orange.

Women players in action.

Czechoslovakia 1956. *5th European Women's Basketball Championships in Prague*

45h. red and grey violet.

Women basketball players.

France 1956. *Sports issue*

30f. blue grey.

In a set depicting popular French sports basketball has an obvious place, as the French are among the leading players in Europe. Also overprinted 'C.F.A.' for use on Réunion.

Russia 1956. *National Spartacist Games*

1r. rose brown.

Women players in action.

Hungary 1956. *16th Olympic Games*

3fo. red lilac and brown.

A goal throw.

Bulgaria 1956. *16th Olympic Games*

80s. brown.

A woman player near the basket—though there is no women's basketball event in the Olympic Games.

Japan 1956. *11th National Games in Hyogo*

5y. grey green.

Women basketball players.

Ecuador 1956. *6th South American Women's Basketball Championships in Quito*

1s. red violet, 1.70s. green.

Not among the most beautiful, these stamps have two designs: one the coat-of-arms of Ecuador, with a woman player making a throw; the other a map of South America with the flags of the participating nations and two women players.

Peru 1956. *16th Olympic Games in Melbourne*

2s. red brown.

The Olympic design of 1948 overprinted 'MELBOURNE 1956'.

Bulgaria 1957. *European Basketball Championships in Sofia*

44s. dark green.

Players in action in front of the basket.

Brazil 1957. *2nd World Women's Basketball Championships in Rio de Janeiro*

3.30c. orange and green.

Women players in action.

Spanish Guinea 1958. *Sports issue*
10c. red brown, 2p. red violet.
A beautiful design showing two coloured players fighting for the ball.

Somalia 1958. *Sports issue*
1.50s. wine red.
Coloured player making a goal throw.

Ifni 1958. *Children's Charity issue*
10+5c. orange brown, 20c. grey green.
Coloured players in an incident in front of the basket.

Ecuador 1958. *South American Basketball Championships in Quito*
1.30s. yellow brown and dark green.
A player jumping to make a goal throw.

Russia 1959. '*Victory' in the World Basketball Championships in Chile*
1r. brown and red brown.
1954 sports issue surcharged 'Victory for U.S.S.R.'s basketball team, Chile 1959'. The Russian team won all its matches, but refused to meet Formosa (Nationalist China) in the final match and was disqualified. Brazil was awarded the championship.

Turkey 1959. *11th European Basketball Championships in Istanbul*
25k. orange red and black.
A goal throw.

Brazil 1959. *Victory in the World Basketball Championships in Chile*
3.30c. red brown and blue.
The team captain with the Victory trophy. A reply to the Russian stamp.

Argentina 1959. *3rd Pan American Games in Chicago*
50+30c. orange yellow and black.
A goal throw.

Panama 1959. *3rd Pan American Games in Chicago*
50c. ultramarine and orange brown.
A goal throw.

Albania 1959. *1st National Spartacist Games*
1.50l. violet.
A goal throw.

China (Communist) 1959. *1st National Games in Peking*
8d. blue violet, red brown and black.
A goal throw.

Czechoslovakia 1960. *2nd National Spartacist Games (I)*
1.60k. yellow brown.

Paraguay 1960. *17th Olympic Games*
12.45g. red and blue grey, 18.15g. brown violet and olive brown, 36g. green and violet red (also in a forged (!) sheet).

San Marino 1960. *17th Olympic Games*
20l. light violet and violet, 20l. red and brown (imperf. in sheet).

Bulgaria 1960. *7th European Women's Basketball Championships in Sofia*
1.25l. yellow and black.
Women players.

U.A.R. 1960. *8th Anniversary of the Revolution*
5m. yellow brown.

Russia 1960. *17th Olympic Games*
15k. multicoloured.
Russian players in action.

Surinam 1960. *17th Olympic Games*
10+5c. red orange and red brown.
Goal throw.

Maldives 1960. *17th Olympic Games.*
25l. red and olive, 50l. yellow orange and violet, 1r. green and red violet.

Tunisia 1960. *1st Tunisian participation in the Olympic Games*
50m. green and blue.
Bouncing the ball.

Turkey 1960. *17th Olympic Games*
30k. brown grey.
Turkish player.

Panama 1960. *17th Olympic Games*
5c. orange.

Formosa (Nationalist China) 1960. *15th National Taiwan Games*
2s. black, red and yellow.

Philippines 1960. *17th Olympic Games*
6c. light green and brown.

Costa Rica 1960. *17th Olympic Games*
85c. red violet and black.

U.A.R. (Syria) 1960. *17th Olympic Games*
15p. multicoloured.

7. BOBSLEIGH

Bobsleighing dates from 1888 when the American diplomat Townsend constructed the bob out of the Swiss sleigh. The type was improved considerably in the next few years and the first modern bobsleigh track was built at St. Moritz in 1902. The sport developed rapidly in Switzerland in the 1930's and reached U.S.A.

Germany 1935. *4th Olympic Winter Games in Garmisch-Partenkirchen*
25+25pf. blue.
Four-man-bob at full speed.

Roumania 1951. *9th Anniversary Winter Games in Poiana-Stalin*
31l. green.
Four-man-bob. This stamp appeared later as a provisional with a surcharge.

Germany (East) 1951. *2nd East German Winter Sports Championships in Oberhof*
12pf. green blue.
Two-man-bob.

San Marino 1955. *7th Olympic Winter Games in Cortina*
3l. red brown and brown, 50l. blue grey and brown.
A two-man-bob at full speed.

Togo 1960. *8th Winter Olympic Games*
1f. light green and red.
A four-man bobsleigh was not included in the 1960 Olympics!

8. BOXING

Boxing is an ancient sport which was practised, for example in Crete, 2,000 years B.C. Modern boxing originated in England in the 1700's, and the rules as we know them today were introduced at the end of the nineteenth century.

Boxing, as a 'philatelic' sport, got off to a slow start, but in the last six years there have been a number of new issues, most of them depicting amateur boxers (i.e. wearing vests).

Greece 1896. *1st Olympic Games in Athens*
1l. yellow brown, 1l. rose.
An ancient bare-fist fight.

Netherlands 1928. *9th Olympic Games in Amsterdam*
30c. brown.
A stylized boxer on guard.

Panama 1938. *7th Central American Games in Panama*
8c. red brown.
Two boxers, one delivering a perfect straight left.

Ecuador 1939. *Victory in the 1st Bolivar Games in Bogotá, Colombia, 1938*
1s. grey brown.
A boxer going down for the count from a well-placed right-hook.

Nicaragua 1949. *10th World Amateur Baseball Championships in Managua 1948*
25c. blue, 25c. red violet (*airmail*).
Two boxers, one throwing out a straight left.

Bolivia 1951. *5th South American Championships in La Paz 1948*
0.20b. blue and black.
Two boxers, one letting go a left-hook.

Yugoslavia 1952. *15th Olympic Games*
28d. brown and orange.
A boxer on guard. The same stamp was issued with changed colours and an overprinted 'STT–VUJNA' for use in the Yugoslav zone of Trieste.

Luxemburg 1952. *Sports issue*
2.50f. rose and black.
This stamp, showing two boxers and the referee, received second place in the competition for the Bonacossa Medal, 1952.

Poland 1953. *European Boxing Championships in Warsaw*
40g. red brown, 80g. orange, 95g. brown violet.
The two lower denominations show a boxer, the highest a boxing match. The Poles totally dominated these events.

Hungary 1953. *Inauguration of Nép Stadium in Budapest*
1f. violet and red brown.
A fight in progress.

Philippines 1954. *2nd Asian Games in Manila*
50c. red violet.
Two fly-weights in action.

San Marino 1954. *Sports issue*
3l. red brown.
Two boxers in action.

Liberia 1955. *Sports issue*
25c. violet and yellow.
This stamp, showing two boxers in action, also appeared with changed colours in a special sheet; a very small number were also issued imperforate.

Russia 1956. *National Spartacist Games*
60k. violet.
These two fighters have little apparent regard for defence.

Bulgaria 1956. *16th Olympic Games*
1l. dark red.
A good straight right during a match.

Poland 1956. *16th Olympic Games*
20g. grey violet and brown.
The Poles won only two bronze medals in spite of their high expectations.

Czechoslovakia 1957. *European Boxing Championships in Prague*
60h. violet brown and orange brown.
Two boxers in action.

Cuba 1957. *Sports and Youth issue*
30c. orange and violet brown.
Two professional fighters infighting.

Russia 1957. *16th Olympic Games 1956*
40k. grey and violet.
Two amateur boxers in a ring and the emblem of the Melbourne Games.

Japan 1957. *12th National Games in Shizuoka*
5y. brown red.
Two fighters in action.

Spanish Guinea 1958. *Sports issue*
5c. violet brown, 1p. orange red.
Two coloured professional boxers.

Somalia 1958. *Sports issue*
0.25s. grey green.
Two professional native boxers.

Argentina 1959. *3rd Pan American Games in Chicago*
1p.+0.50, brown violet and black.
Knock-down.

Panama 1959. *3rd Pan American Games in Chicago*
5c. grey black and red brown.
Left-hook.

Roumania 1959. *Sports issue*
1.50l. blue, violet, yellow and red.
Right-hook.

Germany (East) 1960. *17th Olympic Games*
5pf. orange brown and brown.
Straight right.

Togo 1960. *17th Olympic Games*
20f. yellow brown, green and dark brown.
Straight left and a right swing.

San Marino 1960. *17th Olympic Games*
4l. red and dark brown, 4l. red and brown (imperf. in sheet).
Guard up.

Roumania 1960. *17th Olympic Games (I)*
1.60l. blue grey and yellow (also imperf.).
Guarding position.

Roumania 1960. *17th Olympic Games (II)*
1l. red.
As above.

Poland 1960. *17th Olympic Games*
2.50z. red brown.
Figure in relief representing *Z. Chycla* welterweight champion 1952.

Italy 1960. *17th Olympic Games*
110l. red violet.
The famous statue of a resting fist fighter by Apollonius (A.D. 300).

Russia 1960. *17th Olympic Games*
25k. dark red and multicoloured.
Straight right.

Hungary 1960. *17th Olympic Games*
20f. brown orange and yellow brown.
Ancient Greek fist-fighters.

The Dominican Republic 1960. *Olympic Victors 1956 (IV)*
5c. ultramarine and brown.
Terry Spinks (Great Britain) flyweight.

Cuba 1960. *17th Olympic Games*
8c. blue, 8c. grey blue (imperf. in sheet).
Stylized boxer.

Morocco 1960. *17th Olympic Games*
40f. brown red, violet and light blue.
Boxers in action.

Lebanon 1960. *17th Olympic Games*
2.50+2.50p. blue brown.
Straight left.

Costa Rica 1960. *17th Olympic Games*
10c. orange red, black.
Two fly-weight boxers.

9. CANOEING

Canoeing had its origin in England, where long-distance voyages by canoe were made in the 1860's. The sport spread to U.S.A. and Sweden, where it developed rapidly. By the start of the twentieth century canoeing had reached the Continent and the Middle European countries now dominate the sport.

Russia 1949. *Sports issue*
25k. green.
Two double kayaks on a river.

Czechoslovakia 1952. *United Czechoslovakian Sports issue*
2k. grey.
The Czechs, who have won many Olympic medals in Canadian canoes, picture a Canadian pair on this stamp. The inscription 'By united sports to socialism' refers to the amalgamation of the old Sokol Movement and the State Sports organization.

France 1953. *French Olympic Successes in 1952*
40f. brown and black.
The French Olympic victors in the Canadian pairs, 10,000 m., in Helsinki, *G. Turlier* and *J. Laudet*. This stamp appeared overprinted 'C.F.A.' for use in Réunion.

Hungary 1956. *16th Olympic Games*
20f. light green blue and brown.
A single kayak.

Yugoslavia 1956. *Olympic Year 1956*
15d. dark blue and brown.
A canoeist minus canoe (!) and a swan form the symbolic and eccentric design.

Roumania 1956. *16th Olympic Games*
1.55l. green.
A stylized drawing of Canadian single canoe.

Czechoslovakia 1958. *World Caneoing Championships in Prague*
40h. grey blue.
Two single Canadians at full speed.

Roumania 1960. *17th Olympic Games (I)*
2.45l. blue grey and green, 3.70l. (imperf.).
Canadian single.

Roumania 1960. *17th Olympic Games (II)*
1.60l. violet red.
As above.

Russia 1960. *17th Olympic Games*
60k. olive and multicoloured.
Canadian pairs.

Bulgaria 1960. *17th Olympic Games*
80s. green blue and light rose, 80s. green blue and yellow (imperf.).
Canadian single.

10. CYCLING

The first cycle races took place in England in the 1870's, first in the form of road races later also on tracks. Track races also became popular in the 1880's in France and in the 1890's in U.S.A.; France took the lead by arranging road races extending over several days. On the track long-distance races and six-day events were introduced.

Cycle-racing is one of the most popular sports with stamp designers. No less than ninety-five different stamps have been issued in an ever-increasing stream. Cycling is, in fact, the most popular sport on stamps over the last five years.

Bulgaria 1931–3. *1st Balkan Games in Sofia*
10l. orange (1931), 10l. brown (1933).
These stamps, issued in two different colours with an interval of two years between, show two track-cyclists in a race.

Russia 1935. *World Spartacist Games in Moscow*
10k. red and violet.
Track race in a velodrome.

Bulgaria 1947. *13th Balkan Games in Sofia*
2l. red violet.
Sprint race with two cyclists.

Poland 1948. *1st Peace Cycle Race, Warsaw–Prague–Warsaw*
15z. red and blue.
A symbolic design showing a cycle wheel with laurels entwined in the spokes and ribbons in the Polish and Czech colours fluttering behind.

Poland 1948. *'Around Poland' Cycle Race*
3z. grey, 6z. brown, 15z. green.
A road race is indicated by the telegraph poles incorporated in the design. Two cyclists, one in silhouette, form the main picture.

Japan 1948. *3rd National Games in Fukuoka*
5y. green.
Two cyclists in a track race.

Germany 1949. *Cycle Race 'Quer durch Deutschland'*
10+5pf. green, 20+10pf. red brown.
Issued in the West Zone of Germany, these have a road-race design to mark the 'Across Germany' race.

Nicaragua 1949. *10th World Amateur Baseball Championships in Managua 1948*
5c. orange, 40c. violet (*airmail*).
Two cyclists.

Russia 1949. *Sports issue*
40k. red brown.
Road race with four cyclists.

Bulgaria 1950. *Sports issue*
9l. red brown.
Cyclists in a road race.

Bolivia 1951. *5th South American Championships in La Paz 1948*
4b. blue violet and black.
Track race.

Roumania 1951. *'Round Roumania' Cycle Race*
11l. red brown.
Road race with mountains in the background.

Italy 1951. *World Cycling Championships in Milan and Varese*
25l. olive black.
Symbolic design showing a cyclist on the globe with Milan Cathedral and the bell tower of Varese in the background. This stamp also appeared overprinted 'AMG-FTT' for use in the A Zone of Trieste.

Trieste, Zone B (Yugoslav) 1952. *Sports issue*
5d. yellow brown.
Three racing cyclists.

Poland 1952. *5th Peace Cycle Race, Warsaw–Berlin–Prague*
40g. blue.
Racing cyclists with the coat-of-arms of the three capitals. This two-week race, arranged annually since 1952, has frequently been commemorated on stamps, not only from Poland but also from East Germany, Czechoslovakia, Russia and Roumania.

Germany (East) 1952. *5th Peace Cycle Race*
12pf. blue.
Cyclists with flags and peace-propaganda signs in the background.

Czechoslovakia 1952. *United Czechoslovakian Sports issue*
3k. red brown.
Racing cyclists. The inscription reads: 'May International Sports Friendship flourish.'

Luxemburg 1952. *World Cycling Championships in Luxemburg*
4f. brown and green.
Cyclist.

San Marino 1953. *Sports issue*
4l. blue and dark green.
A cyclist with a view of San Marino in the background.

Czechoslovakia 1953. *6th Peace Cycle Race*
3k. blue grey
Cyclists under a banner bearing the name of the race, on this occasion starting in Prague.

Poland 1953. *6th Peace Cycle race*
80g. brown, 80g. green, 80g. red.
Though with the same general design, each colour bears a different city emblem: brown, Warsaw; green, Berlin; red, Prague.

Germany (East) 1953. *6th Peace Cycle race*
24pf. green, 35pf. blue, 60pf. brown.
Cyclists in town, country and industrial surroundings, respectively.

Hungary 1953. *Inauguration of Nép Stadium in Budapest*
20f. red brown and orange.
Track race.

France 1953. *50th Anniversary of 'Tour de France'*
12f. red brown and blue.
This classic race celebrated its 50th anniversary in 1953. This stamp shows a cyclist of the old days and a modern one on each side of a map of France, on which the route is marked.

Guatemala 1953. *National Festival issue*
65c. green and blue.
In a large set marking Festival Week one stamp has a poor design showing a track race.

Poland 1954. *7th Peace Cycle Race*
80g. dark blue, 80g. brown.
Symbolic designs showing a wheel with the 'compulsory' peace dove and coats-of-arms of the three cities and silhouettes of well-known buildings from Warsaw (New University), Berlin (Brandenburg Gate) and Prague (Charles Bridge Tower).

Germany (East) 1954. *7th Peace Cycle Race*
12pf. brown, 24pf. green.
The designs show racing cyclists passing through a town and through countryside, respectively.

Russia 1954. *Sports issue*
40k. brown and red brown.
Track race in a velodrome.

Saar 1955. *World Cross Country Cycling Championships in Saarbrücken*
15f. black olive, red, white and blue.
Cyclist with the colours of the Saar in the background.

Poland 1955. *8th Peace Cycle Race*
40g. violet brown, 60g. light blue.
A cycle wheel with the coats-of-arms of the three cities (40g.) and peace doves (80g.), respectively.

Germany (East) 1955. *8th Peace Cycle Race*
10pf. green, 20pf. red.
Racing cyclists with the coats-of-arms of the cities.

Poland 1956. *9th Peace Cycle Race*
40g. dark blue, 60g. green.
A close-up of a cyclist. In the upper right-hand corner are the coats-of-arms of Warsaw, Berlin and Prague.

Czechoslovakia 1956. *9th Peace Cycle Race*
30h. light blue and green.
Cyclists.

Germany (East) 1956. *9th Peace Cycle Race*
10pf. grey green, 20 pf. red.
A hand with a laurel in front of a wheel (10pf.) and the three city coats-of-arms in front of a wheel (20pf.).

Russia 1956. *National Spartacist Games*
40k. green blue.
Track race.

Bulgaria 1957. *4th 'Round Egypt' Cycle Race*
80s. red brown, 80s. blue green.
Cyclists in front of the Pyramids.

China (Communist) 1957. *1st Chinese Workers' Games 1955*
5d. yellow brown, red and green.
A cyclist.

Czechoslovakia 1957. *10th Peace Cycle Race*
30h. grey brown and blue, 60h. grey green.
Cyclists in a road race.

Germany (East) 1957. *10th Peace Cycle Race*
5pf. yellow.
A design symbolizing the route of the race; Prague (Charles Bridge), Berlin (Town Hall in East Berlin), Warsaw (Palace of Culture).

Poland 1957. *10th Peace Cycle Race*
60g. ultramarine, 1.50z. wine red.
Cycle wheel and flower (60g.) and a cyclist bending over the handlebars (1.50z.).

Roumania 1957. *10th Peace Cycle Race*
20b. dark blue, 55b. dark brown.
A peace dove, symbolically resting on the handlebars (20b.), and a cyclist (55b.).

Russia 1957. *10th Peace Cycle Race*
40k. blue grey and violet brown.
Cyclist in front of a Warsaw building.

Colombia 1957. *10th National Cycle Race*
2c. light brown, 5c. light blue.
Used for express letters, these diamond-shaped stamps depict a racing cyclist.

The Dominican Republic 1957. *Olympic Victors 1956 (II)*
7c. grey green, green and red.
Ercole Baldini, the Italian gold medallist in the road race.

Egypt 1958. *5th 'Round Egypt' Cycle Race*
10m. red brown.
Two cyclists.

Liechtenstein 1958. *Sports issue*
90c. olive green and violet brown.
Two cyclists at full speed.

Somalia 1958. *Sports issue*
1.20s. light blue.
Racing cyclist with a stadium in the background.

Ifni 1958. *Children's Charity issue*
15+5c. yellow brown, 70c. grey green.
Two cyclists in a road race.

Indonesia 1958. *1st 'Round Java' Cycle Race*
25f. blue, 50f. orange brown, 1r. grey.
The design, the same on all three stamps, has a racing cyclist superimposed on a map of Indonesia.

Spanish Guinea 1959. *Sports issue*
20+5c. dark green, 50+20c. olive brown.
Two cyclists and the finish of a track race.

China (Communist) 1959. *1st National Games in Peking*
5d. grey, blue violet, red brown and black.
Woman cyclist—for the first time.

Togo 1960. *17th Olympic Games*
10f. dark green, ultramarine and red brown.
Cyclist.

Yugoslavia 1960. *17th Olympic Games*
40d. olive, grey and light green.
Stylized cyclists.

San Marino 1960. *17th Olympic Games*
10l. red brown and blue, 10l. red and brown (imperf. in sheets).
Cyclist.

Poland 1960. *17th Olympic Games*
60g. violet.
Figure in relief representing the 1924 Polish silver cycling team.

Germany (East) 1960. *World Road Cycling Championships in Leipzig*
20+10pf. red and multicoloured, 25+10 light blue and grey.
Cyclist and the finish of a race.

Maldives 1960. *17th Olympic Games*
2l. red violet and dark green, 3l. grey green and red violet, 5l. red brown and violet blue, 10l. green and red brown.
Cyclist and 'shadow'.

Tunisia 1960. *1st Tunisian participation in the Olympic Games*
5m. olive and violet brown.
Cyclist and velodrome.

Bulgaria 1960. *10th Bulgarian Cycle Race*
1l. yellow, black and red.
Group of cyclists.

Panama 1960. *17th Olympic Games*
10c. orange brown.
Two cyclists at finish of race.

Morocco 1960. *17th Olympic Games*
15f. orange brown, blue and green.
Cyclist.

Spain 1960. *Sports issue*
40c. red violet and orange, 2p. violet red and green.
Cyclist.

North Korea 1960. *15th Anniversary of the Republic*
5w. green, orange brown, blue and black.
Cyclist.

Lebanon 1960. *17th Olympic Games*
25+25p. green and brown.
Cyclist.

Costa Rica 1960. *17th Olympic Games*
3c. red and black.
Cyclist.

11. EQUESTRIAN SPORTS

HORSE-RACING

Horse-racing can be traced back to ancient times and was introduced to the Olympic Games in 646 B.C. England is the home of modern horse-racing. As early as the sixteenth century public horse-racing is on record, and the first classics like the Derby and the Oaks originated in the eighteenth century. At the same time steeplechases developed from fox-hunting, the Grand National being inaugurated in 1836. Outside England horse-racing is mainly popular in France, Germany, U.S.A. and Australia.

Surprisingly, therefore, only Germany has used this graceful sport on stamps to any large extent. There are, of course, many stamps showing horses but this section is confined to competitive horse-racing and race-horse breeding.

Tannu Tuva (Northern Mongolia) 1936. *15th Anniversary of the Republic*
40k. brown, 50k. blue black.
Primitive form of Mongolian horse-racing.

Germany 1936–44. '*Brown Ribbon*' *issues*
42+108pf. brown.
The 'Brown Ribbon' ('Braunes Band von Deutschland'), inaugurated in 1934, was an international flat race over 2,400 m. for three-year-olds

or over. To mark this race, every year a stamp of identical denomination and colour was issued. The premium on this stamp was divided between Hitler's culture fund and horse-breeding.

Here is a short description of the various issues:

1936 Three race-horses at full speed. This stamp was also sold in a commemorative sheet.
1938 Allegoric picture of a woman riding a horse.
1939 Man holding two horses who are rearing up on their hindlegs.
1940 Chariot pulled by three horses.
1941 Two amazons on horseback.
1942 Three galloping horses.
1943 Fox-hunter with horn.
1944 Racing mare with foal. This stamp was overprinted 'Österreich 8pf.' for use in Austria after the war.

Germany 1939–42. *Derby of Germany*

25+50pf. blue (1939); 25+100pf. blue (1940–2).

The German Derby ('Deutsches Derby' until 1940, then 'Grosser Preis der Dreijährigen') was Germany's foremost flat race.

Issues:

1939 *70th Anniversary of the Derby*; jockey mounted on horse.
1940 German officer on horse show-jumping (cf. Riding).
1941 Head of a race-horse.
1942 Horse and jockey at full speed.

Germany 1941. *Berlin Grand Prix*

25+50pf. blue.

The Brandenburg Gate in Berlin.

Germany 1943. *Vienna Grand Prix*

6+4pf. grey violet, 12+88pf. red.

A thoroughbred with a Vienna skyline in the background. Under the Russian occupation these stamps were reissued in 1945 overprinted 'Stadt Strausberg 1945'.

Germany 1944. *Vienna Grand Prix*

6+4pf. green, 12+88pf. red.

A horse's head within a laurel crown. This stamp was also overprinted 'Stadt Strausberg 1945'.

Austria 1946. *Austria Prize Race*

16+16g. red, 24+24g. violet, 60+60g. green, 1+1s. blue, 2+2s. brown.

A mare with her foal, two horses' heads, a steeplechase, three galloping horses and three horses' heads.

Austria 1947. *Vienna Grand Prix*

60+20g. blue on rose paper.

A jockey walking his horse.

Japan 1948. *Japanese Derby*

5.00y. brown.

Three race-horses at full speed.

Saar 1949. *Day of the Horse*

15+5f. red, 25+15f. blue.

These attractive stamps show a mare with her foal and a steeplechase design with two riders jumping a fence.

Guatemala 1953. *National Festival issue*

15c. brown and violet.

Race-horses galloping on a track.

Russia 1956. *International Equestrian Events in Moscow 1955*

40k. brown, 60k. green.

Jockey on a galloping horse. In the lower right-hand corner is the symbol of the meeting.

Czechoslovakia 1956. *Pardubice Steeplechase*

60h. grey blue and olive.

A graphic picture of a group of riders jumping a fence.

Germany (East) 1958. *East German Grand Prix*

5pf. dark brown, 20pf. red brown.

A racing mare with her foal (5pf.), a horse-race (20pf.).

Mongolia 1959. *National Sports issue*

5m. orange and multicoloured, 15m. yellow green and multicoloured, 25m. light blue and multicoloured, 70m. orange and multicoloured.

Catching and taming wild horse, a riding lesson and a horse-race.

Australia 1960. *100th Melbourne Cup Race*

5d. brown.

'Archer', winner of 1861 race.

POLO

Polo, one of the world's oldest games, is of Ancient Persian origin. Polo spread eastwards to Tibet and China, where it became very popular between A.D. 700 and 1000. From Tibet the game went to India, where it was adopted by the British who reintroduced it to Europe and America. The first polo stamp did not appear until 1953, from Iran, the home of the game. An Argentine polo stamp of 1951 was withdrawn for political reasons.

Iran 1953. *Ancient Persian Sports*

5r. olive and yellow.

A design depicting an Ancient Persian polo-player.

The Dominican Republic 1959. *Polo match: Dominican Republic v. Jamaica.*

2c. violet, 7c. brown, 10c. green, 11c. orange.

1st Lieut. L. R. Trujillo, in polo dress, the Jamaican team, the Dominican team captain in action and the Dominican team.

Brazil 1959. *9th Childrens' Games*

2.50c. red brown.

Players in action.

Iran 1960. *17th Olympic Games*

1r. violet brown.

Ancient Persian polo-player (similar to 1953 issue).

RIDING

Modern riding has its roots in the jousts and tourneys of the Middle Ages. As part of military training, riding competitions began to be arranged in France in the 1860's. Competitive riding spread rapidly to Austria, Germany, Italy and Belgium. At the Olympic Games in Stockholm, 1912, new international rules were adopted.

Netherlands 1928. *9th Olympic Games in Amsterdam*

15c. blue.

Civilian rider taking a water jump.

Bulgaria 1931–3. *1st Balkan Games in Sofia*

4l. red, 4l. violet (1933).

Jockey and horse jumping.

Germany 1936. *9th Olympic Games in Berlin*

40+35pf. violet.

A perfect jump over the 'oxer'.

Roumania 1937. *25th Anniversary of Roumanian Sports Union*
6+2l. red brown.
Military horseman jumping a fence in a three-day event.

Ecuador 1939. *Victory in the 1st Bolivar Games in Bogotá, Colombia, 1938*
5c. green.
Similar design to above.

Germany 1940. *German Derby*
25+100pf. blue.
Though issued in connection with the Derby, this stamp has also been included in this section because it is typical of competitive jumping. It shows a German cavalryman executing a perfect jump.

Russia 1941. *23rd Anniversary of the Red Army*
45k. green.
A Russian cavalryman in a jump over the double bar.

Japan 1950. *5th National Sports Games in Magoya*
8.00y. red brown.
A civilian horseman in a brilliant jump over a double bar.

Bolivia 1951. *2nd National Sports Congress 1948*
0.20b. violet and black.
A cavalryman jumping over a high fence with bars.

France 1953. *French Olympic Successes in 1952*
75f. wine red and orange.
This stamp honours the French gold medallist in the show-jumping event—*P. J. d'Oriola*—and also the French team which came fifth in the team event. It was overprinted 'C.F.A.' for use on Réunion.

Bulgaria 1954. *Sports issue*
80s. red brown.
A beautiful jump.

Sweden 1956. *16th Olympic Games: Equestrian Events in Stockholm*
20ö. red, 25ö. blue, 40ö. green.
The design was taken from the Parthenon frieze.

Hungary 1956. *16th Olympic Games*
30f. olive green and brown.
A beautiful jump over a bar.

The Dominican Republic 1957. *Olympic Victors 1956 (II)*
11c. light blue, black, red and yellow.
Hans Winkler on 'Halla', Germany, jumping a gate in the Olympic Stadium, Stockholm.

Poland 1959. *Sports issue*
2z. green.
Jumping a bar.

Roumania 1959. *Sports issue*
1l. violet brown, yellow olive, orange and blue.
Jumping a high fence.

China (Communist) 1959. *1st National Games in Peking*
8d. red, brown and black.
Horse jumping.

Yugoslavia 1960. *17th Olympic Games*
80d. red, yellow brown and grey.
Stylized riders.

Monaco 1960. *17th Olympic Games*
0.05f. dark brown, green and red.
Jumping a fence.

San Marino 1960. *17th Olympic Games*
110l. yellow green, red and black, 110l. green, brown (imperf. in sheet).
Horse-jumping.

Poland 1960. *17th Olympic Games*
60g. blue green.
Figure in relief representing the 1936 Polish silver three-day-event team.

U.A.R. 1960. *8th Anniversary of the Revolution*
30m. violet.
Cavalryman jumping crossed bars.

Russia 1960. *17th Olympic Games*
1r. violet brown and multicoloured.
Horse jumping.

Mongolia 1960. *17th Olympic Games*
5m. carmine, blue green and grey.
Horse jumping.

Hungary 1960. *17th Olympic Games*
1fo. violet brown and yellow brown.
Statue taken from the Parthenon frieze (cf. Sweden 1956).

Turkey 1960. *17th Olympic Games*
30k. light brown.
Cavalryman jumping a high fence.

Spain 1960. *Sports issue*
1.25p. red brown and red, 6p. black and red.
Horseman clearing a fence.

U.A.R. (Syria) 1960. *17th Olympic Games*
40p. violet red, red violet.
Military horsemen passing a double fence.

TROTTING

Trotting with horse and carriage has been practised in several countries for centuries, but the modern version has its origin in the U.S.A., whose trotters have dominated the record lists.

Russia 1956. *International Horse Races in Moscow 1955*
1r. blue and brown violet.
Trotting horse with driver and sulky.

Germany (East) 1958. *East German Grand Prix*
10pf. dark green.
A trotting rig at full speed.

12. FENCING

Fencing is one of the oldest sports in the world and was practised in Egypt 2,000 years B.C. Modern fencing, however, dates from the Middle Ages, when it formed part of normal education. It reached its peak as an art in Italy, spreading from there to France and Spain. The leading fencing schools today are French, Italian and Hungarian. It is also popular today in the countries of Eastern Europe.

Hungary 1925. *Sports issue*
500k. brown violet.
The sabre-fencer on the right is executing a lunge which his opponent parries.

Netherlands 1928. *9th Olympic Games in Amsterdam*
2c. red violet.
Épée-fencer on guard.

Bulgaria 1931–3. *1st Balkan Games in Sofia*
6l. blue green, 6l. rose (1933).
A sabre-fencer lunging.

Germany 1936. *9th Olympic Games in Berlin*
15+10pf. red brown.
Foil-fencer lunging.

Bolivia 1951. *2nd National Sports Congress 1948*
0.50b. orange red and black.
Foil lesson.

Hungary 1952. *15th Olympic Games*
60f. red violet.
A beautiful design picturing a sabre-fencer when attacking.

Luxemburg 1952. *Sports issue*
8f. light violet, blue and black.
Épée-fencing.

Monaco 1953. *15th Olympic Games*
50f. blue violet.
Épée-fencing.

France 1953. *French Olympic Successes in 1952*
30f. ultramarine and brown.
A left-handed foil-fencer, honouring the French Olympic gold medallist—*G. d'Oriola* (also a left-hander)—and the victorious French foil team.

Luxemburg 1954. *World Fencing Championships*
2f. red brown and dark brown.
Because of its fencing successes, Luxemburg was honoured with the world championships in 1954. She commemorated this event with a stamp showing a fencing mask, glove, foil, épée and sabre.

Poland 1954. *2nd National Spartacist Games in Warsaw*
25g. brown violet.
A vivid picture of two foil-fencers.

San Marino 1954. *Sports issue*
2l. blue violet and green.
Foil-fencer in a lunge.

Russia 1956. *National Spartacist Games*
40k. brown and green.
Sabre-fencers in action.

Hungary 1956. *16th Olympic Games*
40f. red orange and brown.
Épée-fencing, the right fencer performing a 'flêche'.

Poland 1956. *16th Olympic Games*
10g. brown and grey.
A sabre-fencer in a forceful 'flêche'.

Poland 1957. *World Junior Fencing Championships in Warsaw*
40g. brown violet, 60g. red, 60g. ultramarine.
The lowest value shows a foil, an épée and a sabre, whose blades consist of the words forming the name of the event, against a background of a world map. Each of the two higher values depicts a sabre-fencer, and when placed together the sabre blades meet, giving a vivid and original picture of sabre-fencers in action. These stamps were, of course, printed and sold as a pair.

Lebanon 1957. *2nd Pan Arabian Games in Beirut*
35p. brown violet.
Two foil-fencers closely engaged.

Colombia 1957. *3rd South American Fencing Championships in Bogotá*
4c. violet, 20c. brown.
These diamond-shaped stamps, the higher value being for airmail use, have the same design, a foil-fencer on guard. The 20c. value was re-issued in 1960 with the surcharge 'Unificado'.

Liechtenstein 1958. *Sports issue*
30c. light violet and grey green.
Épée-fencers in action.

Roumania 1958. *World Junior Fencing Championships in Bucharest*
1.75l. rose.
Symbolic design showing an épée-fencer with a mask and also representing the globe.

Somalia 1958. *Sports issue*
0.08s. grey blue.
A native foil-fencer with guard low and mask removed.

The Dominican Republic 1958. *Olympic Victors 1956 (III)*
1c. blue grey and rose.
Gillian Sheen (Great Britain).

Hungary 1959. *24th World Fencing Championships in Budapest*
10f. light blue and grey, 20f. yellow and grey, 30f. violet and grey, 40f. red and grey, 60f. red violet and grey, 1fo. blue green and grey, 1.40fo. orange and grey, 3fo. yellow green and grey.
Viking warrior, medieval knight, Hungarian hussars of the seventeenth, eighteenth and nineteenth centuries and modern fencers representing épée, foil and sabre.

Japan 1959. *14th National Games in Tokyo*
8y. olive brown.
Woman foil-fencer.

Yugoslavia 1960. *17th Olympic Games*
100d. violet, yellow brown and grey.
Stylized fencers.

San Marino 1960. *17th Olympic Games*
5l. brown and light blue, 5l. green and brown (imperf. in sheet).
Épée-fencer doing a 'flêche'.

U.A.R. 1960. *8th Anniversary of the Revolution*
10m. rose red.
Foil-fencers.

WELL-KNOWN SPORTSMEN

Colombia 1935

Kolehmainen and Bouin 1912
Finland France

Japan 1947

Carpenter, U.S.A.

Monaco 1948

Arifon, France

Turkey 1940

Meadows, U.S.A.

Finland 1945

Nurmi, Finland

Turkey 1949

Dogu, Turkey and
Grönberg, Sweden

Yugoslavia 1948

Cowperthwaite, U.S.A.

Sweden 1954

Karlsson, Sweden

Czechoslovakia 1951

Dumbadze, Russia

Czechoslovakia 1953

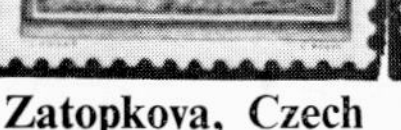

Zatopkova, Czech

France 1953

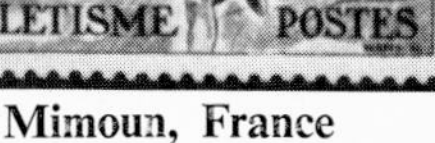

Mimoun, France

Czechoslovakia 1954

Zatopek, Czech

WELL-KNOWN SPORTSMEN
Olympic Victors
Dominican Republic 1957–8

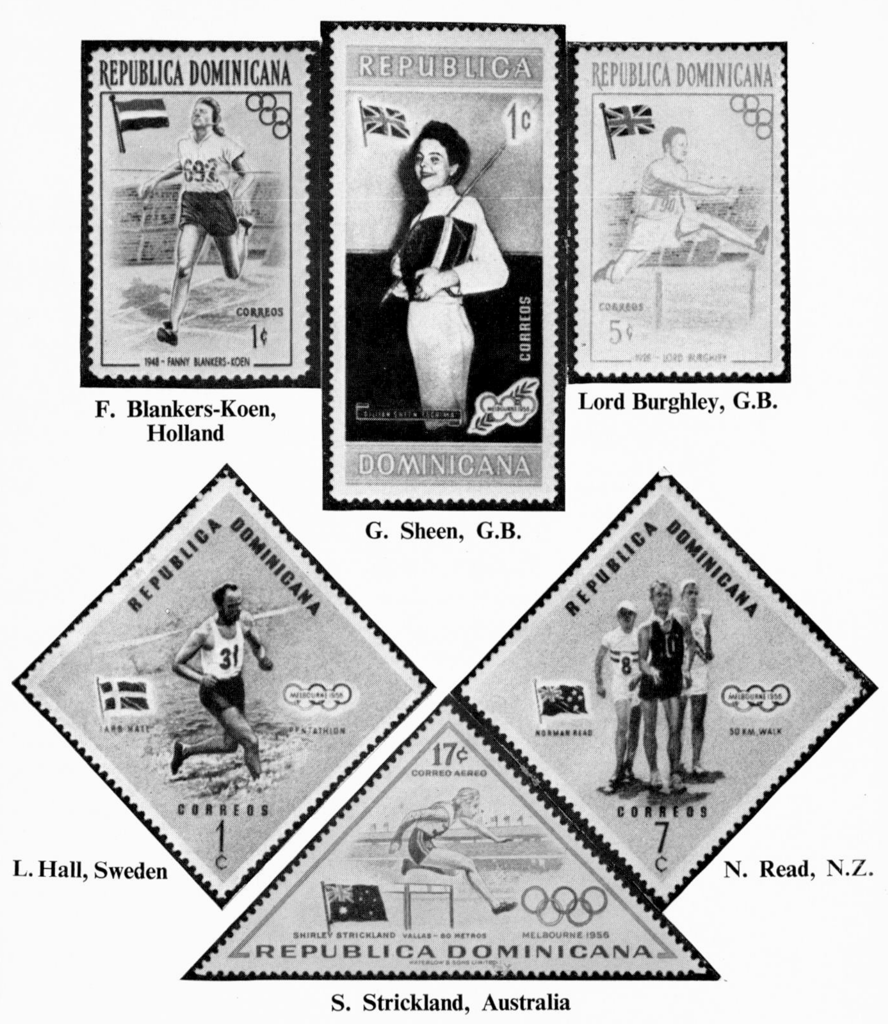

F. Blankers-Koen, Holland

G. Sheen, G.B.

Lord Burghley, G.B.

L. Hall, Sweden

N. Read, N.Z.

S. Strickland, Australia

T. Courtney and C. Jenkins, U.S.A.

OLYMPIC GAMES
1896–1928

Greece 1896

Greece 1906

Belgium 1920 | France 1924 | Netherlands 1928

OLYMPIC GAMES
1932–1956
Summer Games

U.S.A. 1932 Great Britain 1948 Germany 1936

Finland 1952 Australia 1956 Sweden 1956

Winter Games

U.S.A. 1932 Switzerland 1948 Germany 1935

Norway 1951 Italy 1956

OLYMPIC GAMES
1925–1957

Czechoslovakia 1925 Switzerland 1944 Portugal 1928

Austria 1948 Australia 1954–5 Peru 1948 (1957)

Germany (Berlin) 1952 Netherlands 1956 Germany (West) 1956

Saar 1952 France 1956 Saar 1956

OLYMPIC GAMES 1960

Russia

Greece

Ghana

Surinam

Monaco

Roumania

San Marino

Czechoslovakia

Italy

Mongolia

OLYMPIC GAMES 1960

Yugoslavia

Germany (East)

Paraguay

Poland

Italy

Togo

Belgian Congo

AQUATIC EVENTS

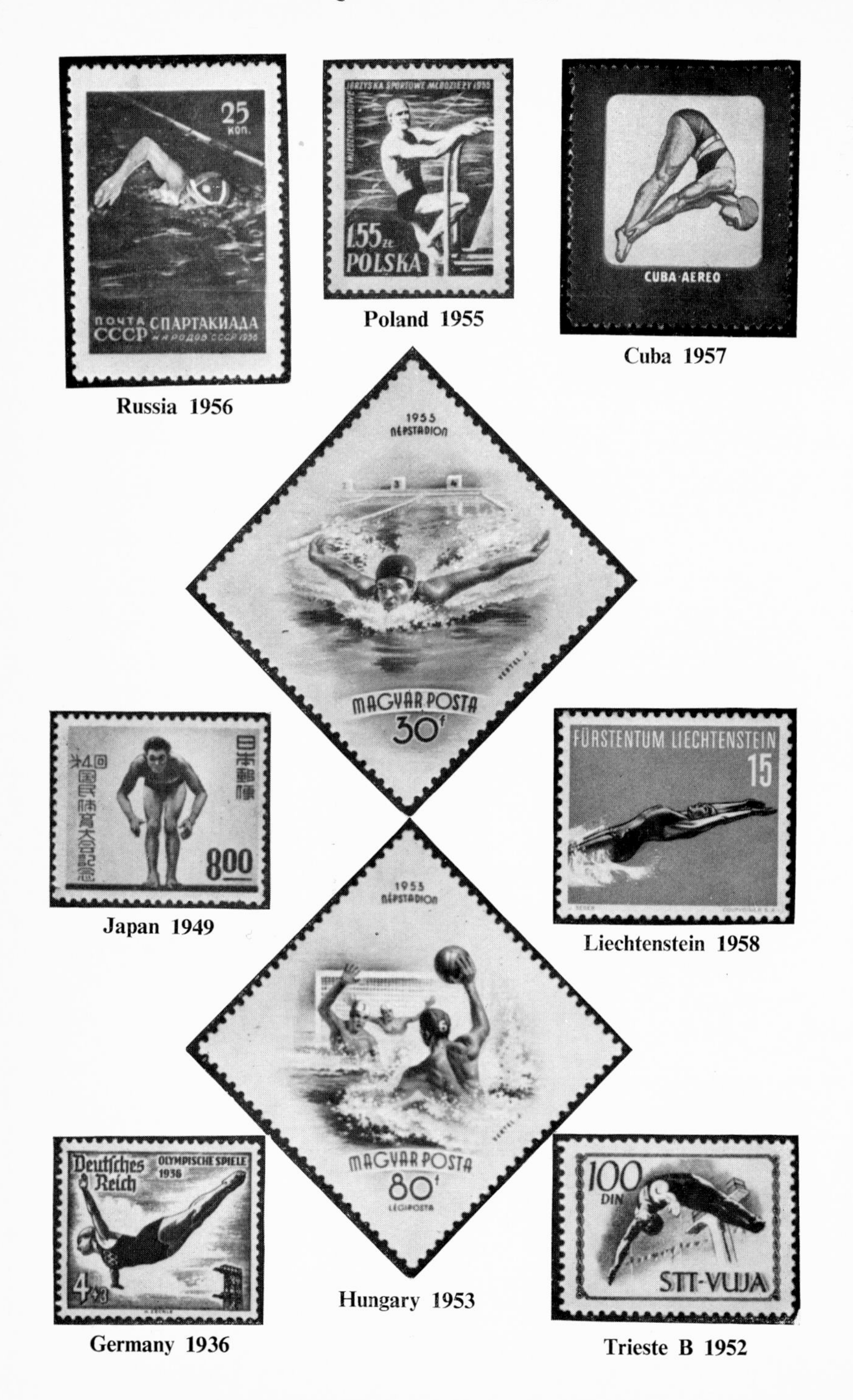

Russia 1956

Poland 1955

Cuba 1957

Japan 1949

Liechtenstein 1958

Germany 1936

Hungary 1953

Trieste B 1952

ATHLETICS

Short-, middle- and long-distance running

Japan 1949 U.S.A. 1932 Liechtenstein 1956

Monaco 1948 Belgium 1950 Spanish Guinea 1958

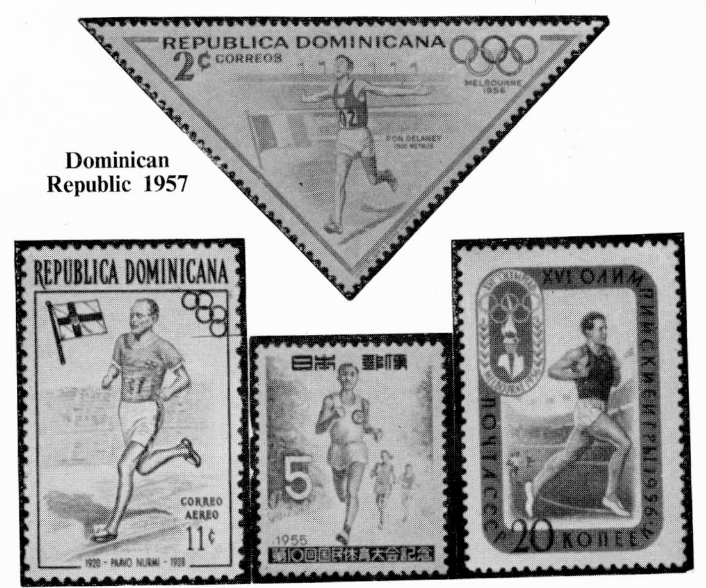

Dominican Republic 1957

Dominican Republic 1957 Japan 1955 Russia 1957

ATHLETICS

Relay-running — Hurdles — Steeplechase

Japan 1948 | Belgium 1950 | Poland 1954

Hungary 1925 | Yugoslavia 1938 | Cuba 1930

Luxemburg 1952 | Belgium 1950 | Liechtenstein 1956

Dominican Republic 1957

ATHLETICS

Discus — Javelin — Shot — Hammer

Russia 1938 Dominican Republic 1957 Monaco 1948

Finland 1945 Bulgaria 1949

Dominican Republic 1957

Yugoslavia 1938 Israel 1958

Bulgaria 1950

ATHLETICS

High-jump — Pole-vault — Hop, step and jump — Long-jump

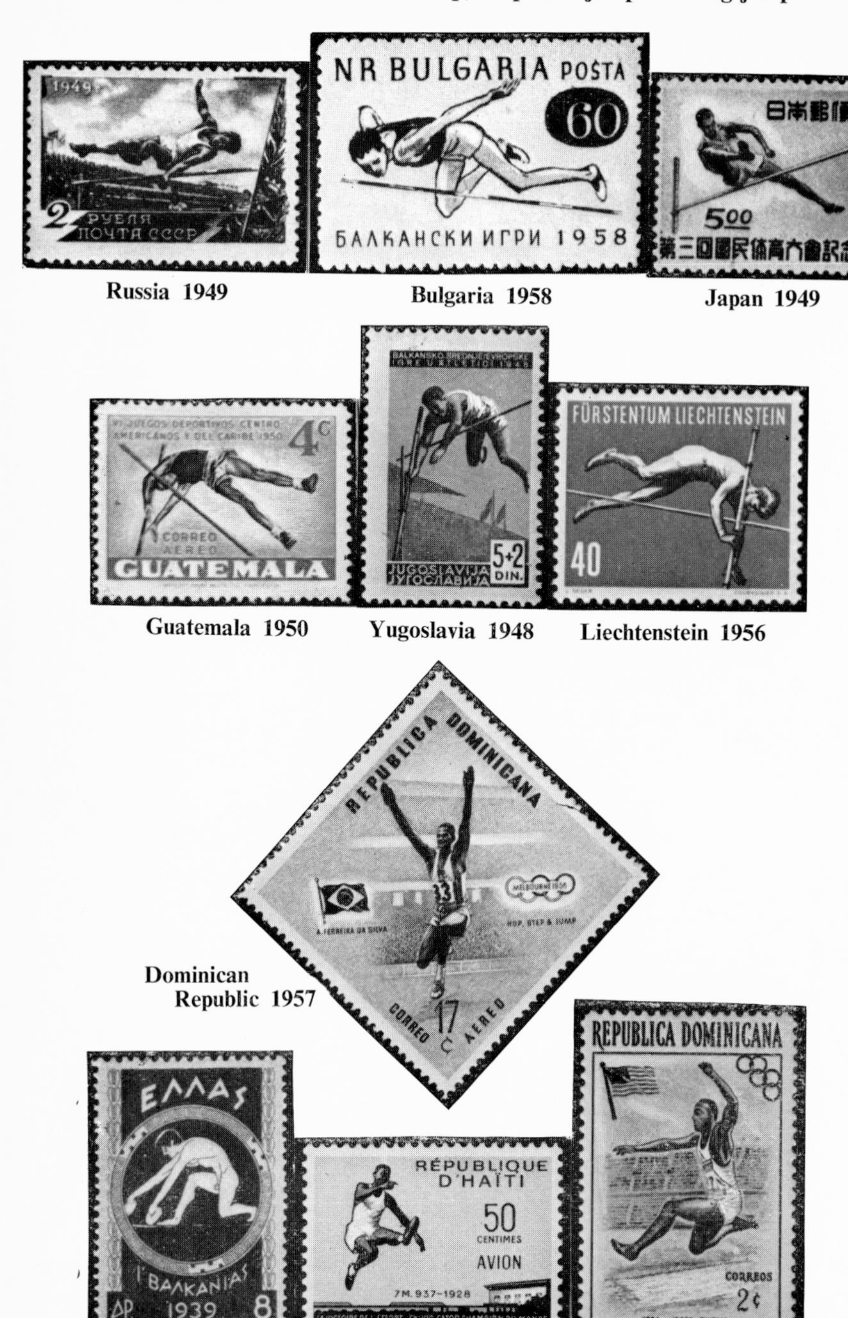

Russia 1949 — Bulgaria 1958 — Japan 1949

Guatemala 1950 — Yugoslavia 1948 — Liechtenstein 1956

Dominican Republic 1957

Greece 1949 — Haiti 1958 — Dominican Republic 1957

ATHLETICS

Walking — Women's events

San Marino 1954

Dominican Republic 1957

Netherlands 1956

Hungary 1956

Sweden 1953

Russia 1938

Poland 1956

Russia 1957

China 1957

Japan 1954

Czechoslovakia 1957

France 1958

Panama 1938

Japan 1958

U.S.A. 1939

Japan 1949

Nicaragua 1949

Liberia 1955

France 1956

Hungary 1956

Czechoslovakia 1956

BOBSLEIGH — BOXING — CANOEING

Germany 1936

San Marino 1955

Germany (East) 1951

Ecuador 1939

Yugoslavia 1952

Panama 1938

Czechoslovakia 1957

Poland 1956

Russia 1956

Yugoslavia 1956

Czechoslovakia 1958

France 1953

CYCLING — FENCING

France 1953

Ifni 1958

Liechtenstein 1958

Monaco 1953

Hungary 1953

Dominican Republic 1957

Hungary 1952

Poland 1954

Liechtenstein 1958

EQUESTRIAN SPORTS

Horse-racing — Riding — Polo — Trotting

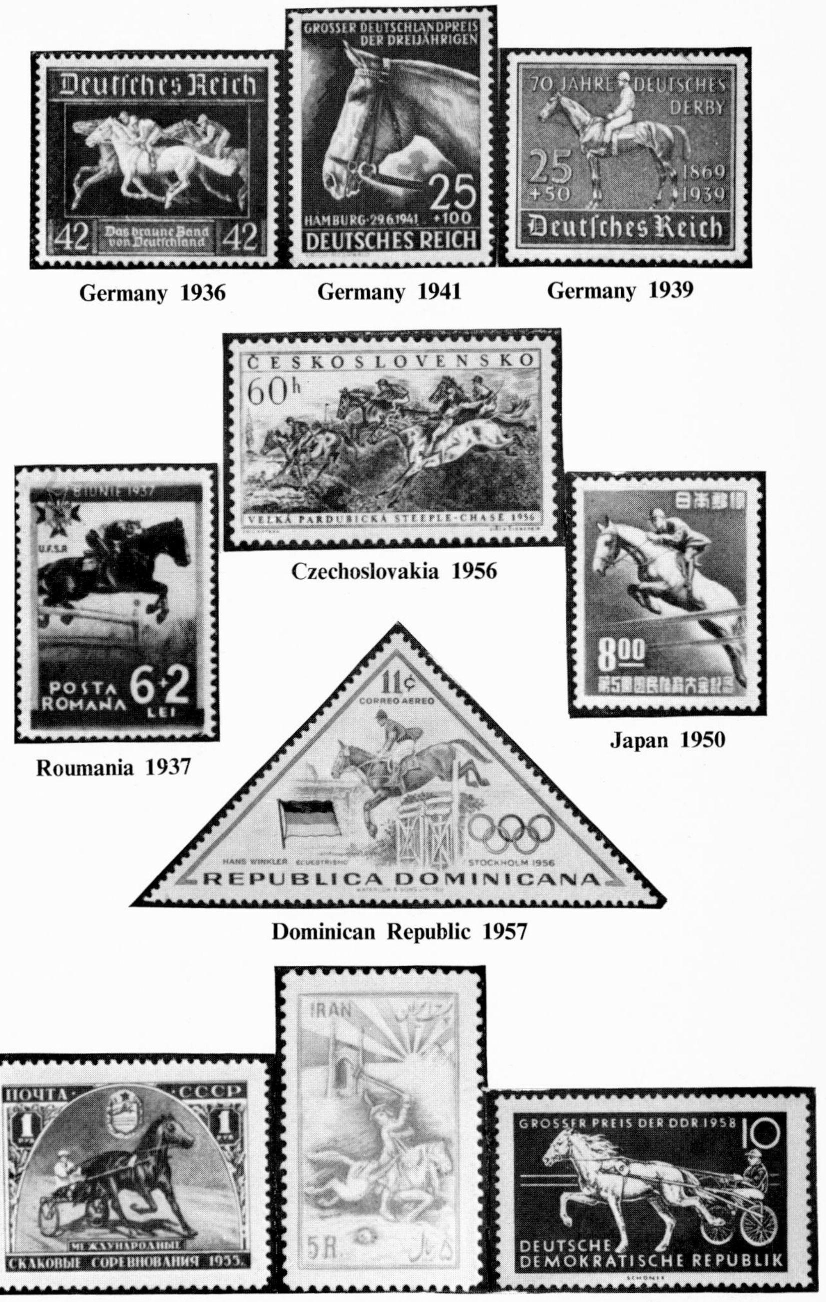

Germany 1936 — Germany 1941 — Germany 1939

Czechoslovakia 1956

Roumania 1937 — Japan 1950

Dominican Republic 1957

Russia 1956 — Iran 1953 — Germany (East) 1958

FLYING

Parachuting — Model-flying — Gliding

Russia 1956

Russia 1951

Czechoslovakia 1958

Hungary 1943

Russia 1951

Brazil 1951

Switzerland 1946

Hungary 1943

Belgium 1951

Hungary 1950

Poland 1954

Bulgaria 1956

FOOTBALL

France 1938

Japan 1950

Russia 1948

Uruguay 1951

Nicaragua 1949

Guatemala 1950

Italy 1934

Switzerland 1954

Spanish Guinea
1955–6

Hungary 1953

Trieste B 1952

Sweden 1958

Finland 1947

Japan 1955

Sweden 1949

Finland 1945

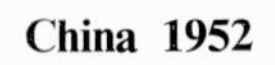

China 1952

Bulgaria 1954

Yugoslavia 1952

Japan 1957

Monaco 1953

Liechtenstein 1957

Liechtenstein 1957

HOCKEY — ICE HOCKEY — ICE YACHTING — JUDO

Japan 1951

Netherlands 1956

Switzerland 1948

Russia 1957

Sweden 1953

Czechoslovakia 1952

Canada 1956

Japan 1953

Hungary 1955

Japan 1956

MOTOR SPORTS

Motor-racing — Motor-boating — Motor-cycling

Germany 1939

Monaco 1955

Yugoslavia 1939

Yugoslavia 1953

Yugoslavia 1953

Russia 1948

Russia 1948

Yugoslavia 1939

San Marino 1954

Czechoslovakia 1957

Somalia 1958

NATIONAL SPORTS

Switzerland 1950

Switzerland 1951

Iceland 1955–7

Switzerland 1950

France 1958

France 1958

Eire 1934

Afghanistan 1957

Burma 1949

MOUNTAINEERING — PELOTA — RUGBY — ROWING — ROLLER-SKATING

Russia 1949

France 1956

Liechtenstein 1955

France 1956

Roumania 1944

France 1956

Roumania 1937

Monaco 1948

Poland 1955

Germany 1936

Portugal 1952

Trieste B 1952

Switzerland 1950

Roumania 1955

Dominican Republic 1957

Germany 1936

San Marino 1955

Norway 1951

Hungary 1925

Hungary 1955

San Marino 1955

SKI-ING

Finland 1938 — Poland 1953 — Czechoslovakia 1950

Norway 1951 — Japan 1949 — Finland 1958

Austria 1936 — Russia 1948 — Austria 1936

Liechtenstein 1955 — Switzerland 1948 — Liechtenstein 1955

TABLE TENNIS — TENNIS — VOLLEY BALL

Nicaragua 1949

Japan 1956

Japan 1954

San Marino 1953

Monaco 1948

Russia 1956

Liechtenstein 1958

Bulgaria 1950

Russia 1956

Czechoslovakia 1953

Russia 1957

Hungary 1956

Japan 1958

Turkey 1949

Finland 1945

Bulgaria 1954

Hungary 1953

Japan 1952

Sweden 1953

Monaco 1948

Bermuda 1936–40

Nicaragua 1949

New Zealand 1951

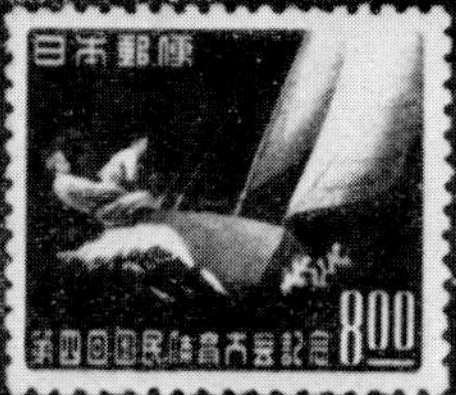

Japan 1948

Bahamas 1954

Trieste B 1952

San Marino 1955–6

Russia 1949

Dominican Republic 1958

SPORTS EVENTS

Italy 1933

Bulgaria 1946

India 1951

Indonesia 1951

Mexico 1955

Indonesia 1951

Egypt 1951

Russia 1956

Israel 1953

France 1957

Japan 1958

Great Britain 1958

SPORTS GROUNDS

Italy 1933

Finland 1951

Greece 1934

Monaco 1939

Italy 1956

Russia 1957

Hungary 1952

Germany (East) 1953

Germany (Berlin) 1953

Nicaragua 1949

Liberia 1956

Japan 1958

Turkey 1943

Bulgaria 1949

Russia 1949

Russia 1938

Czechoslovakia 1950

Roumania 1943

Poland 1951

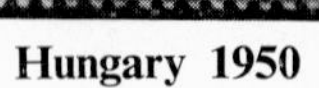

Hungary 1950

Italy 1952

Roumania 1937

Roumania 1958

Brazil 1952

Russia 1960. *17th Olympic Games*
40k. blue and multicoloured.
Foil-fencers.

Hungary 1960. *17th Olympic Games*
1.70fo. yellow brown and light brown.
Ancient Greek warriors fighting.

The Dominican Republic 1960. *Olympic Victors 1956 (IV)*
7c. blue and green.
Carlo Pavesi, Italy, épée champion.

Panama 1960. *17th Olympic Games*
3c. violet.
Foil-fencers.

Morocco 1960. *17th Olympic Games*
70f. black, blue and dark brown.
Épée-fencers.

Lebanon 1960. *17th Olympic Games*
15+15p. red brown.
Foil-fencing.

U.A.R. (Syria) 1960. *17th Olympic Games*
25p. yellow red and violet.
Native *bedouin* fencing.

13. FLYING

This heading undoubtedly covers a larger field than that of an ordinary sports stamps collection. As already mentioned, it is sometimes very hard to fix boundaries between what should be regarded as sports stamps and what should not. In this case personal judgment and interest must decide. The following comments, however, may serve as a guide to the collector:

The first problem to be faced is whether stamps depicting air pioneers should be regarded as sports stamps. One cannot deny the 'sporting' nature of many of these flyers' achievements, but their primary object was scientific. Although not strictly 'sports stamps', here is a short description of most of these issues. It does not have any pretensions to being complete, but should still be of use to those who would like to include these stamps in their collections.

Argentina celebrated the 50th anniversary of her aero club in 1958 by issuing one stamp picturing an old aeroplane.

Australia issued in 1931 three stamps to honour the round-the-world flyer *Kingsford-Smith*. In 1958 the 30th anniversary of his flight to Tasmania was celebrated with a stamp showing *Kingsford-Smith* and his aeroplane.

Belgium marked, in 1951, the 50th anniversary of the Belgian Aero Club with two stamps, one showing a 'Tipsy' sports aeroplane.

Brazil was the home country of *Santos Dumont*, one of the foremost air pioneers. In 1929 he was honoured with three stamps showing an airship, *Dumont* himself and his aeroplane. In 1951 the 50th anniversary of his first flight was celebrated with two stamps. New stamps appeared in 1956 commemorating his feat fifty years earlier of conquering the air with an aeroplane heavier than air. The first flight New York–Rio de Janeiro by *E. Pinto Martin* in 1922 was commemorated with one stamp in 1951.

Cuba issued in 1938 a stamp with an overprint to honour pioneer *Rossillo*. Another Cuban pioneer, *J. Gonzales*, was honoured in a commemorative series in 1955. The aeroplanes of the *Wright brothers* as well as *Lindbergh's* 'Spirit of St. Louis' were illustrated on Cuban airmail stamps in 1955.

Czechoslovakia celebrated the 50th anniversary of the first flight of the Czech pilot and engineer *Kaspar*.

Denmark celebrated in 1956 the 50th anniversary of the first European flight performed by the Dane *Ellehammer* in 1906.

Ecuador marked the centenary of air pioneer *J. A. Castillo* in 1955 with a set of no less than seven values.

France can boast many air pioneers. The French flyer *Blériot* was commemorated in 1939 with a stamp showing his aeroplane over the Channel. He was honoured not only by his home country but also in Latvia in 1932 and Hungary in 1948. Another French pioneer, *M. Noguès*, was commemorated in 1951 with one stamp, as was the French woman flyer *Maryse Bastié* in 1955.

Germany or, more correctly, West Berlin, depicted in 1953 the German pioneer *O. Lilienthal*.

Hungary celebrated 'Air Day' in 1954 with a large set illustrating many forms of flying.

Italy's airmail issues include stamps among others commemorating the Atlantic flights of *General Balbo* in 1931–3, and the first direct flight from Rome to Buenos Aires in 1934.

Latvia honoured the *Wright brothers* with a set in 1932.

Liechtenstein issued in 1948 a series of ten stamps picturing air pioneers from *Icarus* to *Leonardo da Vinci* and *Wilbur Wright*.

Lithuania commemorated in 1935 and 1936 the pilot *F. Valthus*. The year previously the two dead Atlantic flyers *Darius* and *Girenas* had been honoured with a set.

Mexico issued in 1929 a series of six stamps in memory of the Mexican Air Force captain *E. Carranza*.

New Zealand in 1958 also honoured *Kingsford-Smith's* crossing of the Tasman Sea in 1928.

Newfoundland have issued several air-pioneer stamps. The first were surcharges on ordinary stamps of 1919 for mail going partly with flyers *Hawker* and *Grieve*, partly with *Alcock* and *Whitton-Brown*, in their rival attempts to cross the Atlantic first. The latter succeeded. In 1927 *de Pinedo* was also commemorated with a special surcharged stamp. The following year *Hawker* and *Grieve* were celebrated with one stamp showing their aeroplane.

Norway in 1944 honoured *T. Gran*, who crossed the North Sea from Scotland to Norway in 1914.

Peru commemorated in 1937 the Peruvian pioneer *J. Chavez* with three stamps.

Philippines, starting in 1926, have issued a number of stamps with surcharges, to commemorate a series of long-distance flights.

Poland celebrated Aviation Day 1951 with a set of three stamps, one of which shows an aeroplane.

Portugal commemorated in 1923 two pilots who first flew from Lisbon to Brazil.

Roumania featured flying on the highest values in the sports sets of 1945 and 1946. They are showing commercial aeroplanes. In 1953 another set of four stamps was issued illustrating aerial sports, one of which shows a sports plane.

Russia commemorated two flights over the North Pole in 1938, Moscow to Portland, U.S.A., and Moscow to St. Jacinthe, Canada, with one set each. In 1939 three Russian women who performed a long-distance flight from Moscow to the Far East were honoured. On one military sports stamp issued in 1959 there is a helicopter used for sport.

United States commemorated *Charles Lindbergh* in 1927. The following year the *Wright brothers* were honoured on a stamp. In 1950 and 1953 they were again commemorated.

AIR RACES

The first air races took place in France in the early 1900's. Flying for sport naturally ceased during the First World War but developed rapidly in the 1920's and 1930's.

Air races in the proper sense are rarely pictured on stamps, as nowadays such races are few and far between.

Poland 1933. *Victory in the 'Round Europe' Flight in 1932*
3pg. grey green.
Poland, whose interest in sports aviation was great during the 1930's, issued a stamp to honour the winner of the 'Round Europe' flight in 1932. The stamp shows the winning sports plane, flanked by portraits of the winner, *Zwirko*, and the plane's constructor, *Wigura*.

Poland 1934. *'Round Europe' Flight*
20g. olive (*airmail*), 30g. grey green.
Two years afterwards Poland was given the honour of arranging the 1934 tournament. To celebrate this event the 1933 stamp was reissued, together with an ordinary airmail stamp, both being overprinted with 'Challenge 1934'.

Tripolitania 1934. *'Round-the-Oases' Race*
50c. red, 75c. yellow olive, 2.25l. orange red, 4.50l. wine red, 5l. grey brown, 10l. blue, 25l. violet.
Sixteen Italian pilots are said to have taken part in this race, which was commemorated with seven ordinary airmail stamps overprinted 'Circuito Delle Oasi/Tripoli/Maggio 1934–XII'.

Czechoslovakia 1960. *1st World Aerobatics Championship in Bratislava*
60h. violet and blue.
Skoda sports aeroplane looping.

BALLOONING

The history of ballooning goes back about 150 years, but not until the big competitions in the twentieth century did it really become a sport. The balloon was soon superseded by the aeroplane and the only events of importance were the Gordon Bennett races started in 1906 and promoted by the American newspaperman, James Gordon Bennett, Jun. As a result, ballooning has received little attention from designers.

Poland 1936. *24th Gordon Bennett races in Warsaw*

30g. red, 55g. blue.

The stamps issued to celebrate this event were two current values overprinted 'Gordon Bennett 30.VIII/1936'.

Russia 1938. *Flying Sports issue*

15k. red, 50k. green, 80k. brown.

These three stamps, all with various ballooning designs, belong to the fringes of sports philately.

PARACHUTING

Apart from its military uses, parachuting is also practised as a sport, especially in the Soviet Union where it is very popular. From Russia it has spread to all the East European countries and several world championships have been held.

Parachuting, which to us seems a borderline sport, has been included in Eastern Europe sports stamps.

Russia 1938. *Flying Sports issue*

30k. lilac brown.

Parachutists landing.

Russia 1938. *20th Anniversary of Russian Youth Movement*

20k. brown.

Parachutist about to land.

Russia 1949. *Sports issue*

1r. red.

A beautiful stamp showing several parachutists.

Yugoslavia 1950. *Flying Sports Week*

5d. violet.

Parachutists landing.

Yugoslavia 1951. *1st World Parachuting Championships in Bled*

6d. red brown, 50d. dark blue.

Airmail stamps overprinted in red with an inscription announcing the event.

Russia 1951. *Aviation Day*

1r. multicoloured.

Mass parachuting. Inscription: 'Parachuting, the Sport of the Brave'.

Poland 1952. *Flying Sports issue*
90g. grey blue.
Three parachutists.

Roumania 1953. *Flying Sports issue*
20b. orange brown and olive brown.
A parachutist collecting his parachute after landing.

Hungary 1954. *Aviation Sports issue*
1fo. brown and black.
An attractive diamond-shaped stamp showing a parachutist with a double parachute.

Russia 1956. *3rd World Parachuting Championships in Moscow*
40k. multicoloured.
A parachutist landing.

Czechoslovakia 1958. *4th World Parachuting Championships in Bratislava*
80h. grey violet.
A close-up of a parachutist in action.

China (Communist) 1958. *Flying Sports issue*
10f. brown.
A beautiful design showing parachutists with a double parachute in the foreground.

Russia 1959. *Military Sports issue*
60k. blue and yellow brown.
Oxygen-masked parachutist.

Bulgaria 1959. *3rd Parachuting (DOSO) Congress*
1.25l. dark green and yellow.
Parachuting from jumping-tower.

China (Communist) 1959. *1st National Games in Peking*
8d. blue, grey and black.
Parachutist landing.

Portugal 1960. *50th Anniversary of the Portuguese Aero Club*
2e. light green and yellow.
Parachutist and aeroplane.

Belgium 1960. *Belgian Parachuting Club*

40c.+10c. light ultramarine and grey, 1f.+50c. light blue and grey, 2f.+50c. light blue, green and grey, 2.50f.+1f. blue green, grey green and grey, 3f.+1f. light blue and grey, 6f.+2f. light blue, violet, grey green and grey.

Jumping, the descent and collecting parachute after landing.

Roumania 1960. *Aviation Day*

1.75l. light green, blue, red and red brown.

Parachutists landing.

Bulgaria 1960. *5th World Parachuting Championships*

16s. light violet and dark violet, 1.25l. green blue and red violet.

Parachutist about to land and parachutists descending.

FLYING MODEL AIRCRAFT

The history of model aircraft is closely connected with aviation itself, and most of the pioneers of flying tested their ideas on models. When problems of flying had been solved, model-aircraft flying became a sport. The first competitions took place in 1911 in Germany and England, but the real 'break-through' came at the end of the 1920's. The number of competitors multiplied rapidly during the 1930's, especially in Russia.

This pastime, which really belongs to the fringes of sport philately, has a place here because of its great popularity and increasingly competitive character. It is often difficult to fix a dividing line between sport and 'play', but where the models are intended for competitive flying, or the stamp itself forms part of a sports set, reference has been made in this section.

Russia 1938. *Flying Sports Issue*

5k. grey brown.

Children holding a large model aeroplane.

Hungary 1941. *Horthy Aviation Fund*

10+10f. red violet.

A boy holding a model aeroplane.

Croatia 1942. *Model Aircraft Exhibition in Zagreb*

3+3k. red brown.

A boy with a model aeroplane. The stamps in this set were also issued in a jubilee sheet.

Hungary 1943. *Horthy Aviation Fund*
8+8f. green.
A hand holding a model glider.

Russia 1948. *Youth Pioneer issue*
30k. green.
Youngsters holding a large model aeroplane.

Roumania 1948. *Sports issue*
20+20l. dark blue, 20×20l. green blue (imperf.).
A boy holding a model aeroplane.

Yugoslavia 1950. *Flying Sports issue*
2d. olive green.
A boy launching a model glider.

Russia 1951. *Aviation Day*
60k. multicoloured.
Young boys with a model aeroplane.

Brazil 1951. *50th Anniversary of the First Flight of Santos Dumont*
60c. orange, blue and brown.
Boys with model aeroplanes in front of a hangar. In the background is the head of *Santos Dumont*.

San Marino 1953. *Sports issue*
10l. red and blue.
Boy with model aeroplane, the San Marino mountains in the background.

Roumania 1953. *Roumanian Pioneer Movement*
55b. blue.
Boy and girl with model gliders.

Roumania 1953. *Flying Sports issue*
10b. orange and green.
Girl with model aeroplane.

Hungary 1954. *Flying Sports issue*
40f. olive yellow and grey, 50f. grey, red and brown.
Two model-aircraft designs are represented in this set, one showing a boy with a model glider, the other depicting the building of a similar model.

Russia 1958. *Pioneer issue*
25k. multicoloured.
Boy holding a model aeroplane.

U.A.R. (Syria) 1958. *Gliding Week Festival*
7½p. grey green, 12½p. olive.
Boy and girl holding a model glider with a sports plane in the background.

China (Communist) 1958. *Flying Sports issue*
4f. carmine.
Three children with model aeroplanes.

Portugal 1960. *50th Anniversary of the Portuguese Aero Club*
2.50e. blue green, red and yellow brown.
Model glider.

GLIDING

Gliding originated in the 1890's, when the German, Otto Lilienthal, attempted more than 2,000 flights. He was followed by the Americans Wilbur and Orville Wright, who in 1901–2 made more than 1,000 flights before they went over to motor-powered aircraft. In Germany, gliding was practised by schoolchildren early in the century, but the real impetus came after the First World War, when powered flight was banned in Germany. From Germany the sport soon spread.

Russia 1938. *Flying Sports issue*
10k. grey brown.
A glider passing over tractors ploughing a field.

Germany 1939. *German Postal Employees' Fund*
20+10pf. blue.
One of a large set, this design shows a glider workshop, with an airborne glider in the background. The inscription says that there were 100 such factories in the country at that time.

Hungary 1941. *Horthy Aviation Fund*
20+20f. orange red.
An attractive gliding stamp.

Croatia 1942. *Model Aircraft Exhibition in Zagreb*
2+2k. brown, 2.50+2.50k. green.
Gliders.

Hungary 1943. *Horthy Aviation Fund*

12+12f. blue.

One of the most attractive sports stamps ever; it pictures gliders against a background of beautiful cloud formations.

Switzerland 1946. *Airmail Stamp*

1f. 50c. red and grey.

An instructional glider which all would-be glider pilots first have to be able to handle. Inscribed 'Pro Aero'.

Roumania 1948. *Flying Sports issue*

2+2l. blue.

A glider passing over a hill.

Switzerland 1949. *Airmail Stamp*

1.50f. yellow.

This stylized gliding stamp was voted the most beautiful stamp of 1949. Inscribed '*Pro Aero*'.

Yugoslavia 1950. *Flying Sports issue*

3d. red brown.

A glider in flight.

Hungary 1950. *Sports issue*

3fo. brown.

Close-up of a glider named 'Koma', which means 'pal'.

Belgium 1951. *50th Anniversary of the Belgian Aero Club*

6f. grey brown.

A glider over a landscape—probably taken from an aerial photograph. The two stamps in the set form part of a special sheet with a heavy premium for sports flying.

Poland 1952. *Flying Sports issue*

30+15g. grey green.

A glider pilot and flying emblem.

Roumania 1953. *Flying Sports issue*

55b. red violet.

Glider on the ground with the pilot standing beside it.

Hungary 1954. *Flying Sports issue*

60f. red brown and grey.

A large diamond-shaped stamp of beautiful design.

Poland 1954. *International Gliding Competition in Leszno*

45g. green, 60g. violet, 60g. brown, 1.35z. light blue (with light clouds), 1.35z. light blue (with dark clouds).

The stamps in this set all have the same glider design but in three different settings.

Turkey 1954. *47th F.A.I. Congress in Ankara*

20k. olive brown, 35k. grey violet.

In this set there are two gliding designs—one showing advanced flying with a sail plane and the other an ordinary glider. On the first stamp the design also contains a standard bearer and on the latter a portrait of the French air pioneer, *Baron de la Grange.*

Bulgaria 1956. *30th Anniversary of Bulgarian Gliding*

44s. blue, 60s. violet, 80s. dark green.

The designs are: a school glider launched by means of ribbon cable and sail planes, with winch and aeroplane launching, respectively.

Syria 1957. *Gliding Festival in Damascus*

25p. light brown, 35p. dark green, 40p. ultramarine.

The three stamps of this set bear the same design—a stylized drawing of a glider, with a bird and the emblem of the Syrian Air Force in the background.

Poland 1958. *World Gliding Championship in Leszno*

60g. blue green, 2.50z grey.

These artistic designs incorporate gliders in which the name of the event forms the wings and the tail.

China (Communist) 1958. *Flying Sports issue*

8f. green.

A beautiful stamp showing two gliders in flight.

Portugal 1960. *50th Anniversary of the Portuguese Aero Club*

1e. yellow and blue.

Glider.

14. FOOTBALL (ASSOCIATION)

A type of football was played in China as early as the fourth century B.C. In the Middle Ages football was played in Italy as well as in France and England. In England it was even prohibited by law. It was revived in various public schools in the nineteenth century, but with differing sets of rules; from these variations sprang Rugby and Association football, the latter being 'born' in 1863. The International Football Association (F.I.F.A.) was founded in 1904.

Not all football stamps show footballers in action; stadiums, symbols and football personalities are also depicted.

Uruguay 1924. *Olympic Football Victory in Paris 1924*

2c. red, 5c. lilac, 12c. blue.

The 'Victory' of Samothrace is the subject depicted on these stamps, which were also printed on special yellow paper in only 500 sets; they were given to the players themselves and are consequently very rare.

Hungary 1925. *Sports issue*

2,000k. lilac brown.

Hungary was the first country to issue a stamp with a realistic football design, showing a goalkeeper in action.

Netherlands 1928. *9th Olympic Games in Amsterdam*

3c. green.

A football player with the ball.

Uruguay 1928. *Olympic Football Victory in Amsterdam*

2c. lilac brown, 5c. red, 8c. blue.

The Uruguayan players repeated their victory of 1924 at Amsterdam and were accordingly honoured with special stamps of a rather confusing design incorporating a flower-bedecked goal, a football and the rising sun.

Bulgaria 1931–3. *1st Balkan Games in Sofia*

2l. brown lilac, 2l. blue (1933)

This stamp, showing a player with the ball, reappeared in 1933 with changed colours.

Italy 1934. *2nd World Football Championships in Rome*

Ordinary mail: 20c. orange, 25c. green, 50c. violet, 1.25l. blue, 5+2.50l, grey brown; *Airmail:* 50c. red, 75c. blue grey, 5+2.50l. grey green. 10+5l. grey brown.

To commemorate this event three sets were issued—one for Italy, one for the Colonies and finally one for the Aegean Islands; the last being the same as that for Italy but with changed colours and overprinted 'Isole Italiane Dell 'Egeo'. The stamps show various incidents on the field as well as views of the stadiums at Turin, Rome and Bologna.

Italian Colonies 1934. *2nd World Football Championships in Rome*

Ordinary mail: 10c. grey green, 50c. violet, 1.25l. blue, 5l. grey brown, 10l. blue grey; *Airmail:* 50c. orange brown, 75c. lilac brown, 5l. grey green, 10l. orange, 15l. rose, 25l. green, 50l. blue green.

This set has different designs from those mentioned above, having oriental backgrounds. The illustrations include a goal being scored, a footballer giving the Fascist salute, a seaplane over a stadium and a goalkeeper diving to make a save. The highest value shows a large football in the foreground with ancient ruins behind.

Colombia 1935. *3rd National Games in Barranquilla*

2c. yellow and green.

Two players in old-fashioned football kit.

Russia 1935. *World Spartacist Games in Moscow*

4k. red and blue.

This large diamond-shaped stamp shows two footballers in somewhat confused action.

Bulgaria 1935. *5th Balkan Football Cup in Sofia*

1l. green, 2l. grey black, 4l. red, 7l. blue, 14l. orange, 50l. brown.

This poorly designed set is one of the most expensive in sports philately. The designs show a football match in progress, a cathedral in Sofia, four players in line, a herald sounding a trumpet against a map of the Balkans, the captain of the victorious team saluting in front of the cup and the trophy itself.

Germany 1936. *11th Olympic Games in Berlin*

6+4pf. green.

Player kicking a ball.

Colombia 1937. *4th National Games in Manizales*

3c. green.

Football player in a stadium. The stamp appeared later the same year as a provisional stamp, surcharge '1 Centavo'.

Roumania 1937. *25th Anniversary of the Roumanian Sports Union*

25+25b. olive brown.

Two players in a tackle.

Panama 1938. *4th Central American Games in Panama*

15c. blue.

A player with ball.

France 1938. *3rd World Football Championships in Paris*

1.75f. dark blue.

A goalkeeper in action in front of an advancing forward.

Russia 1938. *Sports issue*

50k. blue.

A vivid football incident.

Costa Rica 1941. *Central American and Caribbean Football Championships in San José*

Ordinary mail: 5c. green, 10c. orange, 15c. rose, 25c. blue, 40c. red brown, 50c. violet, 75c. orange red, 1col. carmine. *Airmail:* 15c. red, 30c. ultramarine, 40c. red brown, 50c. violet, 60c. green, 75c. yellow, 1col. violet, 1.40col. rose, 2col. blue green, 5col. black.

For these championships Costa Rica issued two magnificent sets. The first shows a football stadium with a flag-pole in the foreground flying the blue, red and white flag of Costa Rica. In the stamp frame are the flags of the twelve other participating nations in their correct colours. The airmail series is far more interesting as regards design, for the illustration is taken from a photograph of a football match in the same stadium. It also is framed by the flags of the participating nations. These sets are among the most rare and are seldom seen on this side of the Atlantic.

Slovakia 1944. *Sports issue*

70+70h. olive green.

Player in a football ground.

Costa Rica 1946. *Central American and Caribbean Football Championships*

25c. green, 30c. yellow, 55c. blue.

These stamps are identical to the airmail stamps of 1941 except that the date has been changed. The following year these stamps reappeared with a surcharge because of an increase in postal rates.

Roumania 1946. *Sports issue*

10l. dark blue.

Two players in a heading duel.

Bulgaria 1947. *13th Balkan Games in Sofia*

20l. dark blue.

Two players fighting for the ball.

Russia 1948. *Sports issue*

30k. yellow brown.

The famous Moscow Dynamo team in action.

Guatemala 1948. *4th Central American and Caribbean Football Championships*

3c. red and grey, 5c. green and grey, 10c. violet and grey, 30c. blue and grey, 50c. olive yellow and grey.

Footballers in action.

Nicaragua 1949. *10th World Amateur Baseball Championships in Managua 1948*

2c. grey green (*airmail*), 1co. red.

An original design, as only the legs of the footballer are visible as he traps the ball.

Russia 1949. *Sports issue*

40k. green.

Dynamo players in an exciting incident at their Moscow stadium. Their opponents are Spartak.

Guatemala 1950. *6th Central American and Caribbean Games*

1c. violet and black.

An interesting and attractive design showing a goalkeeper punching the ball clear.

Brazil 1950. *4th World Football Championships in Rio de Janeiro*

0.60cr. blue, green and grey, 1.20cr. brown orange and blue, 5.00cr. yellow, green and blue (*airmail*).

These stamps are not among the most beautiful because of their dull colours and poor printing. They depict football players in front of a globe, the Estadio Municipal in Rio de Janeiro and a footballer in front of the Brazilian flag.

Japan 1950. *5th National Sports Games in Nagoya*

8.00y. red brown.

Goalkeeper punching the ball away from an opposing forward.

Hungary 1950. *Sports issue*

70f. red brown and grey.

Two players in a tackle.

Uruguay 1951. *Victory in the World Football Championships in 1950*
3c. green, 7c. blue.
Uruguay honoured her team, which had surprisingly beaten Brazil. The design, which was also used for the official World Cup poster, depicts a footballer's leg wearing a sock made up of the flags of the participating nations.

Bolivia 1951. *2nd National Sports Congress of 1948*
1.40b. yellow and black.
Goalkeeper in action.

Czechoslovakia 1951. *9th Sokol Congress and Games*
3k. red brown.
Two players fighting for the ball.

Finland 1952. *15th Olympic Games*
15+2m. green.
Two players challenging for the ball.

Trieste, Zone B (Yugoslav) 1952. *Sports issue*
10d. green
A goalkeeper in action.

Poland 1952. *Sports issue*
45+15g. violet.
Players with a football trophy in the foreground.

Yugoslavia 1952. *15th Olympic Games*
110d. blue violet and brown.
A player making a powerful kick. The same stamp but with changed colours was issued for Trieste Zone B, overprinted 'STT–VUJNA'.

Luxemburg 1952. *Sports issue*
2f. brown and black.
This stamp, showing players fighting for the ball, was awarded third place in the Bonacossa Medal Competition, 1952.

Roumania 1952. *International Students' Congress in Bucharest*
55b. green.
A football match.

Monaco 1953. *15th Olympic Games*
2f. green and blue.
A forceful kick is shown on this big diamond-shaped stamp.

San Marino 1953. *Sports issue*

5l. green and brown.

Players struggling for the ball.

Hungary 1953. *Inauguration of Nép Stadium, Budapest*

2fo. red brown and green.

A player in the Hungarian national team being chased by an opponent at the Nép Stadium. This stamp was awarded third place in the Bonacossa Medal Competition, 1953.

Hungary 1953. *Football Victory over England*

2fo. red brown and green.

As above but overprinted 'London-Wembley/1953. XI. 25./6:3'. This commemorates the first-ever occasion when England were beaten at home by a foreign national team.

Switzerland 1954. *World Football Championships in Berne*

40c. blue and yellow brown.

A football in front of a map of the world. This stamp won the Bonacossa Medal in 1954.

Liechtenstein 1954. *World Football Championships*

10c. rose brown, 20c. olive green, 25c. brown, 40c. grey violet.

The small, stamp-issuing principality attempted a sports issue for the first time when their neighbour Switzerland was the host for the World Cup. The set shows, according to the official description, two forwards, a full-back, a goalkeeper and two half-backs.

Liberia 1955. *Sports issue*

5c. orange brown and black.

Two players in action.

Spanish Guinea 1955–6. *Sports issue*

25c. grey violet, 50c. olive brown, 1.50p. red brown, 4p. lilac rose, 10p. green.

The highest value in this ordinary airmail issue appeared in 1955 and depicted a heading duel between a white and a coloured player. Six months later the four lower values followed.

Turkey 1955. *Victory in the International Military Football Championships in Rome*

15k. light blue, 20k. light red, 1l. grey green.

These stamps, which can hardly be regarded as beautiful, show footballers, an emblem with the F.I.S.M. badge, the flag of Turkey, a map and sabre and finally the championship plaque with an oak leaf and laurel.

Guatemala 1955–6. *50th Anniversary of Guatemalan Football*
4c. violet, 4c. red, 4c. green, 10c. grey green, 15c. blue.
An excellent goalkeeper design and two, to us, unknown football stars, *Carlos Aguirre Matheu* and *Mario Camposeco* (crouching by the ball). The lowest value reappeared six months later in two new colours.

Germany (East) 1956. *2nd Sports and Gymnastic Festival in Leipzig*
5pf. grey green.
Two players and a ball.

Russia 1956. *National Spartacist Games*
40k. green and brown.
Three players with ball.

Hungary 1956. *16th Olympic Games*
1fo. rose and brown.
Hungarian goalkeeper in action.

Bulgaria 1956. *16th Olympic Games*
44s. dark green.
Two footballers in action, the one on the right belonging to the Bulgarian team.

Yugoslavia 1956. *Olympic Year*
35d. dark brown and brown.
Goalkeeper in action. A panther, symbolizing alertness and mobility, is also featured on the stamp.

China (Communist) 1957. *1st Chinese Workers' Games 1955*
8d. dark blue, brown, red and green.
Two players with a football.

Russia 1957. *16th Olympic Games*
40k. multicoloured.
An incident from the football final in Melbourne between Russia and Yugoslavia.

Dutch Antilles 1957. *7th Central American and Caribbean Football Championships in Curaçao*
6+2½c. orange, 7½+5c. red brown, 15+5c. green, 22½+7½c. blue green.

Player with ball, map of the Caribbean and neighbouring countries, a goalkeeper in action and players fighting for the ball.

Lebanon 1957. *2nd Pan Arabian Games in Beirut*
12½p. grey black.
Two players in a tackle, with the Games' emblem.

Czechoslovakia 1958. *World Football Championships in Stockholm*
1.60k. yellow green.
A match with a member of the Czech team in the foreground.

Somalia 1958. *Sports issue*
0.04s. light green.
Coloured goalkeeper in action.

Sweden 1958. *World Football Championships in Sweden*
15ö. red, 20ö. green, 1.20k. blue.
A player kicking a ball.

Russia 1958. *World Football Championships*
40k. multicoloured, 60k. multicoloured
These two stamps show footballers in front of a globe of the world. Shortly after the championships the same stamps reappeared imperforate, and for one day only, in a very small issue which was sold out the same day.

North Viet-Nam 1958. *Inauguration of Hanoi Stadium*
10d. blue and blue grey, 20d. olive and red orange, 80d. red brown and yellow orange, 150d. dark brown and blue green.
Footballer and parading athletes.

Poland 1959. *Sports issue*
95g. light green and violet brown.
Footballers in action.

Brazil 1959. *Victory in the World Football Championships 1958*
3.30g. yellow green and dark red.
Brazilian player and the Jules Rimet Cup.

Bulgaria 1959. *Youth Football Tournament in Sofia*
2l. red brown.
A match in progress.

Panama 1959. *3rd Pan American Games in Chicago*
1c. grey and green.
High kick.

Roumania 1959. *Sports issue*
20b. green, orange brown, light blue and red violet.
Goalkeeper catching ball.

Bulgaria 1959. *50th Football Anniversary*
1.25l. dark green and yellow, 1.25l. dark red and yellow (imperf.).
Kicking the ball.

Ghana 1959. *West African Football Championships*
½d., 1d., 3d., 8d., 2s.6d., all multicoloured.
Issued to commemorate a tournament that was never held, this set depicts in vivid colours a map of Western Africa and the cup, a Ghana player and opponent, a goalkeeper with flags of participating countries, a Ghana player about to score and the Gold Cup.

Albania 1959. *1st National Spartacist Games*
2l. green.
Players in action.

Ifni 1959. *Sports issue*
10+5c. violet brown, 20+5c. grey green.
Footballer about to shoot and two players in action.

China (Communist) 1959. *1st National Games in Peking*
5d. grey, red, brown and black.
Player with ball.

Paraguay 1960. *17th Olympic Games*
0.30g. red and green, 0.50g. brown violet and grey blue, 0.75g. olive brown and orange, 1.50g. violet blue and green.
Goalkeeper catching ball.

Costa Rica 1960. *3rd Pan American Football Championships in San José*
10c. grey, 25c. ultramarine, 35c. orange, 50c. red brown, 85c. dark green, $5 violet brown, and $2 blue (sheet).
The designs are taken from photographs of actual matches.

Belgian Congo 1960. *17th Olympic Games*
2f.+1f. green and red.
Goalkeeper catching ball.

Ruanda Urundi 1960. *17th Olympic Games*
2f.+1f. brown grey and dark red.
As Belgian Congo.

San Marino 1960. *17th Olympic Games*
60l. grey green and orange brown, 60l. same colour (imperf. in sheet).
Player with ball.

Roumania 1960. *17th Olympic Games (II)*
2l. violet.
Player with ball.

U.A.R. 1960. *8th Anniversary of the Revolution*
5m. violet brown.
Two players in action.

Surinam 1960. *17th Olympic Games*
50x.+20c. green, red brown and black.
Player with ball.

Sudan 1960. *17th Olympic Games*
15m. ultramarine, 55m. green, 3p. yellow.
Sudanese player.

Turkey 1960. *17th Olympic Games*
30k. grey green.
Turkish players.

Bulgaria 1960. *17th Olympic Games*
8s. brown and light rose, 8s. dark brown and yellow (imperf.).
Goalkeeper catching ball.

Panama 1960. *17th Olympic Games*
5c. green.
Player with ball.

Spain 1960. *Sports issue*
70c. green and red, 2.50p. violet red and green.
Player kicking ball.

Formosa (Nationalist China) 1960. *15th National Taiwan Games*
$2.50 light orange, red orange and black.
Two players with ball.

North Korea 1960. *15th Anniversary of the Republic*
5w. orange, green and black.
Two players in action.

Costa Rica 1960. *17th Olympic Games*
25c. green and black.
Player with ball.

15. GYMNASTICS

In China and India there were in about 500 B.C. several 'gymnastic systems' with very closely regulated rules of movement. The gymnastics practised in Ancient Greece approximately corresponded to our athletics. It was not until the end of the eighteenth century that the first regular gymnastic system was founded in Germany by Johann Guts Muth. At the beginning of the nineteenth century the ground was prepared for the two chief systems: Turnen by F. L. Jahn and E. W. B. Eiselen and Swedish Gymnastics by P. H. Ling. The German system laid stress on movements with equipment, whereas the Swedish emphasized the importance of harmony.

This section includes, apart from stamps showing gymnasts in action, those commemorating gymnastic festivals and leading personalities in the sport.

In this connection it is worth mentioning some Swiss stamps depicting the educationalist and philosopher, J. H. Pestalozzi. Pestalozzi, who was born in 1746 and died in 1827, was one of the pioneers of modern gymnastics and originator of elementary gymnastics, from which the three movements of the modern sport have developed. Pestalozzi was shown on the Pro Juventute stamps of 1927, and also on one stamp in 1946.

Modern competitive gymnastics has been given a section of its own.

Hungary 1925. *Sports issue*
100k brown and green.
Gymnastic team in traditional white dress marching past a stadium stand.

Czechoslovakia 1926. *8th Sokol Festival in Prague*
50h. green, 100h. red, 200h. blue, 300h. brown.
The Slavic Sokol Movement is represented on these stamps for the first time. Each of the four stamps has President Masaryk's portrait overprinted 'VIII SLET VSESOKOLSKY/PRAHA 1926' in a semicircle.

Czechoslovakia 1932–3. *Centenary of the birth of Miroslav Tyrš*

50h. green, 1k. red, 2k. blue, 3k. brown; 60h. violet (1933).

Two portraits of *Tyrš*, the first reappearing in 1933 in a somewhat changed form as an ordinary stamp.

Yugoslavia 1933. *Sokol Games in Ljubljana*

75+25p. grey green, 11½+½d. red.

Crown Prince Peter in the Sokol uniform.

Yugoslavia 1934. *20th Anniversary of Sokol Movement in Sarajevo*

0.75+0.25d. green, 1.50+0.50d. red, 1.75+0.25d. brown.

A falcon (Sokol means falcon) over Sarajevo.

Yugoslavia 1934. *60th Anniversary of Sokol Movement in Zagreb*

0.75+0.25d. green, 1.50+0.50d. red, 1.75+0.25d. brown.

A boy with a falcon.

Bulgaria 1935. *8th Junak Games in Sofia*

2l. light blue, 4l. red, 50l. carmine.

The Bulgarian counterpart to Sokol was the Junak Movement, Junak meaning 'young hero'. This national movement was formed in 1898 and had military-style rules. Regular Junak games were arranged every fourth year. The first Junak issue in 1935 contained a pole-vaulting design. Two of the stamps show a man and a woman both wearing the Junak uniform. The highest value illustrates the emblem of the movement.

Czechoslovakia 1938. *Sokol Winter Games in the Tatra Mountains*

50h. green, 1k. red.

A falcon resting among the mountain-tops.

Czechoslovakia 1938. *10th Sokol Games in Prague*

50h. green, 1k. red, 2k. blue grey.

The second of the founders of the Sokol Movement, *J Fügner*, father-in-law of *Tyrš* and his leading co-worker.

Germany 1938. *16th Turn and Sports Festival in Breslau*

3pf. brown, 5pf. green, 12 pf. red, 15pf. red brown.

The Turn Movement Festival in Breslau was marked by four stamps bearing views of the city.

Bulgaria 1939. *9th Junak Games in Sofia*

2l. rose, 7l. blue.

This set included the emblem of the Junak Movement and a girl dancing in national dress.

Sweden 1939. *Centenary of the death of P. H. Ling*
5ö. green, 25ö. brown.
The founder of Swedish Gymnastics, *P. H. Ling* (1776–1839).

Finland 1946. *National Games*
8m. purple.
Athletes holding laurel wreath.

Yugoslavia 1947. *Sports Festival in Belgrade*
1.50d. brown.
Two women's mass-gymnastics teams in action.

Finland 1947. *Finnish Gymnastics and Sports Festival in Helsinki*
10m. blue.
These Games, a rehearsal for the 1952 Olympic Games, included most sports but with gymnastics predominating.

Czechoslovakia 1948. *11th Sokol Games in Prague*
1st Series: 1.50k. brown, 3k. red, 5k. blue; *2nd Series:* 1k. green, 1.50k. grey brown, 2k. blue grey, 3k. red violet.
The Sokol Movement, originally a national gymnastic movement, later included most other sports. Sokol festivals were arranged every 10th year and in 1948 two sets were issued to celebrate the Games. The first depicts athletes, in national dress, paying homage to the republic. The four other values which came later show Sokol leaders *J. Vanicek* and *J. Scheiner*.

U.S.A. 1948. *Centenary of American 'Turners'*
3c. carmine.
The American 'Turners' are a transatlantic counterpart to the German Turn Movement. The stamp commemorating this anniversary is too overcrowded with detail to be attractive. The centre motif consists of the emblem of the movement.

Sweden 1949. *2nd Lingiad in Stockholm*
5ö. blue, 15ö. brown.
In their simplicity and purity of design these stamps are among the best sports issues ever. Two movements from the Ling system are illustrated.

Roumania 1950. *Sports and Work issue* (*F.G.M.A.*)
31l. olive brown.
Mass women's team with a woman gymnast in the foreground.

Italy 1951. *International Gymnastic Festival in Florence*

5l. dark brown and red, 10l. green and red, 15l. blue and red.

Different gymnastics equipment such as dumb-bells, clubs, ropes, rings, etc., and the flags of the participating nations.

This series was also overprinted 'AMG-FTT' for use in Trieste, Zone A.

China (Communist) 1952. *Gymnastics by Radio issue*

4×400d. carmine red, 4×400d. dark blue, 4×400d. red brown, 4×400d. green, 4×400d. light red, 4×400d. blue, 4×400d. yellow orange, 4×400d. violet, 4×400d. light brown, 4×400d. light blue.

This set is remarkable. To persuade people to take up gymnastics by radio these stamps were issued in sheets containing blocks of four, of the same colour and value. Each block of four stamps illustrated one complete gymnastic exercise.

A week later a fresh sheet followed, until the whole programme of gymnastics was covered.

Yugoslavia 1952. *15th Olympic Games*

50d. dark green and green.

Gymnastics with a ball, performed by a woman (officially described as basketball). The same stamp was issued with changed colour and overprinted 'STT-VUJNA' for use in Trieste, Zone B.

Germany (East) 1952. *Centenary of the death of F. L. Jahn*

12pf. blue.

Friedrich Ludwig Jahn, 1778–1852, was the founder of the German 'Turnen'.

Hungary 1953. *Inauguration of Nép Stadium in Budapest*

40f. grey blue and red brown.

A women's gymnastics team performing in the new stadium.

Iran 1953. *Ancient Persian Sports issue*

1r. green.

A man dressed in a special gymnastics suit exercising with clubs in a gymnasium.

Finland 1954. *Centenary of the birth of Ivar Wilskman*

25m. blue.

Ivar Wilskman, 1854–1932, was 'the father of Finnish Athletics'.

Czechoslovakia 1955. *1st National Summer Spartacist Games*
20h. ultramarine, 1.60h. brick red.
A girl in gymnastics kit and a male gymnast.

Japan 1955. *10th National Games of Kanagawa*
5y. red brown.
A women's gymnastic team.

Brazil 1955. *7th Spring Games in Rio de Janeiro*
0.60c. red violet.
Two women gymnasts performing a movement on a gymnastics bar.

Finland 1956. *Finnish Gymnastics and Sports Festival in Helsinki*
30m. blue.
A woman gymnast with a javelin-thrower, a footballer and a high diver in the background.

Germany (West) 1958. *50th Anniversary of 'Turnen'*
10pf. green, grey and black; 12f. green, grey and black (Saar).
The emblem of German 'Turnen' on an oak leaf. The 12f. stamp, bearing the inscription 'Saarland', was for use in the Saar.

Bulgaria 1958. *Student Games in Sofia*
28s. orange brown.
A woman gymnast performing dance movement.

Yugoslavia 1959. *The Partisan Games*
35d. violet brown and grey, 40d. violet grey and grey.
Gymnastics with rings, and 'hornpipe'.

Germany (East) 1959. *3rd German Gymnastics and Sports Festival in Leipzig*
5+5pf. orange, 25+10pf. blue.
Gymnastic exercises.

Bulgaria 1959. *Youth Festival and Spartacist Games in Sofia*
12s. red and yellow, 16s. red brown and light rose.
Acrobatics and gymnastics with rings.

Finland 1959. *Centenary of the birth of E. Kallio*
30m. red violet.
Woman gymnast with ring. *Elin Kallio*, 1859–1927, Finnish woman gymnast, founded gymnastics for women there in 1878.

China (Communist) 1959. *1st National Games in Peking*
8d. ultramarine, blue and brown.
Woman gymnast jumping.

Czechoslovakia 1960. *2nd National Spartacist Games (I)*
30h. rose red and brown.
Woman gymnast.

Czechoslovakia 1960. *2nd National Spartacist Games (II)*
30h. light green and red violet, 60h. rose red and grey, 1k. orange brown and violet blue.
Girls with medicine balls, gymnast with stick and women gymnasts with rings.

COMPETITIVE GYMNASTICS

Competitive gymnastics developed from the German 'Turnen' Movement and only comparatively recently has it become popular in countries favouring the Ling system. However, it has formed a part of all modern Olympic Games.

Bulgaria 1931–3. *1st Balkan Games in Sofia*
1l. yellow green, 1l. pale green (1933).
Gymnast at the parallel bars.

Bulgaria 1935. *8th Junak Games in Sofia*
1l. green.
Exercises at the parallel bars.

Germany 1936. *11th Olympic Games*
3+2pf. brown.
A gymnast on the horizontal bar.

Bulgaria 1939. *9th Junak Games in Sofia*
1l. green.
A gymnast at the horizontal bar.

Finland 1945. *Sports issue*
2+1m. red.
The attractive design shows a gymnast—probably Olympic victor *Saarvala*—at the horizontal bar.

Yugoslavia 1947. *Sports Games in Ljubljana*
1.50+0.50d. green, 2.50+0.50d. red, 4+0.50d. blue.
A gymnast at the parallel bars.

Russia 1949. *Sports issue*
40k. red brown.
Woman gymnast using the rings.

Japan 1950. *5th National Sports Games in Nagoya*
8.00y. red brown.
Gymnast using the rings.

Hungary 1950. *Sports issue*
20f. orange brown.
Gymnast at the parallel bars.

Czechoslovakia 1952. *9th Sokol Congress and Games*
1k. grey green.
Gymnast using the rings.

Hungary 1952. *14th Olympic Games*
1fo. blue.
Balancing exercises on the beam by a woman gymnast.

Poland 1952. *Sports issue*
1.20z. light red.
Girl exercising at the parallel bars. The bars in women's gymnastics, which have a different shape from those in men's, are shown here for the first time.

Yugoslavia 1952. *15th Olympic Games*
5d. yellow brown and dark brown.
Woman gymnast. The same stamp was issued in different colours and overprinted 'STT–VUJNA' for use in the Yugoslav zone of Trieste.

Monaco 1953. *15th Olympic Games*
8f. lilac red and light red.
The vaulting horse.

Poland 1954. *2nd National Spartacist Games in Warsaw*
60g. green blue.
Parallel bars—men.

San Marino 1954. *Sports issue*
4l. light blue and dark blue, 200l. brown and violet.
Rings—men. These stamps won third place in the Bonacossa Medal Competition, 1954.

Bulgaria 1954. *Sports issue*
16s. grey green.
Rings—men. Second prize in the Bonacossa Medal Competition, 1954.

San Marino 1955. *Sports issue*
250l. multicoloured.
This stamp has the same design as the 4l. and 200l. of 1954 but is recess-printed in another value and different colours.

Germany (East) 1956. *2nd Sports and Gymnastic Festival in Leipzig*
20pf. red.
Male gymnast using rings.

Russia 1956. *National Spartacist Games*
60k. violet.
A woman gymnast.

Hungary 1956. *16th Olympic Games*
2fo. yellow green and brown.
A girl performing balancing exercises on the beam.

Bulgaria 1956. *16th Olympic Games*
4s. ultramarine.
Balancing on the beam by a woman gymnast.

Roumania 1956. *16th Olympic Games*
1l. lilac red.
A stylized design based on women's balancing exercises.

Poland 1956. *16th Olympic Games*
1.55z. dark brown and violet.
Another picture of a girl balancing on the beam.

Brazil 1957. *7th Children's Games in Rio de Janeiro*
2.50c. red brown.
Boy exercising at the parallel bars.

Roumania 1957. *1st Women's European Gymnastics Championships in Bucharest*

20b. yellow green, 35b. carmine, 55b. blue, 1.75b. red violet.

The four designs showing women gymnasts represent free standing (20b.), at the parallel bars (35b.), vaulting (55b.) and balancing (1.75b.).

Liechtenstein 1957. *Sports issue*

10c. rose and grey green, 15c. green and brown violet, 25c. brown grey and greyish green, 1.50c. yellow and brown.

This extremely beautiful set, printed by Courvoisier, is entirely devoted to gymnastics and shows horizontal bars, the vaulting-horse, rings and parallel bars.

Yugoslavia 1957. *2nd Gymnaestrada in Zagreb*

10d. olive green, 15d. red brown, 30d. grey blue, 50d. brown.

Artistic stamps with symbolic designs of various movements.

Russia 1957. *3rd World Youth Games in Moscow*

20k. red brown and violet.

Women gymnasts.

Russia 1957. *16th Olympic Games*

25k. light blue and orange.

A Russian gymnast at the horizontal bar, probably *Chukarin.*

Japan 1957. *12th National Games in Shizuoka*

5y. blue.

Parallel bars—women's.

North Viet-Nam 1958. *Physical Culture issue*

150d. light blue and light brown, 500d. rose and light brown.

Woman gymnast.

Russia 1958. *World Gymnastics Championships in Moscow*

40k. multicoloured, 40k. multicoloured.

A girl gymnast and Moscow University, and a man using the rings with the Lenin Stadium in the background.

Yugoslavia 1959. *The Partisan Games*

20d. brown violet and olive brown.

Rings and parallel bars.

Russia 1959. *2nd National Spartacist Games*
15k. red violet and grey.
Woman vaulting.

Germany (East) 1959. *3rd German Gymnastics and Sports Festival in Leipzig*
20+10pf. red.
Vaulting-horse.

San Marino 1960. *17th Olympic Games*
2l. grey and red brown, 2l. grey green and red brown (imperf. in sheet).
Rings.

Roumania 1960. *17th Olympic Games (I)*
55b. grey, black, yellow and green.
Woman at the beam.

Roumania 1960. *17th Olympic Games (II)*
40b. red brown.
Woman gymnast.

Czechoslovakia 1960. *17th Olympic Games*
1.80k. rose red and brown grey.
Woman and beam.

Russia 1960. *17th Olympic Games*
40k. olive brown and violet red.
Woman gymnast.

Mongolia 1960. *17th Olympic Games*
50m. ultramarine, blue green and grey.
Woman gymnast.

Bulgaria 1960. *17th Olympic Games*
45s. violet red and light rose, 45s. dark green and yellow (imperf.).
Woman gymnast.

Morocco 1960. *17th Olympic Games*
10f. brown, blue and orange brown.
Parallel bars.

Japan 1960. *15th National Games in Kumakoto*
5y. brown violet.
Woman vaulting.

Spain 1960. *Sports issue*
80c. dark green and violet red, 3p. deep blue and violet red.
European Champion, *Joaquin Blume*, performing with the rings.

North Korea 1960. *15th Anniversary of the Republic*
5w. blue, grey, orange brown and black.
Rings.

16. HANDBALL

Handball is a relatively modern sport, originating in the late nineteenth century in Germany and Scandinavia. It developed into a competitive game in Germany and from there spread to Central and Northern Europe.

The first handball stamps appeared in 1959, but made up for a late start with three stamps within three months.

Austria 1959. *World Outdoor Handball Championships in Vienna*
1.50s. grey green.
Austrian player about to shoot.

Yugoslavia 1959. *The Partisan Games*
55d. dark green and orange brown.
Players in action; in the background are basketball players.

Roumania 1959. *Sports issue*
55b. olive, orange, light violet and dark blue.
Goal throw.

17. HOCKEY

In Ancient Greece there was a game called *keratizein*, resembling modern hockey. During the Middle Ages hockey-style games were played, particularly in France and England. These games survived in different guises, notably as hockey in England and hurling in Ireland. Hockey received its final shape in the 1880's in England and spread to the Continent, where Holland and Germany took the lead. It became most popular, however, in India, which has remained unbeaten for the past thirty years.

Japan 1951. *6th National Games in Hiroshima*
5y. blue grey.
A hockey player in action.

Netherlands 1956. *16th Olympic Games*
10+5c. grey and black.
Silhouette of a hockey player.

The Dominican Republic 1958. *Olympic Victors 1956 (III)*
16c. orange, green and blue grey.
An incident from the Olympic hockey final in Melbourne in which India beat Pakistan 1—0.

San Marino 1960. *17th Olympic Games*
15l. green and violet, 15l. green and red brown (imperf. in sheet).
Hockey player.

18. ICE HOCKEY

Ice hockey is a Canadian game originating at McGill University during the winter 1879–80. The game grew rapidly popular in Canada and U.S.A. and professionalism got a footing as early as the 1890's. Professional ice hockey is now a really large-scale sport in U.S.A. and Canada. The game was introduced to Europe in 1891 by the British, reaching the Continent in 1906, where it is now very popular.

Switzerland 1948. *5th Winter Olympic Games at St. Moritz*
20+10c. red violet and yellow.
A goalkeeper in action.

Russia 1949. *Sports issue*
50k. blue.
An interesting design. It depicts Russian ice hockey before its rise to popularity in the 1950's. The players on this stamp are wearing equipment more like that for bandy than for modern ice hockey. Ice hockey was then played in Russia under rules differing from the international code.

Roumania 1951. *9th World University Winter Games in Poiana-Stalin*
20l. red brown.
A goalkeeper and a forward in action. The stamp was issued later with a provisional surcharge of fifty-five bani due to monetary reform.

Czechoslovakia 1952. *United Czechoslovakian Sports issue*
4k. blue grey.
The Czech national team in action.

Sweden 1953. *50th Anniversary of Swedish Sports Federation*
15ö. brown.
Ice-hockey player in the Swedish national colours.

Poland 1953. *Winter Sports issue*
2.85z. red brown.
Polish international ice-hockey player.

Hungary 1955. *European Figure Skating Championships in Budapest*
80f. multicoloured.
Two ice-hockey players in action, with a goalkeeper in the background.

San Marino 1955. *7th Olympic Winter Games in Cortina in 1956*
5l. rose and blue, 100l. green and black.
Ice-hockey player. (The higher value was reissued one year later with a special overprint for airmail.)

Canada 1956. *Sports issue*
5c. blue.
The home of ice hockey issued this stamp, showing players in action, in time for the Cortina Olympics. It was, however, a bad omen, as Canada lost her Olympic title for the first time.

Poland 1956. *11th World University Winter Games in Zakopane*
40g. green and dark blue.
Ice-hockey sticks, a puck and an ice crystal.

Russia 1957. *World Ice Hockey Championships in Moscow*
25k. dark violet, 40k. blue, 60k. yellow green.
The badge of the championships, a Russian ice-hockey forward and a Russian goalkeeper.

Czechoslovakia 1959. *World Ice Hockey Championships in Prague*
20h. green grey and violet brown, 60h. light green and blue violet.
Czech player with puck and goalkeeper stopping puck with body.

St. Pierre and Miquelon 1959. *Sports issue*
20f. multicoloured.
This French island's first sports stamp depicted her favourite sport.

Roumania 1959. *Sports issue*
40b. blue, light violet, light orange and red brown.
Two players in action.

Russia 1960. *8th Winter Olympic Games*
10k. light violet and red orange.
Action picture.

Czechoslovakia 1960. *8th Winter Olympic Games*
60h. light blue and brown grey.
Czech player against back and goalkeeper.

Hungary 1960. *8th Winter Olympic Games*
40f. green and yellow brown.
Player with puck.

Togo 1960. *8th Winter Olympic Games,*
0.50f. red and brown black.
A player with puck.

19. ICE YACHTING

Yachting on ice was recorded in the sixteenth century—especially in Holland—but it was not until the end of the nineteenth century that modern competitive ice yachting started in North America.

Hungary 1955. *European Figure Skating Championships in Budapest*
60f. multicoloured.
A beautiful ice-yachting design showing Lake Balaton.

20. JUDO

Judo, or ju-jitsu, is an ancient Japanese form of contest without weapons, which aims at overcoming strength through balance and flexibility. Modern judo was evolved in 1866. It has since spread all over the world.

Japan 1953. *8th National Games in Matsuyama*
5y. green.
A throw over the head (*kataguruma*).

Japan 1956. *1st World Judo Championships in Tokyo*

5y. red violet and green.

A throw called *sumiotoshi.*

21. MODERN PENTATHLON

The modern pentathlon was introduced for the first time in the Olympic programme of 1912, being suggested by the founder of modern Olympics, Baron de Coubertin. Since then it has become one of the leading events in the Games.

The five events—cross-country riding, épée-fencing, pistol-shooting, swimming and cross-country running—have been depicted separately on stamps but only one stamp has been devoted to the modern pentathlon.

The Dominican Republic 1957. *Olympic Victors in Melbourne 1956 (I)*

1c. brown, blue green, blue and yellow.

The Olympic gold medallist in 1952 and 1956, *Lars Hall* of Sweden, in the cross-country-running final.

22. MOTOR-RACING

Motor-racing has existed almost as long as the car itself. The first race was probably held in 1884 in France. After the First World War motor-racing developed rapidly and became one of the crowd-drawing sports.

Motor-racing is not as well represented as might be expected and in the last three years there have been only the Monte Carlo Rally issues. Apart from the 'racing' stamps listed below, there have been various other motoring stamps, notably the set commemorating the fifth anniversary of the Portuguese Automobile Club. They have not been included here (as they do not fit into the 'competitive sports' category).

Germany 1939. *International Motor Show in Berlin*

12+8pf. red.

In this set of three stamps one stamp depicts two racing-cars on a motor circuit. The two cars are an Auto-Union and a Mercedes-Benz.

Germany 1939. *Nürburgring Races*

6+4pf. green, 12+8pf. red, 25+10pf. blue.

The most important motor-race in Germany, the 'Nürburgring-

Rennen' (about forty miles south of Cologne) took place later in 1939. The Motor Show set was accordingly overprinted with the name of the race.

Yugoslavia 1939. *International Motor Races in Belgrade*

1+1d. green, 2+2d. blue.

Racing-cars at full speed, with the buildings of Belgrade in the background.

Germany 1939–44. *Postal Employees' Fund*

12+6 carmine and brown, 12+18 red brown, 16+24 green.

The first of these three identical designs was issued in 1939. The stamp reappeared in 1941 with changed premium and colour, and again in 1944 with a smaller size and changed value, premium and colour. The design shows sports cars driving through a forest in a reliability test.

Bolivia 1948. *South American Grand Prix*

5b. blue and rose, 10b. green and yellow.

A map of South America showing the race route.

Italy 1953. *20th Anniversary of the 'Mille Miglia'*

25l. violet.

The world-famous Mille Miglia ('thousand miles') marked its 20th anniversary in 1953 with this none-too-beautiful stamp depicting sports cars on the road. It was also overprinted 'AMG–FTT' for use in Zone A of Trieste.

Yugoslavia 1953. *International Motor Races in Yugoslavia*

15d. orange red, 50d. yellow brown, 70d. green.

The designs of these three stamps show sports cars and famous tourist views of Yugoslavia. The designs and events chosen were: 2nd Adriatic Rally (Lovcen Mountain in Montenegro), International Races in Belgrade (Kalimegdan Park in Belgrade) and 22nd Yugoslav Alpine Rally (Triglav, Yugoslavia's highest mountain). The same designs 'STT–VUJNA' were issued for the Yugoslav zone of Trieste.

San Marino 1954. *Sports issue*

12l. red and black.

Sports car at full speed.

Monaco 1955. *25th Monte Carlo Rally*

100f. brown and carmine.

The Monte Carlo Rally, the world's most famous reliability test, started in 1911, but because of the wars and other causes the 25th race was not held until 1955. To commemorate this, a giant stamp was issued, showing not only the coat-of-arms of Monaco and its castle but also a steering-wheel and a car, and the seven different starting places with their notable buildings: Glasgow (University), Oslo (Town Hall), Stockholm (Old Town), Munich (Marienplatz), Athens (Acropolis), Palermo (Palazzo Reale) and Lisbon (Teatro Nacional).

Monaco 1956. *26th Monte Carlo Rally*

100f. red brown and carmine.

The route from Glasgow to Monaco. On the upper left corner of the large stamp is a piper and a Scottish view, and the route from there to Monte Carlo with the chief cities on the way.

Monaco 1958. *27th Monte Carlo Rally*

100f. red violet, dark brown and green.

The 27th Monte Carlo Rally took place in 1958, the 1957 event being cancelled because of the Suez crisis. This stamp shows the starting place in Munich, with the route over the mountains to Monte Carlo.

Monaco 1959. *28th Monte Carlo Rally*

100f. blue violet, black green and dark red.

The route from Athens, the Acropolis and the Royal Palace of Monaco.

Monaco 1960. *29th Monte Carlo Rally*

100f. blue, dark red and grey.

The route from Lisbon, Lisbon National Theatre and the rock of Monte Carlo.

23. MOTOR-BOATING

As early as 1895 a private motor-boat race was arranged at Nice in which four yawls took part, equipped with combustion engines. It was not until 1900, however, that the first real race took place, in connection with the World Exhibition in Paris. The first international motor-boat regattas were held in 1901–2 in Nice. The sport then spread rapidly.

Russia 1948. *Sports issue*

45k. dark brown.

Outboard motor-boat at full speed.

Roumania 1959. *Sports issue*

2.80l. blue, orange brown, yellow and violet brown.

Outboard motor-boat at full speed.

24. MOTOR-CYCLING

The first motor-cycle races were held in connection with motor races. Then, from 1899, races for three- and two-wheelers were arranged on the trotting trocks in Germany and Austria. About 1900 long-distance races and weight classification were introduced in France. The Isle of Man TT races, the world's foremost motor-cycle races, were arranged for the first time in 1907. In the 1920's came the international Grand Prix races with England and Germany predominating. At the same time trials and scrambles became popular, while in the 1930's speedway grew to mass popularity.

A postage-due issue of Monaco shows a motor-cycle at full speed, but this must be regarded solely as a means of transportation.

Yugoslavia 1939. *International Motor Races in Belgrade*
0.50+0.50d. orange, 1.50+1.50d. red brown.
These stamps are without doubt two of the most beautiful sports designs ever. The lower value shows a motor-cycle and sidecar, with the 'passenger' leaning inwards to counter the centrifugal force round a curve. The other stamp shows a solo machine at full speed.

Russia 1948. *Sports issue*
20k. dark grey.
Hill-climbing.

Bulgaria 1949. *Sports issue*
20l. dark blue.
One of a set which illustrates the usefulness of sport in military and everyday life, this depicts a racing motor-cycle and a tractor.

Hungary 1950. *Sports issue*
2fo. violet brown.
A solo machine at full speed.

Yugoslavia 1953. *International Motor Races in Yugoslavia*
30d. green and blue.
A motor-cycle design showing the Adriatic coast at Opatija. The same design was issued with changed colours and overprinted 'STT–VUJNA' for use in the Yugoslav zone of Trieste.

Czechoslovakia 1953. *Sports issue*
40h. brown grey.
Motor-cycle at full speed.

San Marino 1954. *Sports issue*
5l. olive brown and green.
Going flat out in a race.

Poland 1955. *13th International Motor-cycle Mountain Race in Tatra*
40g. lilac brown, 60g. green.
Two motor-cyclists in mountain country.

Czechoslovakia 1955. *30th International Six Days Race in Gottwaldow (Zlin)*
60h. grey brown.
This event originated in 1913. It is held every year under the sponsorship of the F.I.C.M. (International Motor Cycle Federation). The winner of the International Trophy becomes the host in the following year. This stamp shows a motor-cyclist and the International Trophy.

Czechoslovakia 1957. *32nd International Six Days Race in Spindleruv Mlýn*
60h. blue grey and blue.
The design is similar to that above.

Somalia 1958. *Sports issue*
0.06s. grey.
Motor-cycle at full speed.

Roumania 1958. *Sports issue*
35b. dark orange, dark blue and light blue.
Two machines in a race.

Russia 1959. *Military Sports Propaganda*
40k. red brown and dark grey.
Solo machine at full speed.

China (Communist) 1959. *1st National Games in Peking*
8d. blue, grey and black.
A somewhat old-fashioned motor-cycle in a race.

25. MOUNTAINEERING

Surprisingly it was not until the sixteenth century that mountaineering was practised in Switzerland. Public interest was first aroused with the climbing of Mont Blanc in 1786. Alpine sport really became popular at the end of the nineteenth century, mostly due to British climbers who dominated the sport for some time.

Although mountaineering is not competitive in the normal sense, it has been included in this book because it is represented by stamps of a sporting character. Some of them do not have any special mountaineering design but have been inspired by the sport.

Roumania 1946. *Sports issue*
80l. dark brown.
This stamp shows that mountaineering is popular in the Carpathians and the Transylvanian Alps.

Russia 1949. *Sports issue*
50k. blue grey.
A very attractive design showing a mountain-climber against a background of snow-covered mountains.

Hungary 1950. *Sports issue*
1fo. green olive.
Mountain-walking.

Yugoslavia 1951. *12th International Alpine Congress in Bled*
3d. red violet, 5d. blue, 20d. green.
Well-known mountains in Serbia (Kopaonik), Slovenia (Triglav) and Croatia (Kaknik).

Japan 1952. *7th National Sports Games in Fukushima*
5y. ultramarine.
Mountain-climber with a peak in the background.

India 1953. *Conquest of Mount Everest*
2a. violet, 14a. brown.
To commemorate the conquest of Mount Everest by *Sir Edmund Hillary* and *Sherpa Tensing*, on 29th May 1953, Indian issued these stamps showing the highest mountain in the world, 29,002 ft.

Iran 1953. *Ancient Persian Sports*
3r. grey.
Mountaineering, probably on the Elburs Mountains.

Czechoslovakia 1954. *Sports issue*
80h. green.
Walking amid a mountain landscape.

Russia 1954. *Sports issue*

1r. blue grey and red brown.

Mountaineering in severe alpine terrain.

Pakistan 1954. *Conquest of K2*

2a. violet.

Pakistan commemorated the conquest of K2, the second-highest mountain of the world, by an Italian expedition led by *A. Desio*. The design shows the peak of K2.

Liechtenstein 1955. *Sports issue*

20c. olive yellow and green, 40c. grey brown and lilac rose.

An alpinist knocking in a piton during an ascent and a climber resting at the top.

France 1956. *Sports issue*

75f. blue grey, green and blue.

A beautiful alpine design. Also overprinted 'C.F.A.' for use on Réunion.

Japan 1956. *Conquest of Manaslu*

10y. multicoloured.

Conquest of Manaslu—the world's eighth-highest mountain—was achieved by a Japanese expedition, 9th–11th May 1956.

Czechoslovakia 1957. *Mountain Rescue Service*

60h. blue grey and grey violet.

The Czech Mountain Rescue Service emblem can be seen on the right-hand portion of the stamp. The rest of the design shows two mountaineers with a sledge.

Austria 1957. *Conquest of Gasherbrum II*

1.50s. dark blue.

Commemorating the conquest of Gasherbrum II (25,300 ft.) in the Karakoram by an Austrian expedition, 7th July 1956.

26. NATIONAL SPORTS

Under this heading have been included sports of an exclusively national character. In some cases, when these closely resemble sports of a wider, international appeal, they have also been included under the appropriate heading, e.g. wrestling.

Switzerland 1932. *Children's Charity issue*

5c. green and red, 10c. orange, 20c. red.

Swiss national sports: *Fahnenschwingen*—banner-swinging; *Steinstossen*—stone-putting (see 'Shot-putting'); and *Schwingen*—the Swiss form of wrestling which is still very popular (see 'Wrestling').

Eire 1934. *50th Anniversary Gaelic Athletic Association*

2d. green.

Hurling player in action. Hurling is a similar game to hockey and has been played in Ireland at least since the ninth century. Authoritative rules were drawn up in 1884.

Tannu Tuva (Northern Mongolia) 1936. *15th Anniversary of Republic*

4k. orange, 6k. green, 40k. brown, 50k. blue grey, 70k. dark violet.

In this set there are six stamps depicting national sports. The two lowest values illustrate Mongolian wrestling (see 'Wrestling'), the two next values a Mongolian horse-race (see 'Equestrian Sports') and the highest values Mongolian archery (see 'Archery').

Burma 1949–54. *Anniversary of Burmese Republic*

1p. orange brown (1954), 3p. ultramarine (1949). 3p. orange brown (1952).

Boys, in a circle, heading a ball in the Burmese game of *Chinlon*. These stamps also appeared with a Burmese overprint meaning 'Service', for use on official correspondence.

Switzerland 1950. *Swiss Federation Festival issue*

10+10c. green, 20+10c. olive brown.

Stone-putting and *Schwingen*

Switzerland 1951. *Swiss Federation Festival issue*

20+10c. olive and grey, 30+10c. red violet and grey.

Fahnenschwingen (see 1932) and *Hornussen*, a strange game played chiefly by the peasants in the valleys of Engadin and Wallis. The game is played with a round wooden disc, latterly changed to a small rubber ball. The wooden disc (*Hornis*) is hit into the air by a flexible club from a rail or a bar, and the fielders try to stop it by throwing up their wooden spades (*Schindeln*), which also can be seen.

Sudan 1951. *Definitive issue*

3p. orange brown and light green.

Nubian wrestling '*Sibr*' (see 'Wrestling').

Sweden 1953. *50th Anniversary Swedish Sports Federation*
40ö. blue.
Slungboll (sling ball) which is now practised in Sweden chiefly by schoolgirls.

Iceland 1955–7. *Sports issue*
75a. dark brown (1955), 1.50k. red (1957).
The Icelandic national sport of *glima*, which is an old Nordic form of wrestling. The opponents grip belts and try to throw each other to the ground. In modern *glima* there are seven different throws of which one, called *leggjarbragd*, is shown here.

Malaya 1957–60. *Ordinary pictorial issues*
$2 red and green
The stamp depicts the traditional Malay art of self defence, *bersilat*, the mastery of which was at one time an essential accomplishment for the adult male. As a modern sport it is accompanied by traditional music, which varies from state to state.

This stamp formed part of a series issued in 1957 by the nine states of the Malayan Federation: Johore (1960), Kedah, Kelantan, Negri Sembilan, Pahang, Perak, Perlis, Selangor, Trengganu, and the two settlements of Malacca and Penang. The state stamps bear the portraits of their respective rulers, whereas Queen Elizabeth is depicted on the settlement stamps.

The Kedah stamp reappeared in 1959 with the picture of the new Sultan, and on the settlement stamps the coats-of-arms of the settlements were substituted for the Queen's portrait in 1960.

Afghanistan 1957. *National Sport 'Buzcashi'*
140p. red violet and light green.
An incident from the national sport of *buzcashi*, which dates back to the Mongol invasion in the thirteenth century. *Buzcashi* is an equestrian sport in which two teams of from 100 to 300 horsemen fight each other to get a buckskin. The ground is a large, flat, sandy field about two miles long. In the middle of the ground there is a hole in which a stuffed buckskin, weighing up to 35 lb., is placed. Around this skin the horsemen are grouped in a circle, and on the signal of the referee the horsemen rush to the hole to seize the buckskin. The two teams fight each other wildly to get the skin, riding at breakneck speed across the ground. The player who succeeds in getting the buckskin back in the hole scores one point for his team.

France 1958. *French National Sports*

12f. red and brown, 15f. green and blue, 18f. green and brown, 25f. brown and blue grey.

The four French sports shown here are *jeu de boules*, *joutes nautiques*, archery (see 'Archery') and Breton wrestling (see 'Wrestling'). *Jeu de boules* is a game similar to the Italian *boccia* and the British bowls. In *joutes nautiques*, or water-jousting, the aim is to push the opponent from his boat and into the water.

Mongolia 1959. *National Sports issue*

10m. violet and multicoloured.

Mongolian wrestling (see 'Wrestling').

Yugoslavia 1959. *The Partisan Games*

10d. blue and orange brown.

Tug-of-war.

North Viet-Nam 1959. *Sports issue*

12x. violet red.

Native wrestling (see 'Wrestling').

China (Communist) 1959. *1st National Games in Peking*

8d. yellow olive and violet brown.

Chinese stick-fencing.

Afghanistan 1960. *Sports issue*

25p. red, 50p. green (also imperf.).

A badly drawn copy of the earlier stamp (1957), depicting national sport, *buzcashi*.

Japan 1960. *15th National Games in Kumakoto*

5y. green blue.

Two *Kendo* fencers. *Kendo*, modern Japanese stick-fencing, developed from Samurai fencing with sharp swords. The weapon is made of bamboo and the fencers are dressed in long, very wide gowns and wear masks.

Afghanistan 1960. *17th Olympic Games*

175p. red brown and green.

Same design as above with green Olympic surcharge.

North Korea 1960. *Sports and pastime issue*

5w. olive grey, brown, and orange brown.

Native wrestlers (see 'Wrestling').

27. PELOTA

Pelota is of ancient origin with its roots in fifteenth-century Italy. Similar games in the Basque provinces of France and Spain developed into pelota, which in its primitive form was played by the peasants. In the nineteenth century the rules were clarified and pelota spread outside the Basque provinces to, among others, America.

It is strange that this very old Basque sport should not be pictured on stamps until 1951 and then in such a distant country as Bolivia.

Bolivia 1951. *5th South American Championships in La Paz 1948*

3.00B. yellow brown and black.

Pelota a mano—a game using the bare hand instead of the basket-like *chistera.*

France 1956. *Sports issue*

40f. dark brown and red brown.

Pelota player with the *chistera* or *cesta* with which the ball is thrown against a wall. Also overprinted 'C.F.A.' for use on Réunion.

Spain 1960. *1st International Philatelic Congress in Barcelona*

1p. red and violet brown, 5p. violet brown and red, 6p. blue black and red violet, 10p. green and red violet.

Spain's first sports stamp shows a pelota player about to hit the ball.

Spain 1960. *Sports issue*

1.50p. violet, 10p. olive green and red violet.

Pelota player with the *pala*, a racketlike bat, which today is more common than the *cesta.*

28. ROLLER-SKATING

The roller-skate was invented in Paris in 1790. It was not, however, until rubber wheels were first fitted in U.S.A. that it could be used for sport. Roller-skating tracks were built as early as the 1870's in Europe and America, and the sport became very popular. An international union was formed in 1924 when speed races, figure-skating and roller-hockey grew to popularity.

Portugal 1952. *8th World Roller-Hockey Championships in Oporto*

1.00e. dark blue and grey, 3.50e. dark brown and grey.

Two hockey players in action.

San Marino 1953. *Sports issue*

100l. grey and olive brown.

A girl roller-skating in front of the San Marino Mountains. The stamp was issued later with a special overprint in connection with a stamp exhibition.

Spain 1960. *Sports issue*

1p. red orange and green, 5p. red brown and blue.

Roller-hockey player.

29. ROWING

Rowing competitions were known in Ancient Greece, though rowing was then regarded more as a military exercise. During the Middle Ages regattas were very popular in Italy, especially in Venice. Modern rowing originated in England and was introduced into schools and universities in the early days.

Rowing has undoubtedly been in favour with the stamp designers. All seven rowing events have been illustrated and it is interesting to see how evenly the designs have been distributed between them.

NOTE: *In 1925 a Hungarian stamp showed a single sculler, but as the main subject was diving it has been included under the latter heading.*

Netherlands 1928. *9th Olympic Games in Amsterdam*

1½c. dark green.

A single sculler.

Yugoslavia 1932. *European Rowing Championships in Belgrade*

75+50p. dark green and blue, 1+½d. carmine and blue, 1½+½d. rose and green, 3+1d. blue, 1+1d. orange and blue, 5+1d. violet.

The standard of this set is rather low, and the print not very clear, making it difficult to distinguish easily the different designs which are as follows:

Single sculls in front of Smederovo, an old fifteenth-century castle on the Danube; coxed fours in front of the Veldes; eights on the Danube at Belgrade; coxswainless pairs in the harbour of Split; double sculls on the Save in front of Zagreb Cathedral; and *Crown Prince Peter* in sailor's uniform framed with oars.

Russia 1935. *World Spartacist Games in Moscow.*

3k. green and black.

Two boats racing.

Germany 1936. *11th Olympic Games*
25+15pf. ultramarine.
Double scullers.

Roumania 1937. *25th Anniversary of Roumanian Athletic Union*
4+1l. orange red.
Coxswainless fours.

Monaco 1948. *14th Olympic Games*
5+5f. grey brown.
The designer took his idea from a photograph of the famous Oxford eight.

Trieste Zone B 1952. *Sports issue*
15d. red.
Coxed fours.

Roumania 1952. *Sports issue*
20l. blue.
Coxswainless fours.

France 1953. *French Olympic Successes in 1952*
50f. green and black.
This badly drawn stamp—among other things the cox is not in time with the oarsmen in the boat in the background—honours the French winners of the coxed pairs, *R. Salles*, *G. Mercier* and *B. Malivoire*, the latter the youngest competitor at the Helsinki Games, being only fourteen years old.

Poland 1955. *2nd World Youth Games in Warsaw*
1.35z. grey violet.
Single sculls.

Roumania 1955. *European University Women's Rowing Championships*
55b. olive green, 1l. blue.
For the first time women's rowing is shown: coxed fours and single sculls.

Russia 1956. *National Spartacist Games*
25k. blue.
Eights with a women's crew.

Poland 1956. *16th Olympic Games*
25g. black and light blue.
A design depicting the single sculls.

Czechoslovakia 1959. *Sports issue*
1.60k. light blue and violet grey.
An oarsman and rowing eight.

Argentina 1959. *3rd Pan American Games in Chicago*
2+1p. blue.
Coxed fours.

China (Communist) 1959. *1st National Games in Peking*
8d. blue green, red brown and black.
Pairs.

San Marino 1960. *17th Olympic Games*
25l. green and red brown, 25l. yellow green and red brown (imperf. in sheet).
Single sculler.

Czechoslovakia 1960. *17th Olympic Games*
2k. blue and grey black.
Eights.

U.A.R. 1960. *8th Anniversary of the Revolution*
10m. grey green.
Coxed fours.

Hungary 1960. *17th Olympic Games*
10f. blue, orange brown and black.
Ancient oarsmen.

Liberia 1960. *17th Olympic Games*
10c. red violet and violet brown.
Single sculler and natives in a canoe.

30. RUGBY FOOTBALL

Rugby football received its name from Rugby School, where, in 1823, William Webb Ellis is reputed to have picked up the ball and run for the opposing line. The Rugby Union was formed in 1871. From England rugby spread over the whole British Empire, and in particular to New Zealand and South Africa. France became the leading rugger country on the Continent.

It is strange to find that this popular sport is depicted on only a few stamps, with none of the leading countries, apart from France, being represented.

Roumania 1944. *30th Anniversary of the Roumanian Rugby Union*
16+184l. red.
This stamp is original in that the Roumanian Rugby Union's title, 'F.R. Rugby', and not the name of the country, dominates the design.

Fiji Islands 1951. *Health Stamp*
2d.+1d. green.
Fijian rugby player with ball.

Japan 1953. *8th National Games in Matsuyama*
5y. black.
A match between Waseda University, Tokyo, and the Oxford University touring team.

France 1956. *Sports issue*
50f. red violet and violet.
A vivid design showing a match in progress. The stamp appeared later overprinted 'C.F.A.' for use on Réunion.

Roumania 1959. *Sports issue*
1.55l. yellow green, red, yellow orange and blue.
Player passing ball.

31. SHOOTING

Shooting has been practised as a sport since time immemorial, and is so evenly spread over the world that no one country can claim to have originated it. Since the end of the nineteenth century, with better design and more accurate weapons, shooting has become increasingly popular and is now a widely practised sport in many countries.

Sweden 1943. *50th Anniversary of the Voluntary Shooting Association*
10ö. violet, 90ö. blue.
The designs of these stamps show very simply the emblem of the Swedish Voluntary Shooting Movement.

Germany 1944. *7th Tyrolean Shooting Festival in Innsbruck*
6+4pf. green, 12+8pf. red.
Neither of these stamps has an actual sports design, but each depicts a medieval Tyrolean musketeer and a modern German soldier.

Peru 1948. *14th Olympic Games*
10s. yellow.
Shooting was the only event in which the Peruvians had any success: a gold medal in the pistol and sixth place in the free-rifle competitions. This design shows a rifleman.

Argentina 1949. *World Shooting Championships in Buenos Aires*
75c. brown.
The trophy 'Copa Argentina' with a target in the background.

Switzerland 1950. *Swiss Federation Festival*
40+10c. blue, white and red.
Three army marksmen kneeling in a line.

Monaco 1953. *15th Olympic Games*
100f. grey green.
A competition rifle, with all its equipment, in front of the target, superimposed upon the coat-of-arms of Monaco.

San Marino 1953. *Sports issue*
25l. grey brown and dark brown.
Clay-pigeon marksman in firing position.

Roumania 1955. *European Shooting Championships in Bucharest*
1l. grey brown.
Aiming a duelling pistol.

Yugoslavia 1956. *Olympic Year*
100d. red brown and brown.
Kneeling army rifleman. The stamp has a falcon in one corner.

Peru 1956. *16th Olympic Games*
10s. yellow.
The rifleman of the 1948 Olympic set returned overprinted 'MELBOURNE 1956'.

The Dominican Republic 1957. *Olympic Victors 1956 (II)*
1c. red brown, red and blue.
Winner of the 50 m. small bore rifle, *Gerald Ouellette*, Canada.

North Viet-Nam 1959. *Sports issue*
1x. ultramarine.
Woman army rifle-shot.

China (Communist) 1959. *1st National Games in Peking*
8d. red brown and black.
Pistol-shooting.

San Marino 1960. *17th Olympic Games*
125l. red and brown, 125l. green and brown (imperf. in sheet).
Clay-pigeon shooting.

Sweden 1960. *Centenary of the Voluntary Shooting Movement*
15ö. violet red (also 3-sides perf.).
Marksmen practising.

Cuba 1960. *17th Olympic Games*
2c. orange, 2c. grey blue (imperf. in sheet).
Pistol-shooting.

Philippines 1960. *17th Olympic Games*
30c. orange and brown.
Kneeling rifle-shooter.

Costa Rica 1960. *17th Olympic Games*
10s. grey violet and black.
Pistol-shooting.

32. SKATING

SPEED-SKATING

Speed-skating was practised in the Middle Ages in the Scandinavian countries. At the beginning of the nineteenth century races were held in Holland and England. The first 'modern' races were arranged in the 1860's in Norway.

Russia 1935. *World Spartacist Games in Moscow*
20k. blue and brown.
Perhaps the most beautiful stamp in this large Russian set.

Germany 1935. *4th Winter Olympic Games in Garmisch-Partenkirchen*
6+4pf. green.
Speed-skater.

Roumania 1951. *9th World University Winter Sport Games in Poiana-Stalin*

5l. light red.

A speed-skater.

Norway 1951. *6th Winter Olympic Games in Oslo*

15+5ö. green.

A Norwegian speed-skater.

Russia 1952. *Winter Sports issue*

40k. multicoloured.

A colourful action picture.

Japan 1954. *World Skating Championships in Sapporo*

10y. light blue.

Two skaters rounding a bend.

Hungary 1955. *European Figure Skating Championships in Budapest*

1.20fo. multicoloured.

A beautiful action picture of two speed-skaters. In the background is the Budapest Ice Palace.

San Marino 1955. *7th Winter Olympic Games in Cortina 1956*

1l. olive brown and yellow.

Speed-skater in action.

Russia 1959. *Women's World Speed Skating Championships in Sverdlovsk*

25k. blue, grey green and red, 40k. blue and grey green.

Women speed-skaters.

Russia 1960. *8th Winter Olympic Games*

25k. grey green, red orange and blue.

Speed-skaters.

Hungary 1960. *8th Winter Olympic Games*

80f. violet and yellow brown.

Woman speed-skater.

FIGURE-SKATING

Figure-skating was practised for pleasure at the end of the eighteenth century but modern figure-skating originated during the middle of the nineteenth century, first in U.S.A., England and Vienna and then spreading to Northern Europe.

One might expect figure-skating to have attracted the attention of the stamp designers, because it is as much an art as a sport. Only recently, however, have figure-skating stamps appeared in any appreciable numbers.

Hungary 1925. *Sports issue*
300k. dark blue.
Figure-skater in the compulsory event. Skates and dress are somewhat dated.

Japan 1949. *4th National Skating Championships in Suwa*
5.00y. violet.
No less than twenty-four years passed before the next figure-skating stamp appeared. The Japanese women's skating champion, *Estu Ibaraki*, was the model for this very beautiful stamp.

Germany (East) 1950. *1st East German Winter Sports Championships in Schierke (Harz)*
24pf. blue.
Woman skater. A stylized design and an out-of-proportion figure make this one of the worst sports stamps.

Poland 1953. *Winter Sports issue*
80g. light blue.
Woman skater. The same comment applies as Germany (East).

Hungary 1955. *European Figure Skating Championships in Budapest*
2fo. multicoloured.
A beautiful pair-skating design.

San Marino 1955. *7th Winter Olympic Games in Cortina 1956*
10l. ultramarine and light rose.
This extremely beautiful stamp of a woman figure-skater won the Bonacossa Medal for the best sport stamp of 1955.

Poland 1956. *11th World University Winter Sports Games in Zakopane*
20g. black and blue.
Skates and an ice crystal.

The Dominican Republic 1957. *Olympic Victors 1956 (II)*
3c. light violet, red and blue.
Tenley Albright, U.S.A., who won the figure-skating event at Cortina in 1956.

Czechoslovakia 1958. *European Figure Skating Championships in Bratislava*
30h. red violet.
Woman figure-skater in action.

China (Communist) 1959. *10th Anniversary of the Pioneer (Scout) Movement*
8d. red violet and red.
Girl figure-skater.

Russia 1960. *8th Winter Olympic Games*
60k. grey green, violet and orange brown.
Woman skater.

Czechoslovakia 1960. *8th Winter Olympic Games*
1.80k. green and grey black.
Pairs.

Hungary 1960. *8th Winter Olympic Games*
1.20fo. violet red and yellow brown.
Woman skater.

Monaco 1960. *8th Winter Olympic Games*
0.25f. dark green and brown violet.
Woman skater.

33. SKI-ING

CROSS-COUNTRY SKI-ING

Ski-ing is mentioned in the old Nordic sagas and during the Viking age there were ski competitions, especially in Norway. As a sport it ceased to be practised after the fifteenth century, not reappearing until the end of the eighteenth century. From Norway it then spread to the rest of the northern countries.

It is rather astonishing that ski-ing, which is necessarily limited to certain regions, should have been illustrated so often on stamps. In this section stamps which have some general connection with ski events are also mentioned. Three stamps have been issued picturing military ski patrols. Two of these stamps (Russia 1941 and Norway 1943) have been omitted as not being real sports stamps. The third stamp from Roumania forms a part of a sports set and has therefore been considered here. A few other stamps showing skis and ski-ing purely as a means of transportation or entertainment have also been omitted.

Austria 1933. *International Ski Championships in Innsbruck*
12g. dark green, 24g. violet, 30g. red.
These stamps, among the gems of sports philately, show skiers carrying their skis on a mountain ridge and cross-country skiers in action.

Russia 1935. *World Spartacist Games in Moscow*
5k. brown and violet.
A skier on a slope.

Lebanon 1936. *Tourist issue*
0.50f. grey green, 2p. black violet, 5p. red brown, 25p. green.
The snow-clad slopes of Lebanon, with cedars and some skiers.

Finland 1938. *World Ski Championships in Lahti*
1.25+0.75m. grey green.
Finland was the first of the Scandinavian countries to illustrate ski-ing on stamps. This is also the only stamp up to the present to depict a relay race.

Russia 1938. *Sports issue*
30k. red violet.
A skier in action.

Poland 1939. *World Ski Championships in Zakopane*
15g. light brown, 25g. brown violet, 30g. red, 55g. blue.
A Polish highlander, or *goral*, in national costume equipped with skis and sticks, looking out over an alpine landscape.

Russia 1940. *Physical Culture Day*
60k. dark blue.
Skier in a cross-country race using the so-called 'diagonal' style.

Finland 1945. *Sports issue*
4.50+2.25m. blue.
A Finnish cross-country skier in action.

Roumania 1945. *Sports issue*
20+180l. green, 20+180l. violet (imperf.).
The central figure in this design is a skier with a rifle on his back. In the background you can see some of his colleagues on the mountain slope.

Poland 1947. *22nd Polish Ski Championships in Zakopane*
5+15z. red (overprint).
This stamp is not a sports design in its real sense but it was specially issued for the event mentioned above. It is an ordinary stamp with the Polish eagle (25g.) overprinted partly with the new denomination 5+15z. and partly with the text 'XXII/MISTRZOSTWA/NARCIARSKIE/POLSKI/1947'.

Würtemburg 1948. *German (West Zone) Ski Championships in Isny*
10+4pf. green, 20+6pf brown red.
These stamps, the first German sport stamps after the Second World War, show the city of Isny, where the events took place. There are two views of the snow-covered city; in the foreground of one are two ski-sticks and the coat-of-arms, and in the other a skier with his skis on his shoulder.

Japan 1951. *Tourist issue*
8y. olive green, 24y. light blue.
Ski-ing in the national park of Zao.

Czechoslovakia 1951. *9th Sokol Congress and Games in Prague*
5k. blue grey.
Skier in action.

Germany (East) 1952. *3rd East German Winter Championships in Oberhof*
12pf. green.
Cross-country skier with spectators in the background.

Russia 1952. *Winter Sports issue*
60k. multicoloured.
Colourful ski-ers in a cross-country race.

Poland 1953. *Winter Sports issue*
95g. green.
Cross-country skier at full speed.

Sweden 1954. *World Ski Championships in Falun and Åre*
20ö. grey.
This much-discussed stamp has a design modelled on the famous Swedish ski idol *Nils Karlsson.* The rhythmic and forceful design has, however, deprived the skier of his hands, legs and eyes.

Hungary 1955. *European Figure Skating Championships in Budapest*
50f. multicoloured.
A woman skier depicted for the first time.

San Marino 1955. *7th Winter Olympic Games in Cortina 1956*
2l. blue and red, 25l. grey black and red.
Cross-country skier at full speed.

Poland 1956. *11th World University Winter Sports Games in Zakopane*
60g. wine red and light violet.
A pair of skis and sticks, together with a snow crystal, symbolize ski sports.

Poland 1957. *50th Anniversary of Polish Ski-ing*
40g. light blue, 1z. light violet.
To celebrate the 50th anniversary of ski-ing in Poland three stamps were issued, two of them showing cross-country ski-ing: one of a skier in the early days of the sport and the other a modern skier.

Finland 1958. *World Ski Championships in Lahti*
30m. grey blue.
A Finnish skier in action.

Czechoslovakia 1960. *2nd National Spartacist Games (I)*
60h. grey blue and grey black.
Woman skier.

Hungary 1960. *8th Olympic Winter Games*
30f. blue and yellow brown.
Cross-country skier.

Bulgaria 1960. *8th Winter Olympic Games*
2l. blue, white, red brown and black (also imperf.).
Cross-country skier.

Yugoslavia 1960. *17th Olympic Games*
30d. blue and grey.
Stylized skiers.

SKI-JUMPING

Ski-jumping is a comparatively modern sport and was born at the beginning of the nineteenth century in Norway. The combined event of downhill ski-ing and ski-jumping was first practised in Norway at the end of the nineteenth century.

U.S.A. 1932. *3rd Winter Olympic Games at Lake Placid*
2c. red.
This is actually not a ski-jumping stamp at all, though it was meant to be! When it was issued there were no alpine events in the Winter Olympics. The designer had apparently not seen any ski-jumping for he depicted the ski-jumper with bent knees, sticks and skis apart, hovering over a beautiful winter landscape, with a scarf fluttering from his neck!

Austria 1933. *International Ski Championships at Innsbruck*
50g. blue.
A ski-jump among snow-covered pine-tops, with a frame of ice flowers.

Germany 1935. *4th Winter Olympic Games in Garmisch-Partenkirchen*
12+6pf. red.
Ski-jumper in a close-up.

France 1937. *World Ski Championships in Chamonix*
1f. 50c. blue.
A ski-jumper in a too-erect style against the background of an alpine landscape.

Finland 1938. *World Ski Championships in Lahti*
2+1m. red.
A ski-jumper with a hill and stylized pines in the background.

Roumania 1946. *Sports issue*
160+1, 340l. dark green.
A ski-jumper.

Japan 1949. *4th National Ski Championships in Sapporo*
5.00y. blue.
Ski-jumping is very popular in Japan and the Japanese jumpers reach a very high standard. This is one of the most beautiful of sports stamps, both in style and composition.

Yugoslavia 1949. *International Ski Championships in Planica*
10d. rose red, 12d. grey.
One of the world's highest ski-jumps—that of Planica—with a jumping record of more than 380 ft. (10d.). The other stamp depicts a perfect jump.

Russia 1949. *Winter Sports issue*
20k. green.
A simple yet nicely drawn stamp with a close-up of a ski-jumper.

Roumania 1951. *9th World University Winter Sports Games in Poiana-Stalin*
4l. dark brown.
A ski-jumper and mountains surrounded by a frame of spruce twigs.

Germany (East) 1951. *2nd East German Winter Sports Championships in Oberhof*
4pf. red.
A ski-jumper in action.

Norway 1952. *6th Winter Olympic Games in Oslo*
30+10ö. red.
A very stylish design illustrating Norway's national sport.

Germany (East) 1952. *3rd East German Winter Sports Championships in Oberhof*
24pf. blue.
Ski-jumper.

Sweden 1953. *50th Anniversary Swedish Sports Federation*
10ö. green.
A stylized design.

Bulgaria 1954. *Sports issue*
2l. ultramarine.
A beautiful close-up of a ski-jumper.

Czechoslovakia 1955. *1st National Winter Spartacist Games*
45k. blue grey.
A ski-jumper against an alpine background.

Hungary 1955. *European Figure Skating Championships in Budapest*
1fo. multicoloured.
Another attractive close-up of a ski-jumper.

San Marino 1955. *7th Winter Olympic Games in Cortina 1956*
200l. orange and black.
An artistic ski-jumping design.

Poland 1957. *50th Anniversary of Ski-ing in Poland*
60g. grey green.
A ski-jumper, using the new 'Finnish' style, surmounting a snow crystal.

Finland 1958. *World Ski Championships in Lahti*
20m. grey green.
An exponent of the new Finnish style provides the design for this stamp.

Germany (East) 1960. *8th Winter Olympic Games*
20pf. red and orange brown.
Ski-jumper.

Russia 1960. *8th Winter Olympic Games*
1r. multicoloured.
Ski-jumper.

Hungary 1960. *8th Winter Olympic Games*
60f. light red and yellow brown.
Ski-jumper.

ALPINE SKI-ING

Alpine ski-ing is the youngest and most modern of all ski-ing events. In its modern form it developed during the 1920's in the Alps, where it was pioneered by the Swiss and the English.

Alpine ski-ing is now the most popular of the ski-ing events, and it is therefore quite natural that it should also be the most popular among ski-stamps.

Hungary 1925. *Sports issue*
200k. green and brown.
That this is the first ski stamp can easily be detected from the old-fashioned design. The man is, in fact, trying to make a 'Telemark' turn, though his style is awkward.

Austria 1936. *International Ski Championships in Innsbruck*
12g. green, 24g. violet, 35g. red, 60g. blue.
This is without doubt one of the most beautiful of all sports stamps sets. The three lower values all depict different alpine ski-movements. The 35g. is said to picture the German Olympic women's champion *Christl Cranz*. The highest value shows a well-known tourist view of Innsbruck.

Roumania 1937. *25th Anniversary of Roumanian Athletic Union*

2+1l. grey green.

A downhill skier against a background of snow-covered spruces. The date '8 JUNIE 1937' was the 7th anniversary of the accession of Carol II as well as the date of issue.

Finland 1938. *World Ski Championships in Lahti*

3.50+1.50 blue.

Although no alpine events were included in these championships, one of the stamps of the set shows downhill ski-ing.

Slovakia 1944. *Sports issue*

1+1k. violet.

A forceful downhill design.

Switzerland 1948. *5th Winter Olympic Games at St. Moritz*

30+10c. green blue and grey.

This ski-ing design is first class, in composition, style and colour. The snow-wake made by the runner shimmers from white to greenish blue, giving the stamp an extremely beautiful appearance.

Russia 1948. *Sports issue*

15k. blue grey.

A slalom-skier passing a gate.

Monaco 1948. *14th Olympic Games*

6+9f. violet.

One stamp in this large Olympic set represented the Winter Games and an alpine event—downhill ski-ing—was chosen for the design.

Czechoslovakia 1950. *51st Tatra Cup Race*

1.50k. blue green, 5k. light blue.

A beautiful downhill design from the Tatra Mountains.

Germany (East) 1950. *1st East German Winter Sports Championships in Schierke (Harz)*

12pf. blue violet.

A downhill skier at full speed.

Roumania 1951. *9th World University Winter Games in Poiana-Stalin*

11l. blue.

Downhill skier within a frame of spruce twigs.

Bolivia 1951. *4th South American Ski Championships 1948*
2.00b. dark red and black.
A downhill skier jumping an obstacle is the only South American contribution to ski-stamps.

San Marino 1953. *Sports issue.*
200l. blue green and yellow green.
A woman alpine skier in a costume which takes you back to the 1920's.

Sweden 1954. *World Ski Championships in Falun and Åre*
1k. blue.
A woman downhill skier.

Russia 1954. *Sports issue*
1r. grey blue and red brown.
A slalom-skier going through a gate.

Hungary 1955. *European Figure Skating Championships in Budapest*
1.50fo. multicoloured.
A slalom-skier just rounding a gate flag.

Lebanon 1955. *Sports and Tourist issue*
5p. green, 15p. red, 20p. violet, 25p. light blue, 35p. olive brown, 50p. dark brown, 65p. dark blue.
Downhill skiers among the cedars of Lebanon.

Liechtenstein 1955. *Sports issue*
10c. green blue, brown and violet, 25c. light ultramarine and grey brown.
The lower value shows slalom and the higher downhill ski-ing. The slalom design was awarded second place in the Bonacossa Medal Competition, 1955.

San Marino 1955. *7th Olympic Winter Games in Cortina 1956*
4l. green and black brown.
Downhill skier in action.

Yugoslavia 1956. *Olympic Year*
20d. ultramarine and brown.
A stylized picture of a downhill skier (without skis!) and a bird, symbolizing speed.

Canada 1957. *Sport and Pastime issue*
5c. light blue.
Downhill ski-ing was one of the four outdoor pastimes in this set.

Poland 1957. *12th Commemorative 'Czech and Marusarz' Ski Races in Zakopane*
60g. grey blue, 60g. grey brown.
These stamps, which had the same design showing a downhill skier at full speed, were issued to mark the races held in memory of the skiers *B. R. Czech* and *E. Marusarz*, who were killed in 1945.

Lebanon 1957. *Sports and Tourist issue*
35p. olive green, 65p. red violet, 100p. grey brown.
The design of these three stamps is the same as that of the 1955 set.

Austria 1958. *World Alpine Championships in Bad Gastein*
1.50s. grey blue.
Mount Graukogel on which the alpine events were held.

The Dominican Republic 1958. *Olympic Victors 1956 (III)*
5c. grey, red and red brown.
Madeleine Berthod, Switzerland, who won the women's downhill-ski-ing event in the Winter Olympics at Cortina 1956.

Bulgaria 1959. *40th Ski-ing Anniversary*
1l. blue.
Slalom-skier.

Russia 1960. *8th Winter Olympic Games*
40k. light violet and blue.
Downhill skier.

Hungary 1960. *8th Winter Olympic Games*
1fo. blue green and yellow brown.
Downhill skier.

Togo 1960. *8th Winter Olympic Games*
0.30f. green and red.
Downhill skier.

Monaco 1960. *8th Winter Olympic Games*
0.50f. dark blue and brown violet.
Slalom-skier.

34. TABLE TENNIS

Table tennis originated in England in the 1880's, though play then bore little resemblance to the modern high-speed game. In the 1890's the game became competitive and spread rapidly to both the U.S.A. and the Continent, where the mid-European countries, particularly Hungary and Czechoslovakia, soon began to dominate events, until their leadership was challenged in the 1950's by the Japanese and the Chinese.

Nicaragua 1949. *10th Amateur Baseball Championships in Managua 1948*

3c. red (*airmail*), 60c. grey green.

Two male table-tennis players in action.

Roumania 1953. *World Table Tennis Championships in Bucharest*

55b. red brown, 55b. grey green.

The world championships' shield.

Japan 1954. *9th National Sports Games in Sapporo (Hokkaido)*

5y. grey brown.

A woman table-tennis player using the well-known Japanese 'pen-grip'.

Japan 1956. *World Table Tennis Championships in Tokyo*

10y. brown.

A match between two men players.

Yugoslavia 1956. *Olympic Year*

70d. lilac brown and brown.

This Olympic set contained, strangely enough, a table-tennis design, although table tennis has no place in the Olympic Games. The design incorporates a woman table-tennis player and a butterfly.

Hungary 1958. *European Table Tennis Championships in Budapest*

20f. carmine, 30f. olive.

A table-tennis bat and ball, and a Hungarian table-tennis player.

China (Communist) 1959. *Victory in the World Championships at Dortmund*

4d. blue and black, 8d. red and black.

Forehand drive from a photo of *Wang Chuan Yao*, Chinese champion 1956–7 and 1959.

China (Communist) 1959. *1st National Games in Peking*

8d. green, olive grey, brown and black.

Backhand drive.

35. TENNIS

The forerunner of lawn tennis was *jeu de paume*, or 'real tennis', which was popular in the Middle Ages and is still played. With this game as a model, lawn tennis was devised in England by Major W. Wingfield in 1874, and has since spread all over the world. Most tennis stamps have been issued by countries outside Europe. The leading tennis countries, however—U.S.A., Australia, England, France etc.—are surprisingly not represented.

Philippines 1934. *10th Far Eastern Games in Manila*
6c. ultramarine.
A player with an old-fashioned racket just finishing a forehand drive.

Colombia 1935. *3rd National Games in Barranquilla*
8c. black and rose.
A backhand stroke up at the net.

Russia 1935. *World Spartacist Games in Moscow*
15k. brown and black.
A stylized design showing both players in a match.

Russia 1938. *Sports issue*
15k. brown.
A forehand drive, the ball being shown for the first time.

Ecuador 1939. *Victory in the 1st Bolivar Games in Bogotá, Colombia, 1938*
50c. red brown.
At the net.

Monaco 1948. *Olympic Games*
10+15f. red.
Although tennis has not been represented in the Olympic programme since 1924 this design was among those selected for the Olympic set. For the first time the traditional white trousers gave place to shorts.

Nicaragua 1949. *19th Amateur Baseball World Championships in Managua 1948*
1c. red (*airmail*), 2c. red violet.
Forehand drive.

Japan 1949. *4th National Sports Games in Tokyo*
8.00y. black.
Low forehand drive.

Guatemala 1950. *6th Central American and Caribbean Games*
8c. lilac and black.
Low forehand drive.

Bolivia 1951. *South American Tennis Championships 1948*
0.50b. red and black.
Forehand drive at the baseline.

San Marino 1953. *Sports issue*
2l. brown and black green.
Forehand drive.

Liberia 1955. *Sports issue*
3c. red and green.
A match between two women at the Antoinette Tubman Stadium in Monrovia.

Russia 1956. *National Spartacist Games*
40k. red brown.
Forehand drive at the baseline.

Liechtenstein 1958. *Sports issue*
40k. rose and grey.
Low backhand.

Roumania 1959. *Sports issue*
1.60l. dark red, olive green and violet brown.
Smash at the net.

Tunisia 1960. *1st Tunisian participation in the Olympic Games*
15m. red and red violet.
Forehand volley by a woman player.

Costa Rica 1960. *17th Olympic Games*
5c. yellow green and black.
Woman tennis player (backhand).

Brazil 1960. *Victories of Maria Bueno at Wimbledon 1959–60*
6.00cr. grey brown.
Mario Bueno, Brazil, women's singles champion at Wimbledon in 1959 and 1960.

36. VOLLEY BALL

In its present form volley ball first appeared in England at the end of the nineteenth century and then spread to the United States. The game received a fresh lease of life in the 1930's, and is now mostly played in Eastern Europe.

Roumania 1945. *Sports issue*
32+168l. wine red, 32+168l. green (imperf.).
Players in front of the net.

Japan 1947. *2nd National Sports Games in Kanazawa*
1.20y. red violet.
Two teams fighting for the ball at the net. This basic design later appeared, with slight variations, on practically all volley ball stamps.

Bulgaria 1950. *Sports issue*
40l. red violet.
Same design as Japan 1947.

Hungary 1950. *Sports issue*
30f. red violet.
Same design as Japan 1947.

Trieste Zone B 1952. *Sports issue*
50d. brown red.
Same design as Japan 1947.

Hungary 1953. *Hungarian Recreation Establishments*
1.70fo. blue.
The new sports and recreation ground of the Steel Works of Csepel, with a volley ball match in progress.

Czechoslovakia 1953. *Sports issue*
30h. red brown.
Fighting for the ball at the net.

Bulgaria 1954. *50th Anniversary Trade Union Movement*

16s. dark green.

A recreation ground with a volley ball match being played in the background.

Roumania 1955. *European Volley Ball Championships in Bucharest*

55b. red violet and rose, 1.75l. red and yellow.

The designs show: net play by men (55b.) and by girls (1.75l.).

Russia 1956. *National Spartacist Games*

25k. brown.

At the net.

Brazil 1957. *9th Spring Games in Rio de Janeiro*

2.50c. orange red.

Woman player at the net.

Czechoslovakia 1958. *European Volley Ball Championships in Prague*

50h. brown.

Players fighting for the ball at the net.

Bulgaria 1958. *Students' Sports Games in Sofia*

45s. emerald green.

Same design as Czechoslovakia.

Brazil 1960. *World Volley Ball Championships in Rio de Janeiro*

11.00cr. blue.

Symbolic picture issued on the occasion of the third women's and the fourth men's world championships.

37. WEIGHT-LIFTING

Modern weight-lifting, with its adjustable bar-bells and other equipment, can be traced back to the athletic trials of strength which were once so popular. Competitive weight-lifting first came into prominence in Austria and Germany in the 1870's, and then spread rapidly to other sports countries. Only quite recently, however, has it found favour with stamp designers.

Bulgaria 1939. *9th Junak Games in Sofia*

2l. red, 14l. red violet.

The lower value shows the emblem of the Junak Movement—a man with a dumb-bell. The higher value, rather attractive in composition and colour, depicts an athlete lifting a large stone.

Russia 1949. *Winter Sports issue*
1r. orange red.
A well-designed stamp showing a perfect two-arm jerk.

Hungary 1956. *16th Olympic Games*
1.50fo. blue violet and brown.
Two-arm snatch.

China (Communist) 1957. *1st Chinese Workers' Games 1955*
1d. red violet, light brown, red and green.
Two-arm snatch.

Russia 1957. *16th Olympic Games*
60k. brown and blue violet.
A weight-lifter performing a two-arm jerk.

Iran 1957. *World Weight Lifting Championships in Teheran*
10r. green blue, green and red.
A stylized design showing a weight-lifter and the national flag of Iran.

Japan 1958. *13th National Sports Games in Toyama*
5y. blue grey.
Two-arm press.

Lebanon 1959. *3rd Mediterranean Games in Beirut*
30p. dark brown.
Two-arm snatch.

China (Communist) 1959. *1st National Games in Peking*
8d. green grey, red brown and black.
Two-arm jerk.

U.A.R. 1960. *8th Anniversary of the Revolution*
5m. grey.
Two-arm jerk.

Russia 1960. *17th Olympic Games*
20k. red, black and violet grey.
Two-arm snatch.

Korea (South) 1960. *17th Olympic Games*
20w. light blue and red brown.
Two-arm jerk.

Liberia 1960. *17th Olympic Games*
5c. green and violet brown.
Two-arm press-up and native carrying basket.

Bulgaria 1960. *17th Olympic Games*
16s. blue green and light rose, 16s. red brown and yellow (imperf.).
Two-arm snatch.

Morocco 1960. *17th Olympic Games*
20f. violet brown, olive and blue.
Two-arm press.

North Korea 1960. *15th Anniversary of the Republic*
5w. yellow green, brown orange and dark green.
Two-arm snatch.

Costa Rica 1960. *17th Olympic Games*
4c. orange yellow and black.
Two-arm jerk.

38. WRESTLING

Wrestling has been practised in every age and by all kinds of people. The oldest known traces of wrestling have been found in Asia Minor and Egypt dating from about 3000 B.C. Modern wrestling originated in the first part of the nineteenth century in Southern France, with the development of the new Greco-Roman style. At the start wrestling was practised by professionals, but in the 1890's amateur wrestling developed strongly. Free-style wrestling began in U.S.A. in the nineteenth century.

Wrestling is one of the most popular sports designs and there are examples of many kinds of incidents and holds, making it a most interesting subject to study on stamps.

Greece 1906. *Special Olympic Games in Athens*
25l. blue, 30l. violet.
The 25l. represents the fight between Hercules and Antaeus and the 30l. shows the well-known Statue of Wrestlers now in the Uffizi Galleries in Florence.

Switzerland 1932. *Pro Juventute issue*

20c. red.

An ancient form of wrestling called *Schwingen*, which is still practised in Switzerland.

Tannu Tuva (Northern Mongolia) 1936. *15th Anniversary of the Tuvinian Republic*

4k. orange, 6k. grey green.

The ancient form of wrestling still practised in Asian countries.

Ecuador 1939. *Victory in the 1st Bolivar Games in Bogotá, Colombia, 1938*

1s. violet.

American free-style wrestling ('catch as catch can') is depicted here. One wrestler has a head-lock on his opponent, who is on his way to the mat.

Finland 1945. *Sports issue*

1m.+50p. green.

More orthodox holds can be seen on this stamp. The model was said to have been the Finnish wrestler *O. Friman.*

Turkey 1949. *5th European Free Style Wrestling Championships in Istanbul*

15k. red violet, 20k. blue, 30k. grey brown, 60k. green.

This set marks a milestone in sports philately. Beautifully printed in photogravure by Courvoisier, they actually show well-known wrestlers both Turkish and Swedish: *Grönberg* (Sweden) and *Dogu* (Turkey); *Akar* (Turkey) and *Pettersén* (Sweden); *Akar* and *Persson*; and finally *Möller* (Sweden) and Izmir (Turkey).

Switzerland 1950. *Swiss Confederation Festival*

20+10c. olive, white and red.

A closer view of *Schwingen.*

Sudan 1951. *Definitive issue*

3½p. red brown and green.

Two Nubian wrestlers about to join battle.

Japan 1952. *7th National Sports Games in Fukushima*

5y. brown.

Pressing down a 'bridge'.

Sweden 1953. *50th Anniversary of the Swedish Sports Federation*

1.40k. red violet.

A half-*linđéna*, a somersault throw named after the Swedish-Finnish wrestler Lindén.

Hungary 1953. *Inauguration of Nép Stadium in Budapest*
60f. red brown and olive yellow.
Free-style wrestling: head-and-arm lock.

Japan 1954. *World Free Style Wrestling Championships in Tokyo*
10y. green.
Reversed waist-lock.

San Marino 1954. *Sports issue*
25l. green and blue.
The Uffizi statue of two wrestlers, earlier reproduced on the Greek issue of 1906.

Bulgaria 1954. *Sports issue*
44s. red.
A waist-hold from behind.

Iceland 1955–7. *Sports issue*
75a. brown, 1.50k. red (1957).
Glima, the ancient Icelandic form of wrestling which dates from the tenth century. About fifty years ago it was revived and is now practised under modern rules. The stamp reappeared two years later with a different value and colour.

Iran 1955. *Persian Wrestling Successes in 1955*
2.50 green, red, brown and blue.
A somewhat complicated manœuvre in which the wrestler on the right seems to have made a throw by means of a back-heel.

Turkey 1956. *16th Olympic Games*
40k. brown and yellow green, 60k. red and grey.
The two designs depict free-style and Greco-Roman wrestling.

Russia 1957. *3rd World Youth Games in Moscow*
25k. red violet and light green.
Reversed waist-hold with overthrow.

Mongolia 1958. *Sports issue*
50m. red brown and rose.
Mongolian wrestlers in action, watched by referees.

France 1958. *French National Sports*

25f. grey and light brown.

Breton wrestling, which is similar to modern free-style wrestling but of older origin.

Bulgaria 1958. *World Free Style Wrestling Championships in Sofia*

60s. red brown, 80s. dark brown.

Overthrow with thigh pick-up.

Hungary 1958. *World Greco-Roman Wrestling Championships in Budapest*

40s. red violet and yellow, 60f. brown and grey blue.

Overthrow with reverse waist pick-up (40s.), and the pressing down of a 'bridge' (60f.).

The Dominican Republic 1958. *Olympic Victors 1956 (III)*

3c. multicoloured.

The Japanese winner of the free-style wrestling (feather-weight), *Shozo Sasahara* applying a 'half-nelson'.

Mongolia 1959. *National Sports issue*

10m. violet and multicoloured.

Mongolian wrestlers.

North Viet-Nam 1959. *Sports issue*

12x. violet red.

Native wrestling.

Iran 1959. *World Free Style Championships in Teheran*

6r. blue, green, red, orange brown and black.

Stylized wrestlers, globe and Iranian flag.

Yugoslavia 1960. *17th Olympic Games*

35d. brown violet and grey.

Coming to grips.

Italy 1960. *17th Olympic Games*

200l. dark green.

The famous statue 'Apoxyomenos' (a wrestler scraping off sand).

Germany (West) 1960. *Olympic Year 1960*

7pf. red brown.

Ancient Greek wrestlers.

Russia 1960. *17th Olympic Games*
10k. dark brown, yellow and blue.
Waist-lift.

Mongolia 1960. *17th Olympic Games*
20m. rose red, light blue and grey.
Reversed waist-grip.

Hungary 1960. *17th Olympic Games*
1.40fo. ultramarine and yellow brown.
Ancient Greek wrestlers.

Turkey 1960. *17th Olympic Games*
30k. blue grey.
Backhammer.

Bulgaria 1960. *17th Olympic Games*
12s. violet and light rose, 12s. red violet and yellow brown (imperf.).
Gripping.

The Dominican Republic 1960. *Olympic Victors 1956 (IV)*
1c. grey green and red, 16c. red brown and red.
Gholam Takhti, Iran, and *Mithat Bayrak*, Turkey,

Morocco 1960. *17th Olympic Games*
5f. red brown, violet blue and olive green.
Professional wrestlers (neck-swing).

Lebanon 1960. *17th Olympic Games*
5+5p, orange and brown.
Pressing down a 'bridge'.

North Korea 1960. *Sports and pastime issue.*
5w. olive grey, brown and orange brown.
Native wrestlers.

39. YACHTING

Although the Ancient Egyptians knew how to sail light boats, yachting can be said to have started in sixteenth-century Holland, when competitions formed part of the sailor's education. Organized yachting did not appear, however, until the end of the seventeenth century in England.

Yachting is one of the most popular subjects on the world's sports stamps. Not all the designs, however, come strictly into the category of competitive sport, and it is no easy matter in many cases to decide whether a particular stamp should be included.

Several of the stamps listed below can therefore be included or excluded according to one's personal inclination.

Netherlands 1928. *9th Olympic Games in Amsterdam*

5c. light blue.

The yacht depicted in this set was a cutter, a type of boat not represented in the Olympics!

Colombia 1935. *3rd National Games in Barranquilla*

20c. green and violet.

Barranquilla Bay, where the yachting events took place; with a little difficulty one can also distinguish a yacht on the horizon.

Canada 1935. *George V's Silver Jubilee issue*

13c. blue.

The royal yacht *Britannia* which took part in several races at the beginning of this century.

Austria 1935. *Airmail stamp—ordinary issue*

10s. grey.

Sailing boats on the Attersee with a glider overhead.

Bermuda 1936–40. *Definitive issue*

2d. blue and black (1936), 2d. black, brown and blue (1938), 2d. red and ultramarine (1940).

A beautiful design, showing the yacht *Lucie*, formed part of the 1936 set, returning with changed colours in 1938 and 1940.

Denmark 1937. *Christian X's Silver Jubilee issue*

5ö. green.

Marselisborg, the summer castle of the Danish king, with a yacht in the foreground.

Danzig 1938. *Winter Relief issue*

5+5pf. green.

The yacht *Peter von Danzig* which took part in the Atlantic race between Bermuda and Cuxhaven in 1936.

Monaco 1948. *14th Olympic Games*

15+25f. blue.

A yachting regatta outside Monte Carlo.

Roumania 1948. *Naval and Air issue*

2+2l. dark green.

A yachting regatta on the Black Sea.

Bahamas 1948. *300th Anniversary of the Bahamas*

1s. brown.

A star boat race.

Netherlands 1949. *Summer Relief issue*

20+5c. blue.

For simplicity of design this stamp surpassed any previously issued. A few skilful lines and white dots have resulted in a vivid picture of a yacht race.

Nicaragua 1949. *10th World Amateur Baseball Championships in Managua 1948*

5c. green blue (*airmail*), 40c. violet.

Yacht race.

Russia 1949. *Sports issue*

20k. blue.

A beautiful picture of a regatta.

Japan 1949. *4th National Sports Games in Tokyo*

8.00y. black.

A vivid picture of a yawl under full sail with the crew leaning overboard to prevent capsizing.

Yugoslavia 1950. *Naval issue*

12d. black blue.

Two yachts under full sail.

New Zealand 1951. *Health Stamps*

½d. red and orange, 1d. green and orange.

Small-boat regatta.

Trieste Zone B 1952. *Sports issue*

28d. blue.

Yacht race.

Poland 1952. *Harbour Workers' Day*

30+15g. green.

Yachts racing.

Monaco 1953. *15th Olympic Games*
3f. dark blue and light blue.
Yachts outside Monte Carlo.

Gibraltar 1953. *Definitive issue*
1½d. red.
Sailing in Gibraltar Bay.

Bermuda 1953. *Definitive issue*
2d. red and blue.
A racing dinghy.

Bahamas 1954. *Definitive issue*
1s. brown and blue.
Same design as for the anniversary set of 1948, but with a portrait of Queen Elizabeth II.

Russia 1954. *Sports issue*
40k. blue and red brown.
Yachting regatta.

San Marino 1955. *7th International Stamp Exposition in Riccione*
100l. blue and grey.
A beautiful picture of a yacht.

Bermuda 1956. *50th Anniversary of the Ocean Race*
8d. red and black, 1s. 3d. blue and red.
Two definitive stamps—showing a seabird and a map of Bermuda—were overprinted '50th anniversary/U.S.-Bermuda/Ocean Race 1956'.

San Marino 1956. *8th International Stamp Exposition in Riccione*
100l. brown and green.
Same design as 1955 issue but with changed colours and date.

Netherlands 1956. *16th Olympic Games*
2+3c. blue and black.
A stylized stamp depicting a yacht.

The Dominican Republic 1958. *Olympic Victors 1956 (III)*
17c. multicoloured.
A 5.5 m. race, with the winning Swedish yacht *Rush V* in the foreground.

Poland 1959. *Sports issue*
40g. light blue
Small yacht.

Hungary 1959. *Balaton Tourist issue*
30f. blue and yellow.
Yacht on Lake Balaton.

Brazil 1959. *World Snipe Championships in Porto Alegro*
6.50c. dark green.
Stylized yachts.

Germany (East) 1960. *17th Olympic Games*
25pf. blue and orange brown.
Yawl.

Yugoslavia 1960. *17th Olympic Games*
55d. dark green and grey.
Stylized yachts.

Cuba 1960. *17th Olympic Games*
1c. light violet, 1c. grey blue (imperf. in sheet).
Two yachts.

Morocco 1960. *17th Olympic Games*
45f. ultramarine, red violet and dark green.
Yawl.

40. SPORTS EVENTS

In the introductory chapters I mentioned the problem of dealing with stamps in the various sports sets which had no specific connection with sport. One of the ways of solving this problem is to include such issues under the heading 'Sports Events', where applicable.

Costa Rica 1924. *National Games in San José*
10c. red, 20c. blue.
These stamps, which bear the wrong inscription 'Juegos Olimpicos', were issued with a surcharge of 10c. to finance the Games and the building of the stadium. They also exist imperforate.

Bulgaria 1931–3. *1st Balkan Games in Sofia*
50l. brown, 50l. red brown (1933).
A man with a trumpet and a laurel wreath standing on a victory rostrum.

Italy 1933. *World University Championships in Turin*

10c. yellow brown, 20c. red, 50c. violet, 1.25c. blue.

A statue of an athlete from Turin Stadium, with a pillar in the background bearing the inscription 'Dux Mussolini'.

Colombia 1935. *3rd National Games in Barranquilla*

15c. blue and red brown, 50c. ultramarine and orange, 1p. olive green and light blue, 2p. dark green and light blue, 5p. violet and light blue, 10p. black and light blue.

The six values in this set not previously described are: an athlete, Barranquilla Harbour, G.P.O. Barranquilla, 'Flag of the Race' Monument, coat-of-arms of Barranquilla and a condor.

Italy 1935. '*Littoriali*' *Championships in Rome*

20c. red, 30c. brown, 50c. violet.

These championships in science and sports for university students in Rome took place every year. The designs have nothing to do with sport, but as it played an important part in the championships the set has been included here.

Ecuador 1939. *1st Victory in the Bolivar Games in Bogotá, Colombia, 1938*

2s. red.

The only stamp in this set not devoted to a special event is the 2s., which depicts the Olympic flame.

Monaco 1939. *8th World University Championships in Monaco*

40c. green, 70c. black brown, 90c. violet, 1.25f. red brown, 2.25c. blue.

The beautiful Louis II Stadium in Monaco.

Germany 1942. '*Wehrkampftage*' *of the S.A.*

6pf. violet.

The Nazi organization S.A. arranged sports events of largely military character between 15th August and 15th September 1942. The stamp shows the S.A. emblem.

Finland 1946. *3rd Workers' Sports Games in Helsinki*

8m. brown violet.

A man and a woman holding a crown of laurels.

Bulgaria 1946. *12th Balkan Games in Tirana, Albania*

100l. black brown.

The Bulgarians commemorated the first post-war Balkan Games by issuing a stamp showing the participating nations' coats-of-arms and flags.

Colombia 1946. *5th Central American and Caribbean Games*

50c. red (overprinted in black and green).

To mark these Games a current stamp showing Cartagena Clock-tower was overprinted in two colours: 'V Juegos C/A Y DEL C/1946.' ('Juegos Centroamericanos y del Caribe.')

Roumania 1947. *13th Balkan Games in Sofia, Bulgaria*

2+2l. violet.

A current stamp (32,000l.) bearing the picture of King Michael overprinted with the new value and the letters 'C.B.A. 1947'.

Bulgaria 1947. *13th Balkan Games in Sofia*

60l. red brown.

The only stamp in the set without a specific sporting design, this reproduced the coats-of-arms of the four participating countries.

Roumania 1948. *Victories in the 13th Balkan Games in Sofia 1947*

5+5l. blue.

A boy's and a girl's head within a laurel chaplet.

Indonesia 1951. *1st Asian Games in New Delhi*

5+3s. grey green, 10+5s. dark blue, 20+5s. carmine, 30+10s. brown, 35+10s. light blue.

A map of South-East Asia and Olympic emblems.

India 1951. *1st Asian Games*

2a. red violet and orange, 12a. brown and ultramarine.

Map of South-East Asia and a torch.

Egypt 1951. *1st Mediterranean Games in Alexandria*

10m. brown, 22m. green, 30m. green and ultramarine.

A triumphal arch (10m.), the coat-of-arms of Alexandria (22m.) and King Farouk (30m.). These stamps were also issued in a special commemorative sheet.

Indonesia 1951. *2nd National Games in Djakarta*

5+3s. grey green, 10+5s. grey blue, 20+5s. carmine, 30+10s. dark brown, 35+10s. light blue.

The design for these stamps shows the emblem of the Games: the wings of the holy bird Garuda surrounding a lotus flower—the symbol of purity—and a flame—the symbol of fighting spirit.

Israel 1953. *4th Maccabiah Games in Tel-Aviv*

110p. blue and yellow orange.

A beautiful design showing a hand holding a football that is also a globe of the world.

Mexico 1954. *7th Central American Games in Mexico City*

20c. blue green and rose, 25c. olive brown and dark green, 35c. grey green and red violet.

An Aztec athlete (20c.), a Mayan building and bas relief of pelota (25c.) and Mexico City Stadium (35c.).

Colombia 1954. *7th National Games in Cali*

5c. blue, 10c. carmine, 15c. brown, 20c. green.

A torch and Olympic rings (5c. and 15c.) and an athlete with coat-of-arms (10c. and 20c.).

Brazil 1954. *6th Spring Games in Rio de Janeiro*

60c. violet brown.

A girl's head and a flower.

Czechoslovakia 1955. *1st National Winter Spartacist Games*

30h. carmine.

A woman athlete in a Czech training suit holding a torch.

Mexico 1955. *2nd Pan American Games in Mexico City*

20c. grey green and brown, 25c. blue green and red violet, 35c. dark brown and red.

An Indian torch-bearer (20c.), Mayan art and a map of America (25c.) and a stadium (35c.).

Czechoslovakia 1955. *1st National Summer Spartacist Games*

60h. grey green.

Czech folk-dancers.

Poland 1955. *2nd World Youth Games in Warsaw*

20g. dark brown.

White, yellow and black athletes shaking hands.

Russia 1956. *5th National Trade Union Spartacist Games in Moscow*

1r. red violet and green.

The emblem of the Games, with a stadium and industrial buildings in the background.

Egypt 1956. *Arab Festival in Cairo*
10m. red brown and green, 35m. light yellow, yellow and grey violet.
Map of Africa and Southern Asia (10m.) and a globe, torch and peace dove (35m.).

Russia 1956. *National Spartacist Games*
40k. orange and yellow.
Medallion depicting a man and a woman athlete.

Russia 1957. *3rd World Youth Games in Moscow*
40k. blue violet and red.
A diamond-shaped stamp showing a European, an Asian and an African holding a peace dove.

France 1957. *International University Games in Paris*
18f. blue grey and grey.
Leo Lagrange, French Minister for Sport between 1936 and 1940, who was killed during the war. In the background is the stadium of Charlety, outside Paris.

Lebanon 1957. *2nd Pan Arabian Games in Beirut*
50p. grey green.
A stadium with the flags of the participating countries. Inset: President Chamoun.

Japan 1958. *3rd Asian Games in Tokyo*
10y. multicoloured.
The emblem of the Games.

Great Britain 1958. *6th Empire and Commonwealth Games*
3d. violet, 6d. red violet, 1s. 3d. green.
To commemorate the Empire Games held in Cardiff in July three stamps were issued, all bearing the portrait of Queen Elizabeth II together with the Dragon of Wales.

Germany (East) 1958. *1st Spartacist Games of the Eastern Armies in Leipzig*
10pf. green and brown violet, 20pf. red brown and yellow, 25pf. light blue and red.
Open to the soldiers of the Communist nations, these Games were marked with three stamps: an East German soldier surmounting an obstacle (10pf.), the emblem of the Games (20pf.) and a parade of sportsmen carrying a red flag (25pf.).

Venezuela 1959. *8th Central American Games in Caracas*

5c. yellow, 10c. red brown, 15c. orange, 30c. grey, 50c. dark green—*airmail*.

Flame and laurel.

Yugoslavia 1959. *The Partisan Games*

100d. brown violet and yellow brown.

Three symbolic figures.

Russia 1959. *2nd National Spartacist Games*

30k. olive brown and red.

Young athletes holding an emblem.

Germany (East) 1959. *3rd German Gymnastics and Sports Festival in Leipzig*

40+20pf. violet red.

Fireworks over the stadium tower.

Lebanon 1959. *3rd Mediterranean Games in Beirut*

40p. ultramarine.

Hand holding a torch.

Thailand 1959. *The SEATO Games in Bangkok*

10s. orange, 25s. violet brown, 2b. light blue.

These stamps feature symbolic Siamese objects.

Albania 1959. *1st National Spartacist Games*

11l. ultramarine.

Athletes holding torch and flag.

North Korea 1959. *3rd National Games in Pyongyang*

5w. light blue, red and red violet.

Sports emblem.

China (Communist) 1959. *1st National Games in Peking*

8d. yellow olive and black.

Communist statue in front of symbolic race track.

Malagasy 1960. *1st Tananarivo Games*

25f. brown, orange brown and ultramarine.

A coloured and a white athlete shaking hands.

Riu Kiu Islands 1960. *8th National Games of Kyushu and Okinawa*

3c. grey, black and red.

A strip of land on the horizon and a torch.

41. SPORTS GROUNDS AND STADIUMS

Although only qualifying as 'sports stamps' in the widest sense, issues featuring famous 'Homes of Sport' could make an interesting sideline for a sports stamps collection. The following section lists stamps which have stadiums, etc., as their main object, and which have not been mentioned earlier.

Greece 1896. *1st Olympic Games in Athens*
1d. blue.
Olympic stadium.

Peru 1906. *Hippodrome Santa Beatriz, Lima*
1s. violet and green.

Italy 1933. *Flights of Graf Zeppelin*
10l. red and blue grey.
Foro Italico, Rome.

Greece 1934. *Olympic Stadium in Athens*
8d. blue.

Colombia 1935. *3rd National Games in Barranquilla*
5c. brown and yellow, 12c. blue black.
Baseball and swimming stadium.

Bulgaria 1935. *8th Junak Games in Sofia*
14l. dark brown.
Stadium of Sofia.

Colombia 1937. *Stadium of Barranquilla*
15c. blue.

Germany 1938. *16th Turn and Sports Festival in Breslau*
5pf. green.
Hermann Göring Sportfield.

Monaco 1939. *Inauguration of the Monaco Stadium*
10f. green.
Stade Louis II.

Nicaragua 1947. *Horse Track Tribune of Managua*
3c. olive grey.

Roumania 1948. *Victories in the 13th Balkan Games in Sofia 1947*
7+7l. violet, 10+10l. grey green (imperforate).

Nicaragua 1949. *10th World Amateur Baseball Championships in Managua 1948*
4c. black (*airmail*), 5c. blue green, 10c. green.
Stadium of Managua.

Honduras 1949. *National Stadium of Tegucigalpa*
30c. grey olive.

Guatemala 1950. *6th Central American and Caribbean Games*
65c. green.
Stadium of Guatemala City.

Panama 1950–2. *Sports issue*
0.01b. red brown and black, 0.01c. green and black.
Stadium of Panama (1950) and swimming stadium (1952).

Bolivia 1951. *2nd National Sports Congress*
5.00b. carmine and black.
Stadium of La Paz.

Finland 1951. *15th Olympic Games in Helsinki 1952*
30+3m. blue.
Olympic Stadium.

Venezuela 1951. *3rd Bolivar Games in Caracas*
5c. green, 10c. violet rose, 20c. brown, 30c. blue.
National Velodrome.

Hungary 1952. *15th Olympic Games in Helsinki*
2fo. olive brown.
Nép Stadium of Budapest.

Portugal 1952. '*28th May Stadium*' *in Braga*
1.40e. violet and yellow.

Nicaragua 1952. *Stadium of Managua*
5c. red.
Same as 1949.

Monaco 1953. *15th Olympic Games in Helsinki 1952*
15f. blue, green and brown.
Louis II Stadium in Monaco.

Hungary 1953. *Sports Buildings*
50f. violet grey, 60f. grey green.
Sport hall in Sztàlinvàros and recreation ground in Kekes.

Germany (East) 1953. *German Sports Hall in East Berlin*
35pf. blue (photogravure and typography).

Hungary 1953. *Inauguration of Nép Stadium in Budapest*
5fo. olive brown and grey blue.

Surinam 1953. *National Sports Week*
10+5c. red violet, 15+7½c. brown, 30+15c. grey green.
Stadium of Paramaribo

Germany (West Berlin) 1953. *Berlin Olympic Stadium*
20pf. red.

Colombia 1954. *Girardot Stadium in Medellin*
$1 blue and black.

Poland 1955. *2nd World Youth Games in Warsaw*
60g. grey blue.

Italy 1956. *7th Olympic Winter Games*
10l. green, brown and orange brown, 12l. grey and olive yellow, 25l. grey violet and red orange, 60l. blue and yellow orange.
The Olympic arenas among the Dolomites in Cortina.

Honduras 1956. *National Stadium in Tegucigalpa*
10c. green and black, 10c. brown and black (Official).

Russia 1956. *National Spartacist Games*
40k. green and red.
Lenin Stadium in Moscow.

Liberia 1956. *16th Olympic Games*
10c. violet and green.
Olympic Park; Melbourne.

Russia 1957. *3rd World Youth Games in Moscow*
40k. green, olive and red.
Lenin Stadium, Moscow.

Russia 1957. *6th World Peace Festival in Moscow*
40k. dark violet and black.

Panama 1957. *Hippodrome 'President G. A. Remon Cantera'*
10c. grey and blue.

Japan 1958. *3rd Asian Games in Tokyo*
5y. dark green, olive and rose.
National (Olympic) Stadium.

Malaya 1958. *Anniversary of Malayan Independence*
10c. multicoloured.
Merdeka stadium, Kuala Lumpur.

Venezuela 1959. *8th Central American Games in Caracas*
5c. green, 10c. red, 20c. light blue, 30c. dark blue, 50c. red violet.

The Dominican Republic 1959. *3rd Pan American Games in Chicago*
9c. dark green and grey.
Baseball stadium, 'Estadio Trujillo'.

Roumania 1959. *'20th August' Stadium in Bucharest*
1.75l. green and grey.

Germany (East) 1959. *Central Stadium, Leipzig*
40pf. olive yellow, red, orange and black.

Italy 1960. *17th Olympic Games*
10l. orange and blue grey, 25l. violet and grey brown, 60l. grey green and grey brown, 150l. light blue and grey brown.

U.A.R. 1960. *8th Anniversary of the Revolution*
100m. red brown and red (sheet).
New Stadium in Cairo.

Haiti 1960. *17th Olympic Games (I) and (II)*
1g. blue and black, 1g.+25c. blue and black.
Olympic stadium of Athens, 1906.

North Korea 1960. *15th Anniversary of the Republic*
10w. yellow green, blue and red.
Stadium of Pyongyang.

42. SPORTS PARADES

Sports parades are depicted on a number of stamps, especially in the sports series of East European countries. Most of these stamps are reproduced from photographs.

Switzerland 1932. *Youth Charity issue*
5c. green red white.
Fahnenschwingen.

Russia 1935. *World Spartacist Games in Moscow*
40k. brown red.

Russia 1938. *Sports Propaganda issue*
20k. green, 80k. blue.
Woman flag bearer, and women's sports parade in Red Square.

Ecuador 1939. *Victory in the 1st Bolivar Games in Bogotá, Columbia, 1938*
5c. red.
Inauguration parade.

Russia 1940. *Day of Physical Culture*
30k. brown.

Turkey 1943. *20th Anniversary of the Turkish Republic*
4½k. olive yellow.
Parade of football players.

Russia 1946. *Sports Propaganda issue*
30k. green.
A large stamp depicting a parade in the Dynamo Stadium.

Yugoslavia 1947. *Day of Physical Culture in Belgrade*
4d. ultramarine.
A large display of club colours and political emblems.

Russia 1948. *30th Anniversary of the Youth Movement*
20k. brown violet.

Roumania 1948. *Sports Propaganda issue*
10 + 10l. red violet, 10 + 10l. red (imperf.).
An athlete against a background of parading sportsmen with flags.

Russia 1949. *International Women's Day*
1r. green.
A parade of women headed by a woman carrying a cup and a flag.

Bulgaria 1949. *Sports Propaganda issue*
50l. red brown.

Switzerland 1951. *Swiss Federation Festival*
20+10c. olive red.
Fahnenschwingen.

Roumania 1952. *Sports Propaganda issue*
1.75l. carmine.

43. SPORTS PROPAGANDA

A great number of sports stamps have been issued with no connection whatever with any special sports event or any particular sport. Again many of these come from the East European countries.

Italy 1932. *10th Fascist Anniversary*
1.75l. orange.
An athlete hoisting the Italian flag over a stadium, symbolizing the Government's interest in sports.

Germany 1935. *German Postal Workers' Fund issue*
5+3pf. green

Roumania 1937. *25th Anniversary of the Roumanian Athletic Union*
10+4l. blue.
This stamp celebrates the anniversary of the founding of the Roumanian Athletic Union (UFSR) in 1912. The name was changed in 1940 to OSR, and again more recently to OSP.

Russia 1940. *Day of Physical Culture*
50k. blue black.
A boy and a girl hold the Russian Athletic Youth badge, BGTO ('be prepared to work and defend').

France 1943. *National Relief issue*
4+10fr. violet.
A man and a woman athlete salute the tricolour.

Roumania 1943. *Day of Sport*
16+24l. brown, 16 + 24l. light blue.
The emblem of OSR, consisting of representations of discus throwing, rifle shooting, ski-ing and swimming.

Indo-China 1944. *Sports Propaganda issue*
10c. yellow violet, 50c. brown red.
Overprinted in 1945 VIET-NAM/DAN-CHU CONG-HOA, for use in the new born state of Vietnam.

Roumania 1945. *Sports Propaganda issue*
35+165l. blue, 35 + 165l. olive green (imperf.)

Algeria 1946. *Charity issue*
8+27fr. red violet.
The laurelled head of an athlete and three rings in the background.

Israel 1948. *Sports Propaganda (Jewish National Fund) issue*
10p. dark green.
A Jewish sports emblem with the star of David and a hand holding a laurel.

Czechoslovakia 1950. *51st. Tatra Cup Ski Race*
3k. red brown, yellow brown.
The athletic badge of Czechoslovakia, a man and a woman within a cog-wheel.

Hungary 1950. *5 Year Plan issue*
10ft. yellow, olive brown.

Roumania 1950. *Sports Propaganda—Sports and Work G.M.A. issue*
3l. red, 5l. brown, 5l. blue.

Hungary 1950. *Sports Progapanda issue*
60f. brown olive, red white green.

Poland 1951. *1st National Spartacist Games in Warsaw*
45gr. green.

Panama 1951-52. *Sports Propaganda issue*
0.01b. blue black, 0.01b. yellow black.

Italy 1952. *1st International Sports Stamps Exposition in Rome*
25c. brown black.
This, the sports philatelist's own stamp, honours the first sports stamps exposition.

Brazil 1952. *50th Anniversary of Fluminense Football Club*
1.20cr. green blue.

Roumania 1953. *1st World Youth Games in Bucharest*
20b. yellow orange.

Greece 1957. *Historical series*
50l. brown black.
Diagoras of Rhodes, who won the boxing event at the 79th Olympic Games in 464 B.C.

Roumania 1958. *25th Anniversary of Sports Medicine*
1.20l. red violet, light green.
An aesculapian emblem against the background of a stadium track.

44. THE FRINGES OF SPORTS PHILATELY

Earlier an attempt was made to draw a line between sports stamps and those dealing with pastimes. This is extremely difficult and the fixing of boundaries should be left to individual taste. As the aim of this book has been to show the development and spread of sports stamps from every angle, this section deals with stamps whose inclusion is a matter of opinion. This small list is far from complete and should be regarded only as a sample.

Children at play, bathing and other pastimes have often attracted stamp designers. For example, FRANCE issued a Postal Workers' Sports Fund set in 1937, with designs depicting a tug-of-war on the beach and ramblers outside a mountain youth hostel. NEW ZEALAND regularly issues 'health' stamps which often depict playing children. The 1937 issue shows a boy climbing a mountain; 1939: boys playing with ball; 1942: children on a see-saw; 1948: children playing leap-frog, etc.

Among others, RUSSIA has a stamp (1938) showing children playing in the Crimea, and a Hungarian issue of 1940 depicts a boy playing with a kite. Children at play can also be seen on stamps from HUNGARY in 1951, 1953 and 1955. FINLAND in 1947 pictured infant gymnastics on a tuberculosis issue. On a Red Cross issue of 1949 pictures of the Finnish hot bath (*sauna*) can be seen.

In her 300th anniversary pictorial set of 1948 the BAHAMAS depicted motifs from the islands, one design showing the Paradise Beach and another water ski-ing. BULGARIA also depicted beach activities in 1948, and HOLLAND has often shown children playing. Other similar designs have come from the DUTCH ANTILLES (Curaçao) 1951; BULGARIA, 1951; FIJI ISLANDS, 1951 (in the same set as the rugby stamp); INDONESIA, 1955; RED CHINA, 1956; AFGHANISTAN, 1956, etc.

Among 'pastime' stamps are two issues from POLAND in 1956 depicting youth hostels, rucksacks and map, a canoe and a pair of skis.

Hunting, Shooting and Fishing must also be mentioned. There are, of course, a number of hunting and fishing stamps, but few can strictly be called sports stamps. For example, ROUMANIA issued a stamp in 1937 with a picture of King Carol II out hunting. The BAHAMAS depicted tuna-fishing in 1948 and 1954; RUSSIA pictured wolf-hunting in 1949; and CANADA covered both hunting and fishing in 1957.

Chess is another pastime that might be included. BULGARIA had a chess stamp in a sports set of 1947. In 1948 RUSSIA issued three stamps in connection with a chess tournament in Moscow. To mark the World Chess Championship in Budapest in the spring of 1950 HUNGARY also issued three stamps. The 9th 'Olympic' Chess Games were held in Dubrovnik, YUGOSLAVIA, 1950, and were commemorated by a series of five really beautiful stamps. In 1951 a large set was issued by CUBA, to mark the 30th anniversary of Capablanca's world-championship victory in 1921. The 10th Chess 'Olympics' in Helsinki, 1952, were also commemorated by FINLAND, and the World Deaf Mute Chess Championships in POLAND, 1956, produced two interesting stamps. In 1958 a stamp was issued for the 5th World University Chess Championships in Varna, BULGARIA.

Country	No.	Year	Date	Reason for Issue
Afghanistan	1	1957	23.11	National sport *buzcashi*
Albania	1	1946	1.10	12th Balkan Games in Tirana
Algeria	1	1946	9.10	Charity issue
Argentina	1	1949	4.11	World Shooting Championships in Buenos Aires
Australia	1	1954	1.12	16th Olympic Games in Melbourne
	2	1955	30.11	16th Olympic Games in Melbourne
	3	1956	31.10	16th Olympic Games in Melbourne
Austria	1	1933	9. 1	Int. Ski (F.I.S.) Games at Innsbruck
	2	1935	15. 8	Yachting (ordinary airmail stamp)
	3	1936	20. 2	Int. Ski (F.I.S.) Games at Innsbruck
	4	1946	20.10	Austria-Preis in Wien-Freudenau
	5	1947	29. 6	Vienna Derby in Wien-Freudenau
	6	1948	16. 1	Olympic Games 1948
	7	1952	22. 1	Olympic Games 1952
	8	1957	24. 7	Conquest of Gasherbrum II 1956
	9	1958	29. 1	World Ski Championships (alpine events) in Badgastein
Bahamas	1	1948	11.10	Yacht race (in Tercentenary set) (1 stamp)
	2	1954	1. 1	Yacht race (ordinary pictorial issue) (1 stamp
Belgium	1	1920	20. 5	7th Olympic Games in Antwerp
	2	1950	1. 7	European Athletic Championships in Brussel
	3	1951	25. 7	50th Anniversary Royal Belgium Aero Club (1 stamp)
Bermuda	1	1936–1940		Yacht (ordinary pictorial issue) (1 stamp)
	2	1953	9.11	Racing dinghy (ordinary pictorial issue (1 stamp)
	3	1956	22. 6	50th Anniversary Ocean Race
Bolivia	1	1948	23.10	South American Grand Prix
	2	1951	18. 7	2nd Sports Congress, 5th South American Championships in La Paz, South American Tennis Championships, etc.
Brazil	1	1950	27. 6	4th World Football Championships in Rio de Janeiro
	2	1951	19.10	50th Anniversary of Santos Dumont (1 stamp
	3	1952	21. 7	50th Anniversary of Fluminense F.C.
	4	1954	23.10	2nd World Basketball Championships in Rio de Janeiro
	5	1954	6.11	6th Spring Games (for women and girls)
	6	1955	30. 4	5th Children's Games (for children 6–15 years
	7	1955	12.11	7th Spring Games
	8	1956	30. 4	6th Children's Games
	9	1956	22. 9	8th Spring Games

Observations	*Events* (*for abbreviations see table 3*)	*No. of Stamps*
	Na	1
	Ath	7
so imperf.	Spo	1
DC spec. cancell.	Sho	1
	OG	1
	OG	1
DC '55 spec. cancell.	OG	4
ec. cancell.	Ski	4
so imperf.	Ya	1
so imperf., spec. cancell.	Ski	4
ec. cancell.	Eq	5
ec. cancell.	Eq	1
	OG	1
	OG	1
DC	Mt	1
DC spec. cancell.	Ski	1
so water ski-ing and tuna fishing	Ya	1
so water ski-ing and tuna fishing	Ya	1
ec. cancell.; supplementary stamps with surcharge 1921	OG, Ath	3
so imperf., spec. cancell., spec. sheet	Ath	5
so imperf., also with aeroplane in spec. sheet (18.6)	Fl	1
fferent colours: 14.4.1936; 20.1.1938; 12.11.1940	Ya	3
	Ya	1
	Ya	2
	Mo	2
	Aq, Ath, Bk, Bx, Cy, Eq, Fe, Fo, Pe, Ski, Te, Spo	14
ec. cancell.	Fo	3
	Fl	1
ec. cancell	Spo	1
ec. cancell.	Bk	1
ec. cancell.	Spo	1
ec. cancell.	Ath	1
ec. cancell.	Gy	1
ec. cancell.	Ath	1
ec. cancell.	Ath	1

Country	*No.*	*Year*	*Date*	*Reason for Issue*
Brazil (cont.)	10	1957	27. 4	7th Children's Games
	11	1957	28. 9	9th Spring Games
	12	1957	19.10	World Women's Basketball Championships Rio de Janeiro
	13	1958	20. 4	8th Children's Games
	14	1958	14. 9	10th Spring Games
Bulgaria	1	1931	18. 9	1st Balkan Games in Sofia
	2	1933	4. 1	1st Balkan Games in Sofia
	3	1935	14. 6	5th Balkan Football Cup in Sofia
	4	1935	10. 7	8th Junak Games in Sofia
	5	1939	8. 7	9th Junak Games in Sofia
	6	1946	6. 7	12th Balkan Games in Tirana (Albania)
	7	1947	25. 9	13th Balkan Games in Sofia (4 stamps)
	8	1949	5. 9	Sports issue
	9	1950	21. 8	Sports issue—'Fiskultura'
	10	1954	21.12	Sports issue
	11	1954	28.12	50th Anniversary of Trade Unions (1 stam
	12	1956	3.10	16th Olympic Games in Melbourne
	13	1956	15.10	30th Anniversary Bulgarian gliding
	14	1957	18. 3	4th Int. Egyptian Cycle Race
	15	1957	20. 6	10th European Basketball Championships Sofia
	16	1958	20. 6	World Free Style Wrestling Championsh in Sofia
	17	1958	22. 8	International Student Games in Sofia
	18	1958	29.11	Balkan Games in Sofia
Burma	1	1949–1954		Chinlon Game (ordinary pictorial issue (1 stamp)
Canada	1	1935	4. 5	Yacht (George V Silver Jubilee issue) (1 stan
	2	1956	23. 1	Canadian national sport: ice hockey
	3	1957	7. 3	Sports and pastime issue (2 stamps)
China (Communist)	1	1952	June-Sept.	Radio Gymnastics issue
	2	1957	20. 3	1st Chinese Workers' Games 1955
	3	1958	30.12	Air Sports issue (3 stamps)
China (Nationalist)—*see* Formosa				
Colombia	1	1935	26. 1	3rd National Games in Barranquilla
	2	1937	4. 1	4th National Games in Manizales
	3	1937	4. 1	Stadium (Exhibition in Barranquilla) (1 stan
	4	1946	6.12	5th Central American and Caribbean Gam
	5	1954	3. 1	Girardot Stadium in Medellin (ordinary mail)
	6	1954	17. 8	7th National Games in Cali
	7	1957	8. 7	7th Colombian Cycle Race
	8	1957	22.11	3rd South American Fencing Championsh in Bogotá

Observations	Events (*for abbreviations see table 3*)	No. of Stamps
c. cancell.	Gy	1
. cancell.	Vo	1
	Bk	1
C spec. cancell.	Ath	1
c. cancell.	Ar	1
	Aq, Cy, Eq, Fe, Fo, Gy, Spo	7
1931, with colour change	Aq, Cy, Eq, Fe, Fo, Gy, Spo	7
c. cancell.	Fo	6
c. cancell.	Ath, Gy, We, Spo	6
c. cancell.	Ath, Gy, We	5
	Spo	1
) one stamp depicting chess	Bk, Cy, Fo, Spo	4
	Ath, Mo, Spo	4
	Ath, Cy, Vo	4
c. cancell.	Eq, Gy, Ski, Wr	4
	Vo	1
C	Ath, Bk, Bx, Fo, Gy	6
	Fl	3
	Cy	2
c. cancell.	Bk	1
C	Wr	3
	Aq, Gy, Vo	3
	Ath	5
plementary stamps in 1952 and 954, also official stamps	Na	3
	Ya	1
c. cancell.	Ih	1
er stamps show fishing and hunting	Aq, Ski	2
	Gy	40
	Ath, Cy, Fo, We	5
ther stamp depicts aeroplanes	Fl	3
st expensive sports set! (About £100 he set)	Aq, Ath, Fo, Te, Ya, Spo	16
) one provisional stamp with sur-harge (3.11.)	Ath, Fo	3
	Spo	1
inary stamps with surcharge	Spo	2
	Spo	1
c. cancell.	Spo	4
c. cancell.	Cy	2
c. cancell; spec. surcharge (on air nail stamp): 'UNIFICADO' in 1960.	Fe	2

Country	No.	Year	Date	Reason for Issue
Costa Rica	1	1924	8.12	National Games in San José
	2	1941	9. 5	Central American Football Champions 1941
	3	1941	9. 5	Central American Football Champions 1941 (airmail)
	4	1946	13. 5	Central American Football Champions 1946 (airmail)
Croatia	1	1942	25. 3	Model Aircraft Exhibition in Zagreb
Cuba	1	1930	15. 3	2nd Central American Games in Havana
	2	1957	17. 5	Sports and Youth Propaganda (3 stamps)
Czechoslovakia	1	1925	10. 5	8th Int. Olympic Congress in Prague
	2	1926	1. 6	8th Sokol Congress and Games in Prague
	3	1932	16. 3	9th Sokol Congress and Games in Prague
	4	1938	25. 1	10th Sokol Winter Games in Tatra
	5	1938	18. 6	10th Sokol Congress and Games in Pragu
	6	1948	7. 3	11th Sokol Congress and Games in Pragu
	7	1948	10. 6	11th Sokol Congress and Games in Pra (2nd issue)
	8	1950	15. 2	51st Tatra Cup Ski Race
	9	1951	21. 6	Sokol Congress in Prague
	10	1952	2. 8	United Czechoslovakian Sports issue
	11	1953	29. 4	6th Int. Peace Cycle Race (Prague-Be Warsaw)
	12	1953	15. 9	Sports issue
	13	1954	24. 4	Sports issue
	14	1955	20. 1	1st National Winter Spartacist Games Prague
	15	1955	21. 6	1st National Summer Spartacist Games Prague
	16	1955	28. 8	30th Int. Motor-cycle Six-days Race Gottwaldov
	17	1956	25. 4	Sports events in 1956
	18	1956	8. 9	Sports events in 1956 (2nd issue)
	19	1957	30. 4	Sports events in 1957
	20	1957	5. 7	32nd Int. Motor-cycle Six-days Race Špindlerův Mlýn
	21	1958	25. 1	Sports events in 1958
Danzig	1	1938	28.11	Yacht (Winter Relief issue) (1 stamp)
Denmark	1	1937	15. 5	Yacht (Christian X Silver Jubilee issue (1 stamp)

Observations	Events (*for abbreviations see table 3*)	No. of Stamps
imperf.	Spo	3
	Fo	8
	Fo	10
provisional issue with surcharge 947	Fo	3
special sheet; spec. cancell.	Fl	4
	Ath	5
one stamp showing ballet dancing	Aq, Ba, Bx	3
inary stamps with surcharge; spec. ancell.	OG	3
inary stamps with surcharge; spec. ancell.	Gy	4
plementary stamp appeared .2.1933; spec. cancell.	Gy	5
c. cancell; with ppendant tab (overprinted for use in the Sudet'l'd Oct. 1–18 1938)	Gy	2
c. cancell; with ppendant tab (overprinted for use in the Sudet'l'd Oct. 1–18 1938)	Gy	3
c. cancell; with appendant tab	Gy	3
c. cancell; with appendant tab	Gy	4
OC spec. cancell	Ski, Spo	3
OC spec. cancell	Ath, Fo, Gy, Ski	4
OC	Ath, Ca, Cy, Ih	4
OC spec. cancell.	Cy	1
OC spec. cancell.	Ath, Mo, Vo	3
OC	Aq, Ath, Mt	3
OC spec. cancell.	Ski, Spo	2
OC spec. cancell.	Gy, Spo	3
OC spec. cancell.	Mo	1
OC spec. cancell.	OG, Bk, Cy	3
OC spec. cancell.	OG, Ath, Eq	3
OC spec. cancell.	Ar, Bx, Cy, Mt	5
OC spec. cancell.	Mo	1
OC spec. cancell.	Ca, Fl, Fo, Ska, Vo	5
	Ya	1
	Ya	1

Country	No.	Year	Date	Reason for Issue
Dominican Republic	1	1937	16. 8	1st National Sports Games in Ciudad Truj
	2	1957	24. 1	Famous Olympic Victors
	3	1957	18. 7	Olympic Victors in Melbourne 1956 (I)
	4	1957	12.11	Olympic Victors in Melbourne 1956 (II)
	5	1958	30.10	Olympic Victors in Melbourne 1956 (III)
Dutch Antilles	1	1957	6. 8	6th Central American and Caribbean Fo ball Championships in Curaçao
Ecuador	1	1939	17. 3	Victory in the 1st Bolivar Games in Bogotá (Colombia) (I)
	2	1939	17. 3	Victory in the 1st Bolivar Games in Bogotá (Colombia) (II)
	3	1956	15.10	6th South American Women's Basket Championships in Quito
	4	1958	1. 9	South American Basketball Championship Quito
Egypt	1	1951	5.10	1st Mediterranean Games in Alexandria
	2	1956	28. 7	Afro-Asian Festival in Cairo
	3	1958	12. 1	5th Int. Egyptian Cycle Race
Eire (Ireland)	1	1934	27. 7	50th Anniversary Gaelic Sports Union
Fiji	1	1951	17. 9	Rugby (Charity Health issue) (1 stamp)
Finland	1	1938	20. 1	World Ski Championships in Lahti (Nor Events)
	2	1945	16. 4	Sports issue
	3	1946	1. 6	3rd Workers' Sports Games in Helsinki
	4	1947	2. 6	Finnish Gymnastics and Sports Festival Helsinki
	5	1951	16.11	15th Olympic Games in Helsinki (I)
	6	1952	15. 2	15th Olympic Games in Helsinki (II)
	7	1954	26. 2	Centenary of Ivar Wilskman
	8	1956	28. 6	Finnish Gymnastics and Sports Festival Helsinki
	9	1958	1. 2	World Ski Championships in Lahti (Nor Events)
Formosa (Nationalist China)	1	1954	12. 3	Athletic Championships
France	1	1924	1. 4	8th Olympic Games in Paris
	2	1937	18. 1	World Ski Championships in Chamonix
	3	1937	16. 6	Athletics (P.T.T. Sports and Recreation iss (1 stamp)

Observations	*Events (for abbreviations see table 3)*	*No. of Stamps*
	Ath	3
c. sheets; also Hungarian Relief urcharge issue	OG, Ath	8
c. sheets; also Scouting surcharge ssue	OG. Ath, Mp	8
c. sheets; also Refugee Relief sur-charge issue	OG, Aq, Ath, Cy, Eq, Sho, Ska	8
c. sheets; also Geophysical Year sur-charge issue	OG, Aq, Ath, Fe, Ho, Ski, Wr, Ya	8
OC spec. cancell.	Fo	4
linary mail	Aq, Ath, Bk, Wr, Spo	5
mail	Ath, Bx, Eq, Te, Spo	5
ec. cancell.	Bk	2
ec. cancell.	Bk	1
OC spec. cancell.; spec. sheet	Spo	3
	Spo	2
	Cy	1
	Na	1
so one stamp showing children playing)	Ru	1
ec. cancell.	Ski	3
	Ath, Gy, Ski, Wr	5
ec. cancell.	Spo	1
OC spec. cancell.	Gy	1
OC spec. cancell.	Aq, Spo	2
OC spec. cancell.	Ath, Fo	2
OC spec. cancell.	Gy	1
OC spec. cancell.	Gy (also Aq, Ath, Fo)	1
OC spec. cancell.	Ski	2
	Ath	2
so imperf.; also surcharge issues for Lebanon and Syria; spec. cancell.; also non-official stamp (Stadium of Nîmes)	OG	4
so imperf.	Ski	1
so 'pastime' stamps	Ath	1

Country	No.	Year	Date	Reason for Issue
France (cont.)	4	1938	1. 6	3rd World Football Championships in Pa
	5	1943	7. 6	Sports issue (National Relief issue) (1 stan
	6	1953	26. 7	50th Anniversary 'Tour de France'
	7	1953	28.11	French Olympic Victories in Helsinki 195
	8	1956	9. 7	Sports issue (Popular French Sports)
	9	1956	26.11	Olympic Games 1956—Pierre de Coubertin
	10	1957	31. 8	World University Games in Paris—Le Lagrange
	11	1958	28. 4	French National Sports
Germany	1	1935	25.11	4th Winter Olympic Games in Garmisch Partenkirchen
	2	1936	8. 5	11th Olympic Games in Berlin
	3	1936	22. 6	'Brown Ribbon' Horse Race 1936 in Muni Riem
	4	1937	1. 8	'Brown Ribbon' Horse Race 1937
	5	1938	21. 6	German Turn and Sports Festival in Bresl
	6	1938	20. 7	'Brown Ribbon' Horse Race 1938
	7	1939	16. 2	Motor-Racing (Int. Motor Show issue) (1 stamp)
	8	1939	18. 5	'Nürburgring' Motor Race
	9	1939	18. 6	'Blue Ribbon'—German Derby 1939 in Hamburg
	10	1939	12. 7	'Brown Ribbon' Horse Race 1939
	11	1939	15. 9	Sports designs (German Postal Fellow iss (4 stamps)
	12	1940	22. 6	German Derby 1940
	13	1940	20. 7	'Brown Ribbon' Horse Race 1940
	14	1941	19. 5	Sports designs as 1939 but change of col (2 stamps)
	15	1941	20. 6	German Derby 1941
	16	1941	20. 7	'Brown Ribbon' Horse Race 1941
	17	1941	9. 9	Grand Prix Horse Race of Berlin 1941
	18	1942	16. 6	German Derby 1942
	19	1942	14. 7	'Brown Ribbon' Horse Race 1942
	20	1942	8. 8	S.A. Sports Games in Nürnberg
	21	1943	27. 7	'Brown Ribbon' Horse Race 1943
	22	1943	14. 8	Grand Prix Horse Race Vienna 1943
	23	1944	20. 5	Sports designs type 1939–41 (small size (2 stamps)
	24	1944	14. 7	7th Tyrolean Shooting Festival in Innsbruc
	25	1944	6. 8	'Brown Ribbon' Horse Race 1944

Observations	Events (*for abbreviations see table 3*)	No. of Stamps
c. cancell.	Fo	1
	Spo	1
) imperf.; spec. cancell.	Cy	1
C spec. cancell.; also imperf.; surcharge CFA for Réunion (2 stamps)	Aq, Ath, Ca, Eq, Fe, Ro	6
C surcharge CFA for Réunion	Bk, Mt, Pe, Ru	4
C spec. cancell.	OG	1
C spec. cancell.	Spo	1
C	Ar, Na, Wr	4
c. cancell.	OG, Bb, Ska, Ski	3
c. cancell.; spec. sheets	OG, Aq, Ath, Eq, Fe, Fo, Gy, Ro	8
c. cancell.; spec. sheets	Eq	1
c. cancell.; spec. sheets; (same as above with surcharge)	Eq	1
c. cancell.	Gy, Spo	4
c. cancell.	Eq	1
c. cancell.	Mo	1
c. cancell.; (Motor Show issue above surcharged)	Mo	3
c. cancell.	Eq	1
c. cancell.	Eq	1
	Ath, Fl, Mo, Spo	4
	Eq	1
c. cancell.	Eq	1
	Fl, Mo	2
c. cancell.	Eq	1
c. cancell.	Eq	1
c. cancell.	Eq	1
c. cancell.	Eq	1
c. cancell.	Eq	1
c. cancell., surcharged 'Stadt Strausberg 1945' (Russian Occup.)	Spo	1
c. cancell.	Eq	1
c. cancell., surcharged 'Stadt Strausberg 1945' (Russian Occup.)	Eq	2
rcharged 'Stadt Strausberg 1945' (Russian Occup.)	Fl, Mo	2
c. cancell.	Sho	2
c. cancell.; surcharged 'ÖSTERREICH 1945' for use in Austria	Eq	1

Country	No.	Year	Date	Reason for Issue
Germany (cont.)	26	1944	21. 8	Grand Prix Horse Race of Vienna 1944
—, Am. and Br. Zones	27	1949	15. 5	Cycle Race 'Quer durch Deutschland'
—, East	28	1950	2. 3	1st East German Winter Sports Champi ships in Schierke
—, East	29	1951	3. 2	2nd East German Winter Sports Champi ships in Oberhof
—, East	30	1952	12. 1	3rd East German Winter Sports Champi ships in Oberhof
—, East	31	1952	5. 5	5th Int. Peace Cycle Race (Warsaw-Berlin Prague)
—, West Berlin	32	1952	20. 6	Pre-Olympic Games in Berlin
—, East	33	1952	15.10	Centenary of Friedrich Ludwig Jahn
—, East	34	1953	2. 5	6th Int. Peace Cycle Race
—, East	35	1953	10. 8	Sports Hall (Five Year Plan issues) (2 stam
—, West Berlin	36	1953	29. 8	Olympic Stadium (Ordinary stamp)
—, East	37	1954	30. 4	7th Int. Peace Cycle Race
—, East	38	1955	30. 4	8th Int. Peace Cycle Race
—, East	39	1956	30. 4	9th Int. Peace Cycle Race
—, West	40	1956	9. 6	Olympic Year of 1956
—, East	41	1956	25. 7	2nd German Turn and Sports Festival Leipzig
—, East	42	1956	28. 9	Olympic Games 1956
—, East	43	1957	30. 4	10th Int. Peace Cycle Race
—, West and Saar	44	1958	21. 7	German Turn Festival in Munich
—, East	45	1958	22. 7	East German Horse Grand Prix 1958
—, East	46	1958	19. 9	1st Eastern Armies Summer Spartacist Gan in Leipzig
Gibraltar	1	1953	19.10	Yachting (ordinary issue) (1 stamp)
Great Britain	1	1948	29. 7	14th Olympic Games in London
	2	1958	18. 7	6th Empire & Commonwealth Games in Wa
Greece	1	1896	6. 4	1st Olympic Games in Athens
	2	1906	6. 3	Special Olympic Games in Athens (10th Anniversary)
	3	1934	10.12	Athens Olympic Stadium
	4	1937	1.11	Diagoras of Rhodos (ordinary pictorial issu (1 stamp)
	5	1939	1.10	10th Balkan Games in Athens
	6	1940	3. 8	Javelin Thrower (Falangist Youth issue) (1 stamp)

Observations	Events (*for abbreviations see table 3*)	No. of Stamps
ec. cancell., surcharged 'Stadt Straus-berg 1945' (Russian Occup.)	Eq	2
ec. cancell.	Cy	2
ec. cancell.	Ska, Ski	2
ec. cancell.	Bb, Ski	2
OC spec. cancell.	Ski	2
OC spec. cancell.	Cy	1
OC spec. cancell.	OG	3
	Gy	1
OC spec. cancell.	Cy	3
ferent printing processes: photo-gravure and typography	Spo	2
OC: (Athletic match Germany *v.* England)	Spo	1
OC spec. cancell.	Cy	2
ec. cancell.	Cy	2
OC	Cy	2
ec. cancell.	OG	1
OC spec. cancell.	Ath, Fo, Gy	4
OC spec. cancell.	OG, Ath	2
OC spec. cancell.	Cy	1
r the Saar, special inscription: 'Saarland'	Gy	2
OC spec. cancell.	Eq	3
OC spec. cancell.	Spo	3
	Ya	1
OC spec. cancell., overprinted for use in Bahrain, Kuwait, Morocco, Muscat and Dubai and Tangier	OG	4
OC spec. cancell.	Spo	3
pplementary denominations 1900-1 with surcharge	OG, Ath, Bx, Spo	12
ec. cancell.	OG, Ath, Wr	14
	Spo	1
erprinted for use in Albania 1940 and Korfu 1941	Spo	1
ec. cancell.	Ath	4
erprinted for use in Albania 1940	Ath	1

Country	No.	Year	Date	Reason for Issue
Greece (cont.)	7	1954	15. 5	Torch runner (5th Anniversary NATO issu (1 stamp)
Guatemala	1	1948	31. 8	4th Central American and Caribbean Footl Championships
	2	1950	25. 2	6th Central American and Caribbean Gam
	3	1953	18.12	Sports issue (National Festival issue) (2 stamps)
	4	1955	21. 9	50th Anniversary Football in Guatemala
Haiti	1	1939	3.10	Pierre de Coubertin (Olympic issue)
	2	1958	16. 8	Silvio Cator (National Olympic Day issue)
Honduras	1	1949	17. 9	Stadium of Tegucigalpa (Presidential Picto issue) (1 stamp)
	2	1956	7. 9	Stadium of Tegucigalpa (ordinary airm issue) (1 stamp)
Hungary	1	1925	27. 4	Sports issue (Int. Sports Events in Budape (7 stamps)
	2	1941	24. 3	Gliding (Air issue) (2 stamps)
	3	1943	13. 7	Gliding (Air issue) (2 stamps)
	4	1950	12. 3	Sports issue (Five Year Plan) (1 stamp)
	5	1950	26.11	Sports issue
	6	1952	26. 5	15th Olympic Games in Helsinki
	7	1953	Apr–Dec	Sports establishments (Buildings issue) (3 stamps)
	8	1953	20. 8	Inauguration of Nép Stadium in Budapest
	9	1953	3.12	Hungarian Football Victory over England
	10	1954	25. 6	Sports designs (Air issue) (4 stamps)
	11	1955	27. 1	European Figure Skating Championships Budapest (5 stamps 25.2)
	12	1956	25. 9	Olympic Games, 1956
	13	1958	30. 8	European and World Championships in Budapest 1958
Iceland	1	1955	9. 8	Sports issue
	2	1957	1. 4	Sports issue (changed denominations and colours)
Ifni	1	1958	1. 6	Children's Charity issue
India	1	1951	4. 3	1st Asian Games in New Delhi
	2	1953	2.10	Conquest of Mount Everest
Indo-China	1	1944	10. 7	Youth Sports issue
Indonesia	1	1951	2. 1	1st Asian Games in New Delhi
	2	1951	23.10	2nd National Games in Djakarta
	3	1958	15. 8	Victory in Thomas Cup tournament 195 (badminton)

Observations	Events (*for abbreviations see table 3*)	No. of Stamps
	Ath	1
	Fo	5
	Aq, Ath, Fo, Te, Spo	6
	Cy, Eq	2
supplementary stamps (4 c.) in changed colours in 1956 (12.3 and 14.4)	Fo	5
rcharge for the stadium of Port-au-Prince	OG	3
th Anniversary of long-jump world record	Ath	7
so surcharged for Central Bank Issue	Spo	1
so surcharged for official use (different colour.)	Spo	1
00% premium for benefit of sports), one stamp also showing scouting	Aq, Ath, Fe, Fo, Gy, Ska, Ski	7
so imperf.	Fl	2
	Fl	2
so imperf.	Spo	1
so imperf., FDC	Aq, Ath, Bk, Fl, Fo, Gy, Mo, Mt, Vo, Spo	10
so imperf., spec. cancell.	Aq, Ath, Fe, Gy, Spo	6
so imperf.	Spo	3
so imperf., FDC spec. cancell.	Aq, Ath, Bx, Cy, Fo, Gy, Wr, Spo	10
so imperf., FDC spec. cancell., as above with surcharge	Fo	1
so imperf.	Fl	4
so imperf., FDC spec. cancell., (one stamp also showing sledging)	Ih, Iy, Ska, Ski	4
so imperf., FDC	Ath, Bk, Ca, Eq, Fe, Fo, Gy, We	8
so imperf., spec. cancell., FDC	Aq, Ta, Wr	7
DC	Aq, Na, Wr	2
DC	Aq, Na, Wr	2
DC	Bk, Cy	4
DC spec. cancell.	Spo	2
ec. cancell.	Mt	2
rcharged in 1945 for use in Viet-Nam	Spo	2
	Spo	5
	Spo	5
	Bm	3

Country	No.	Year	Date	Reason for Issue
Indonesia (cont.)	4	1958	15.11	Javanese Cycle Race
Iran	1	1953	26.10	Ancient Persian Sports (Shah's Birthday iss
	2	1955	25.10	Iranian Wrestling Successes 1955
	3	1956	16. 5	10th Anniversary Iranian Olympic Commit
	4	1957	8.11	World Weight-lifting Championships i Teheran
Israel	1	1948	2. 5	Sports issue (Jewish National Fund) (1 stan
	2	1950	27. 9	3rd Maccabiah in Tel-Aviv
	3	1953	20. 9	4th Maccabiah in Tel-Aviv
	4	1958	20. 1	25th Anniversary of Maccabi–5th Maccabi
Italy	1	1932	27.10	Sports issue (10th Fascist Anniversary iss (1 stamp)
	2	1933	24. 4	Stadium (Graf Zeppelin issue) (1 stamp)
	3	1933	16. 8	5th World University Games in Turin
	4	1934	24. 5	2nd World Football Championships in Ro
	5	1935	23. 4	4th National 'Littoriali' University Games Rome
	6	1951	18. 5	Int. Gymnastics Festival in Florence
	7	1951	23. 8	World Cycle Championships in Milan and Varese
	8	1952	21. 3	1st Int. Sports Stamps Exposition in Rome
	9	1953	21. 4	20th 'Mille Miglia' Race
	10	1956	26. 1	7th Winter Olympic Games in Cortina d'Ampezzo
Italian colonies	1	1934	5. 6	2nd World Football Championships in Ro
Japan	1	1947	30.10	2nd National Games in Kanazawa
	2	1948	6. 6	25th Anniversary Derby of Japan
	3	1948	16. 9	3rd National Swimming Championships in Yawata
	4	1948	29.10	3rd National Games in Fukuoka
	5	1949	27. 1	4th National Skating Championships in Su
	6	1949	3. 3	4th National Ski Championships in Sappor
	7	1949	15. 9	4th National Swimming Championships Yokohama
	8	1949	30.10	4th National Games in Tokyo
	9	1950	28.10	5th National Games in Nagoya
	10	1951	15. 2	Winter Sports issue—National Park, Zao
	11	1951	27.10	6th National Games in Hiroshima
	12	1952	18.10	7th National Games in Fukushima
	13	1953	22.10	8th National Games in Matsuyama

Observations	Events (*for abbreviations see table 3*)	No. of Stamps
	Cy	3
	Ar, Eq, Gy, Mt	5
	Wr	1
)C	OG	1
)C	We	1
e provisional stamp made valid by urcharge 'DOAR'	Spo	1
)C spec. cancell., with appendant ab	Ath	1
)C spec. cancell.	Spo	1
C spec. cancell., with appendant ab	Ath	1
	Spo	1
	Spo	1
c. cancell.	Spo	4
rcharge and different colours for he Aegean Islands)	Fo	9
c. cancell.	Spo	3
c. cancell., (surcharge for Trieste, zone A)	Gy	3
c. cancell., (surcharge for Trieste, zone A)	Cy	1
c. cancell., (surcharge for Trieste, zone A)	Spo	1
c. cancell., (surcharge for Trieste, zone A)	Mo	1
)C spec. cancell.	OG, Spo	4
	Fo	12
C spec. cancell.	Aq, Ath, Vo	4
C spec. cancell.	Eq	1
)C spec. cancell.	Aq	1
)C spec. cancell.	Ath, Ba, Cy	4
)C spec. cancell.	Ska	1
)C spec. cancell.	Ski	1
)C spec. cancell.	Aq	1
)C spec. cancell.	Ath, Te, Ya	4
)C spec. cancell.	Ath, Eq, Fo, Gy	4
)C spec. cancell.	Ski	2
)C spec. cancell.	Ath, Ho	2
C spec. cancell.	Mt, Wr	2
)C spec. cancell.	Ju, Ru	2

Country	No.	Year	Date	Reason for Issue
Japan (cont.)	14	1954	16. 1	World Speed Skating Championships i Sapporo
	15	1954	22. 5	World Wrestling Championships (Free St in Tokyo
	16	1954	22. 8	9th National Games in Sapporo (Hokkaid
	17	1955	30.10	10th National Games in Yokohama (Kanaga
	18	1956	2. 4	World Table Tennis Championships in Tok
	19	1956	3. 5	World Judo Championships in Tokyo
	20	1956	28.10	11th National Games in Hyogo
	21	1956	3.11	Conquest of Mount Manaslu
	22	1957	26.10	12th National Games in Shizuoka
	23	1958	24. 5	3rd Asian Games in Tokyo
	24	1958	19.10	13th National Games in Toyama
Korea	1	1948	1. 6	14th Olympic Games in London
(South)	2	1955	23.10	36th National Games (80th Birthday o Syngman Rhee)
	3	1956	1.11	16th Olympic Games in Melbourne
Lebanon	1	1936	12.10	Winter Sports (Tourist issue) (4 stamps)
(*see also* France)	2	1955	15. 3	Winter Sports
	3	1957	—	Winter Sports
	4	1957	12.10	2nd Pan Arabian Games in Beirut
Liberia	1	1955	26. 1	Sports issue
	2	1956	15.11	16th Olympic Games in Melbourne
Liechtenstein	1	1954	18. 5	Sports issue (Football)
	2	1955	14. 6	Sports issue (Ski-ing and Mountaineering)
	3	1956	21. 6	Sports issue (Athletics)
	4	1957	14. 5	Sports issue (Gymnastics)
	5	1958	18. 3	Sports issue (Miscellaneous)
Lithuania	1	1938	13. 7	National Sports Festival in Kaunas
	2	1939	20. 5	3rd European Basketball Championships i Kaunas
Luxemburg	1	1952	20. 8	Sports issue (World Cycle Championships i Luxemburg and Olympic Games)
	2	1954	6. 5	World Fencing Championships in Luxembu
Malaya	1	1957	21. 8	*Bersilat* (ordinary pictorial issues) 1 sta each)
	2	1958	31. 8	Stadium of Kuala Lumpur (Federal An versary issue)
Mexico	1	1941	4. 9	National Revolution Games in Mexico Cit
	2	1954	6. 3	7th Central American and Caribbean Gan in Mexico City
	3	1955	12. 3	2nd Pan American Games in Mexico City
Monaco	1	1939	23. 4	Inauguration of Louis II Stadium in Mon
	2	1939	15. 8	8th World University Games in Monaco

Observations	*Events (for abbreviations see table 3)*	*No. of Stamps*
)C spec. cancell.	Ska	1
)C spec. cancell.	Wr	1
)C spec. cancell.	Ar, Ta	2
)C spec. cancell.	Ath, Gy	2
)C spec. cancell.	Ta	1
)C spec. cancell.	Ju	1
)C spec. cancell.	Ath, Bk	2
)C spec. cancell.	Mt	1
)C spec. cancell.	Bx, Gy	2
)C spec. cancell.	Aq, Ath, Spo	4
)C spec. cancell.	Bm, We	2
)C spec. cancell., special sheet	OG, Ath	2
	Ath	2
)C spec. cancell., special sheet	OG	2
o imperf.	Ski	4
	Ski	7
plementary stamps (as above)	Ski	3
)C spec. cancell.,	Ath, Fe, Fo, Spo	4
c. sheets of 2 stamps in different colours (also imperf.)	Ath, Ba, Bx, Fo, Swi, Te	6
)C, highest denomination (40c.) in spec. sheet	OG, Ath, Spo	7
	Fo	4
	Mt, Ski	4
	Ath	4
	Gy	4
	Aq, Cy, Fe, Te	4
o surcharged for a scout meeting	Aq, Ar, Ath	4
c. cancell.	Bk	3
c. cancell.	Aq, Ath, Bx, Cy, Fe, Fo	6
c. cancell.	Fe	1
ues for Kedah, Kelantan, Negri Sembilan, Pahang, Perak, Perlis, Selangor, Trengganu, Malacca, Penang	Na	10
	Spo	1
	Ath	1
	Spo	3
	Spo	3
o imperf.	Spo	1
o imperf.	Spo	5

Country	No.	Year	Date	Reason for Issue
Monaco (cont.)	3	1948	19. 7	Olympic Games 1948
	4	1953	23. 2	15th Olympic Games in Helsinki 1952
	5	1955	14. 1	25th Monte Carlo Rally
	6	1956	15. 4	Olympic Games 1956
	7	1956	15. 4	26th Monte Carlo Rally
	8	1958	15. 5	27th Monte Carlo Rally
Mongolia	1	1958	. 2	Sports issue
Netherlands	1	1928	27. 3	9th Olympic Games in Amsterdam
	2	1949	2. 5	Yachting (Summer Relief issue) (1 stamp)
	3	1956	27. 8	16th Olympic Games in Melbourne
New Zealand	1	1951	1.11	Charity Health issue
Nicaragua	1	1937	10. 7	4th Central American and Caribbean Gam in Panama 1938
	2	1947	29. 8	Horse-track tribune in Managua (ordinar issue) (1 stamp)
	3	1949	16. 7	10th World Amateur Baseball Championsh in Managua 1948
	4	1949–1952		National Stadium in Managua (surcharg stamp in small size)
North Viet-Nam	1	1958	8. 3	Physical Culture issue
Norway	1	1951	1.10	6th Winter Olympic Games in Oslo
Pakistan	1	1954	25.12	Conquest of 'K2' in Himalayas
Panama	1	1938	2. 2	4th Central American and Caribbean Gam in Panama
	2	1950–1952		Sports issue (surcharge stamps)
	3	1957	1.11	Hippodrome (ordinary airmail pictorial issu (1 stamp)
Peru	1	1907	18. 2	Hippodrome in Santa Beatriz (ordinar issue) (1 stamp)
	2	1948	29. 7	14th Olympic Games in London
	3	1956	19.11	16th Olympic Games in Melbourne (onl valid 15.4.1957)
Philippines	1	1934	14. 4	10th Far Eastern Games in Manila
	2	1954	31. 5	2nd Asian Games in Manila
Poland	1	1933	15. 4	Victory in the Int. Round Europe Air Rac 1932
	2	1934	28. 8	Int. Round Europe Air Race
	3	1936	15. 8	24th Int. Gordon Bennett Balloon Race i Warsaw
	4	1939	6. 2	World Ski Championships in Zakopane
	5	1947	22. 2	22nd Polish Ski Championships in Zakopan
	6	1948	2. 5	1st Int. Peace Cycle Race (Warsaw–Pragu Warsaw)

Observations	*Events (for abbreviations see table 3)*	*No. of Stamps*
o imperf.	OG, Aq, Ath, Bk, Ro, Ski, Te, Ya	9
o imperf.	OG, Ath, Bk, Cy, Fe, Fo, Gy, Sho, Ya, Spo	10
	Mo	1
	OG	2
	Mo	1
	Mo	1
	Wr	1
c. cancell.	OG, Ath, Bx, Eq, Fe, Fo, Ro, Ya	8
	Ya	1
C spec. cancell. (surcharge for Olympic team, later Hungarian Relief)	OG, Aq, Ath, Ho, Ya	5
	Ya	2
o spec. sheet, (to promote participa-ion in the Games)	Ba	4
	Spo	1
mail: same designs, another size; also two stamps showing scouting)	Aq, Ath, Ba, Bk, Bx, Cy, Fo, Ta, Te, Ya, Spo	24
ferent colour in 1952 (15.8)	Spo	2
	Gy	2
C spec. cancell.	OG, Ska, Ski	3
	Mt	1
o spec. sheet	Aq, Ba, Bk, Bx, Fo	5
	Ath, Spo	5
	Spo	1
	Spo	
c. cancell., also spec. sheet	OG, Ath, Bk, Sho	4
ne as above with overprint	OG, Ath, Bk, Sho	4
c. cancell.	Ba, Bk, Te	3
c. cancell.	Aq, Ath, Bx	3
o imperf.	Fl	1
c. cancell., stamps overprinted 'Challenge 1934'	Fl	2
linary stamps overprinted	Fl	2
c. cancell.	Ski	4
c. cancell., ordinary stamp over-printed	Ski	1
c. cancell., surcharged 1950 because of monetary reform	Cy	1

Country	No.	Year	Date	Reason for Issue
Poland (cont.)	7	1948	22. 6	7th Poland Round Cycle Race
	8	1951	8. 9	1st National Spartacist Games in Warsaw
	9	1952	30. 4	5th Int. Peace Cycle Race (Warsaw–Berl Prague)
	10	1952	21. 6	Sports issue
	11	1952	28. 6	Yachting (Harbour Workers' Day issue) (1 stamp)
	12	1952	23. 8	Sports designs (Aviation Day issue) (2 stam
	13	1953	30. 4	6th Int. Peace Cycle Race
	14	1953	17. 5	European Boxing Championships in Wars
	15	1953	31.12	Winter Sports issue
	16	1954	29. 4	7th Int. Peace Cycle Race
	17	1954	31. 6	Int. Gliding Competitions in Leszno
	18	1954	17. 7	2nd National Spartacist Games
	19	1955	25. 4	8th Int. Peace Cycle Race
	20	1955	27. 7	2nd World Youth Games in Warsaw
	21	1955	7. 8	13th Int. Motor-cycle Mountain Race in Ta
	22	1956	7. 3	11th World University Winter Games Zakopane
	23	1956	25. 4	9th Int. Peace Cycle Race
	24	1956	2.11	16th Olympic Games in Melbourne
	25	1956	12.12	16th Olympic Games in Melbourne (Krzesinska)
	26	1957	18. 1	50th Anniversary of Ski-ing in Poland
	27	1957	22. 3	12th 'Czech and Marusarz' Ski Race Zakopane
	28	1957	20. 4	World Junior Fencing Championships Warsaw
	29	1957	4. 5	10th Int. Peace Cycle Race
	30	1958	14. 6	6th World Gliding Championships in Lesz
Portugal	1	1928	30. 4	9th Olympic Games in Amsterdam 1928
	2	1952	28. 6	8th World Roller Hockey Championships Oporto
	3	1952	10.12	Stadium (Centenary Public Works Minis issue) (1 stamp)
Roumania	1	1937	8. 6	25th Anniversary Roumanian Sports Uni (7 stamps)
	2	1937	1. 9	8th Balkan Games in Bucharest
	3	1943	26. 9	National Sports Week
	4	1944	16. 3	30th Anniversary Roumanian Rugby Unio
	5	1945	5. 8	New Sports Union (OSP)
	6	1946	6. 3	Hurdling (Youth Sports issue) (1 stamp)
	7	1946	1. 5	Sports Union (OSP)
	8	1947	6. 9	Balkan Athletic Championships in Buchar

Observations	Events (for abbreviations see table 3)	No. of Stamps
c. cancell.	Cy	3
c. cancell.	Spo	1
c. cancell.	Cy	1
c. cancell.	Aq, Ath, Fo, Gy	4
	Ya	1
	Fl	2
c. cancell.	Cy	3
c. cancell.	Bx	3
	Ih, Ska, Ski	3
c. cancell.	Cy	2
c. cancell.	Fl	5
C spec. cancell.	Ath, Fe, Gy	5
C spec. cancell.	Cy	2
C spec. cancell.	Aq, Ath, Bk, Ro, Spo	6
C spec. cancell.	Mo	2
C spec. cancell.	Ih, Ska, Ski	3
C spec. cancell.	Cy	2
C spec. cancell.	Ath, Bx, Fe, Gy, Ro	6
C spec. cancell.	Ath	1
C spec. cancell.	Ski	3
C spec. cancell.	Ski	2
C spec. cancell.	Fe	3
C spec. cancell.	Cy	2
C spec. cancell.	Fl	2
rcharge for the Portuguese Olympic team	OG, Ath	2
ec. cancell.	Rs	2
	Spo	1
so imperf. (also one stamp showing Carol II hunting)	Aq, Ath, Eq, Fo, Ro, Ski, Spo	7
	Ath	5
	Spo	2
	Ru	1
rf. and imperf. (diff. col.); also sheets; airmail stamp in big size	Aq, Ath, Ski, Vo, Spo	11
so 4-sheet	Ath	1
so imperf.; also sheets	Aq, Ath, Fo, Mt, Ski, Spo	8
dinary stamp overprinted; spec. cancell.	Spo	1

Country	No.	Year	Date	Reason for Issue
Roumania (cont.)	9	1948	20. 2	Roumanian Victories in the 13th Balk Games in Sofia 1947
	10	1948	26. 7	Gliding and Yachting (Aviation and Mar issue) (2 stamps)
	11	1948	31.12	Sports Union (OSP)
	12	1950	30.10	Sport and Work (GMA)
	13	1951	28. 1	9th World University Winter Games Poiana-Stalin
	14	1951	9. 7	'Round Roumania' Cycle Race
	15	1952	3. 9	Football (Int. Student Congress issue) stamp)
	16	1952	20.10	Sports issue
	17	1953	24. 3	World Table Tennis Championships Bucharest
	18	1953	21. 5	Model Aircraft (Pioneer issue) (1 stamp)
	19	1953	2. 8	1st World Youth Games (Peace Festival iss (1 stamp)
	20	1953	20.10	Flying Sports (Aviation issue) (3 stamps)
	21	1955	17. 6	European Volley Ball Championships in Bucharest
	22	1955	20. 8	European University Women's Rowing Championships on Lake Snagov
	23	1955	11. 9	European Shooting Championships in Bucharest
	24	1956	29.10	16th Olympic Games in Melbourne
	25	1957	5. 5	1st European Women's Gymnastics Champic ships in Bucharest
	26	1957	29. 5	10th Peace Cycle Race (Prague-Berlin-Warsa
	27	1957	14. 9	10th Int. Athletic Championships in Buchar
	28	1958	6. 4	World Junior Fencing Championships in Bucharest
	29	1958	16. 4	25th Anniversary of Sports Medical Activit
	30	1958	9.12	3rd Youth Spartacist Games in Bucharest
Russia	1	1935	22. 4	World Spartacist Games in Moscow
	2	1938	7.11	Flying Sports (Aviation Exhibition issue) (6 stamps)
	3	1938	7.12	Parachuting (20th Anniversary Komsomol issue) (1 stamp)
	4	1938	28.12	Sports issue
	5	1940	21. 7	Physical Culture Day 1940
	6	1941	17. 2	Riding (23rd Anniversary Red Army issue) (1 stamp)
	7	1946	7. 8	Sports parade in Moscow
	8	1948	23. 2	Sports issue

Observations	Events (*for abbreviations see table 3*)	No. of Stamps
c. cancell.; also in sheets	Ath, Spo	5
	Fl, Ya	2
f. and imperf. (different colours); pec. cancell. also in sheets	Ath, Fl, Spo	6
c. cancell.; also one overprinted upplementary stamp 1952	Ath, Gy, Spo	5
C spec. cancell.; also two over-rinted supplementary stamps 1952	Bb, Ih, Ska, Ski	5
C spec. cancell.	Cy	1
	Fo	1
	Ro, Spo	2
c. cancell.	Ta	2
	Fl	1
	Spo	1
	Fl	3
ec. cancell.	Vo	2
ec. cancell.	Ro	2
OC spec. cancell.	Sho	1
OC spec. cancell.	OG, Aq, Ath, Ca, Gy	5
OC spec. cancell.	Gy	4
	Cy	2
OC spec. cancell.	Ath	3
OC spec. cancell.	Fe	1
	Spo	1
ec. cancell.	Ath	1
	Aq, Ath, Cy, Fo, Ro, Ska, Ski, Te, Spo	10
o aeroplane stamps; overprinted for Aviation Day 1939	Fl	6
	Fl	1
	Aq, Ath, Fo, Ski, Te, Spo	8
	Ath, Ski, Spo	5
	Eq	1
	Spo	1
ur stamps issued 15.9.	Aq, Ath, Fo, Mo, Ski	6

Country	No.	Year	Date	Reason for Issue
Russia (cont.)	9	1948	26.10	Model Aircraft (Pioneer issue) (1 stamp)
	10	1948	29.10	Sports parade (30th Anniversary Komsom issue) (1 stamp)
	11	1949	8. 3	Sports parade (Int. Women's Day issue) (1 stamp)
	12	1949	7. 8	Sports issue
	13	1949	8.10	Winter Sports issue
	14	1951	17.10	Flying Sports (Aviation issue) (2 stamps)
	15	1952	3. 3	Winter Sports issue
	16	1954	29. 5	Sports issue
	17	1956	9. 1	Int. Horse Races in Moscow 1955
	18	1956	18. 1	5th National Trade Union Spartacist Gan in Moscow
	19	1956	5. 8	National Spartacist Games in Moscow
	20	1956	5. 8	3rd World Parachuting Championships in Moscow
	21	1957	24. 2	World Ice Hockey Championships in Mosc
	22	1957	20. 6	10th Peace Cycle Race (Prague-Berlin-Wars
	23	1957	15. 7	3rd World Youth Games in Moscow
	24	1957	20. 7	Russian Victories at the Olympic Games Melbourne
	25	1957	28. 7	Central Moscow Stadium (6th Peace Festiv issue) (1 stamp)
	26	1958	28. 5	Model Aircraft (Pioneer issue) (1 stamp)
	27	1958	5. 6	World Football Championships in Stockho
	28	1958	24. 6	World Gymnastics Championships in Mosc
Saar	1	1949	25. 9	Day of the Horse in Gübingen
(*see also*	2	1952	29. 3	15th Olympic Games in Helsinki
Germany)	3	1955	28. 2	World Cross Country Cycle Championship Saarbrücken
	4	1956	25. 7	16th Olympic Games in Melbourne
Salvador	1	1935	16. 3	3rd Central American and Caribbean Gan in San Salvador
	2	1935	16. 3	3rd Central American and Caribbean Gan in San Salvador (airmail)
San Marino	1	1953	20. 4	Sports issue
	2	1954	28. 8	Sports issue
	3	1955	10. 3	Sports issue
	4	1955	25. 6	1st Olympic Stamps Exposition in San Mari
	5	1955	27. 8	7th Int. Philatelic Fair in San Marino-Riccio
	6	1955	15.12	7th Winter Olympic Games in Cortina d'Ampezzo

Observations	*Events (for abbreviations see table 3)*	*No. of Stamps*
	Fl	1
	Spo	1
	Spo	1
	Aq, Ath, Ca, Cy, Fl, Fo, Mt, Ya	8
o one stamp showing wolf-hunting	Gy, Ih, Ski, We	4
o two stamps showing emblems and military aeroplanes, respectively	Fl	2
	Ska, Ski	2
	Aq, Ath, Bk, Cy, Mt, Ski, Ya	8
	Eq	3
	Spo	1
	Aq, Ath, Bk, Bx, Cy, Fe, Fo, Gy, Ro, Te, Vo, Spo	14
	Fl	1
	Ih	3
	Cy	1
	Ath, Gy, Wr, Spo	5
	OG, Ath, Bx, Fo, Gy, We	6
	Spo	1
	Fl	1
o imperf. 1.7. in small numbers	Fo	2
	Gy	2
ec. cancell.	Eq	2
rcharge for Olympic team	OG	2
ec. cancell.	Cy	1
rcharge for Olympic team	OG	2
er overprinted 'HABILITADO'	Ath	5
er overprinted 'HABILITADO'; one overprinted supplementary stamp 1937	Ath	5
o Rs stamp overprinted for a Stamps Exposition	Ath, Cy, Fl, Fo, Rs, Sho, Ski, Te	9
ec. cancell.	Ath, Bx, Fe, Gy, Mo, Wr	10
y stamp as above but for diff. colour and print	Gy	1
ec. cancell.	OG, Ath	2
ec. cancell.	Ya	1
OC; also 100l. stamp overprinted 1956 for airmail use	OG, Bb, Ih, Ska, Ski	10

Country	No.	Year	Date	Reason for Issue
San Marino (cont.)	7	1956	25. 8	8th Int. Philatelic Fair in San Marino-Riccio
Slovakia	1	1944	30. 4	Sports issue
Somalia	1	1958	28. 4	Sports issue
Spanish Guinea	1	1955	18. 7	Sports issue (airmail)
	2	1957	19. 9	Javelin thrower (30th Anniversary Flight t Fernando Poo)
	3	1958	10. 4	Sports issue
Spanish Sahara	1	1954	2. 6	Children's Charity issue
Sudan	1	1951	1. 9	Nubian wrestling 'sibr' (ordinary pictoria issue) (1 stamp)
Surinam	1	1953	28. 8	Sports Week—Paramaribo Stadium
Sweden	1	1939	25. 2	P.H. Ling Centenary
	2	1943	22. 7	50th Anniversary Swedish Voluntary Rifl Organization
	3	1949	27. 7	2nd Ling Games in Stockholm
	4	1953	27. 5	50th Anniversary Swedish Sports Federatio
	5	1954	13. 2	World Ski Championships in Falun and År
	6	1956	16. 4	16th Olympic Equestrian Games in Stockho
	7	1958	8. 5	6th World Football Champs. in Stockholm
Switzerland	1	1932	1.12	Children's Charity issue (3 stamps)
	2	1944	21. 3	50th Anniversary I.O.C.
	3	1946	1. 5	Aviation issue—Pro Aero 1946
	4	1948	15. 1	5th Winter Olympic Games in St. Moritz
	5	1949	11. 4	Aviation issue—Pro Aero 1949
	6	1950	1. 6	Swiss Confederation Festival 1950 (4 stam
	7	1951	1. 8	Swiss Confederation Festival 1951 (2 stamp
	8	1954	15. 3	5th World Football Championships in Bern
Syria (*see also* France *and* U.A.R.)	1	1957	8.11	Gliding Festival
Tannu-Tuva (Northern Mongolia)	1	1936	—	Sports designs (15th Anniversary Tuvinia Republic issue) (5 stamps)
Trieste, Zone B (*see also* Italy *and* Yugoslavia)	1	1952	26. 3	Sports propaganda
Tripolitania	1	1934	1. 5	Round the Oases Flight
Turkey	1	1940	5.10	11th Balkan Games in Ankara
	2	1943	9.10	Sports parade (20th Anniversary Turkis Republic issue) (1 stamp)
	3	1949	12. 6	European Wrestling (Free Style) Champion ships in Istanbul
	4	1954	20. 9	47th F.A.I. Congress in Istanbul (2 stamps)
	5	1955	30. 8	Victory in the Int. Military Football Champio ships in Rome
	6	1956	8.12	16th Olympic Games in Melbourne
U.A.R. (Syria) (United Arab Republic)	1	1958	.12	Gliding Festival

Observations	*Events (for abbreviations see table 3)*	*No. of Stamps*
ec. cancell., as 1955 with diff. colour	Ya	1
	Aq, Ath, Fo, Ski	4
ec. cancell.	Ar, Ath, Bk, Bx, Cy, Fe, Fo, Mo	10
stamps appeared 20.4.1956, FDC	Fo	5
	Ath	1
	Ath, Bk, Bx	8
DC	Ath	4
so overprinted 'S.G.' for official use	Na, Wr	1
	Spo	3
DC spec. cancell., also 3-sides perf.	Gy	2
DC spec. cancell., also 3-sides perf.	Sho	2
DC spec. cancell., also 3-sides perf.	Gy	2
DC spec. cancell., also 3-sides perf.	Ath, Ih, Ski, Wr	4
DC spec. cancell., also 3-sides perf.	Ski	2
DC spec. cancell., also 3-sides perf.	OG, Eq	3
DC spec. cancell., also 3-sides perf.	Fo	3
	Ath, Na, Wr, Spo	3
ec. cancell.	OG	3
	Fl	1
DC spec. cancell.	OG, Ih, Ski	4
	Fl	1
DC spec. cancell.	Ath, Na, Sho, Wr	4
DC spec. cancell.	Na, Spo	2
DC spec. cancell.	Fo	1
	Fl	3
	Ar, Eq, Na, Wr	5
	Aq, Cy, Fo, Ro, Vo, Ya	6
rdinary airmail stamps with surcharge, spec. cancell.	Fl	7
	Ath	4
so imperf.	Spo	1
ec. cancell.	Wr	4
ne stamp also showing Kemal and military aeroplanes	Fl	2
so in spec. sheet	Fo	3
DC	OG, Wr	2
	Fl	2

Country	No.	Year	Date	Reason for Issue
U.S.A.	1	1932	25. 1	3rd Winter Olympic Games at Lake Placid
	2	1932	15. 6	10th Olympic Games in Los Angeles
	3	1939	12. 6	Baseball Centenary
	4	1948	20.11	American Turners' Centenary
Uruguay	1	1924	29. 7	Victory in the Olympic Football Tournam in Paris 1924
	2	1928	28. 8	Victory in the Olympic Football Tournam in Amsterdam 1928
	3	1951	20. 2	Victory in the World Football Championsh in Rio de Janeiro 1950
	4	1958	14. 1	14th South American Swimming Champi ships in Montevideo
Venezuela	1	1944	12.10	7th World Amateur Baseball Championsh in Caracas
	2	1952	20. 1	3rd Bolivar Games in Caracas 1951
Württemberg	1	1949	11. 2	German West Zone Ski Champ. at Isny
Yugoslavia	1	1932	1. 9	European Rowing Championships in Belgr
	2	1933	7. 8	Sokol Games in Ljubljana (60th Anniversa
	3	1934	1. 6	60th Anniversary Sokol Movement in Zag
	4	1934	1. 6	60th Anniversary Sokol Movement ir Sarajevo
	5	1938	1. 8	Torch runner (Railway Officials' Chari issue) (1 stamp)
	6	1938	11. 9	9th Balkan Games in Belgrade
	7	1939	3. 9	1st Int. Motor Races (Motor Show) in Belgra
	8	1947	15. 6	Sports Festival in Belgrade
	9	1947	5. 9	Sports Games in Ljubljana
	10	1948	7. 9	14th Balkan Games in Belgrade
	11	1949	20. 3	International Ski Games at Planica
	12	1950	2. 7	Sports designs (Flying Sports Week iss (3 stamps)
	13	1950	29.11	Yachting (Naval Day issue) (1 stamp)
	14	1951	7. 7	12th Int. Alpinist Congress in Bled
	15	1951	16. 8	1st World Parachuting Championships in B
	16	1952	10. 7	15th Olympic Games in Helsinki
	17	1953	10. 5	Four International Motor Races in Yugosla
	18	1956	24.10	Olympic Year, 1956
	19	1957	1. 7	2nd Gymnastic Games in Zagreb

Observations	Events (*for abbreviations see table 3*)	No. of Stamps
	Ski	1
	OG, Ath	2
	Ba	1
	Gy	1
ɔec. cancell., also on yellow paper (500)	OG, Fo	3
lso punched for official use	OG. Fo	3
stamp also imperf.	Fo	2
	Aq	2
	Ba	9
lso in spec. sheet	Spo	4
pec. cancell.	Ski	2
	Ro	6
	Gy	2
pec. cancell.	Gy	3
pec. cancell.	Gy	3
	Ath	1
pec. cancell.	Ath	4
pec. cancell.	Mo	4
pec. cancell.	Ath, Gy, Spo	3
	Gy	3
	Ath	3
FDC spec. cancell.	Ski	2
lso stamps showing aeroplanes	Fl	3
lso stamps showing ships	Ya	1
	Mt	3
pec. cancell., ordinary stamps with surcharge	Fl	2
urcharged 'STT-VUJNA' for use in Trieste Zone B (different colours)	Aq, Ath, Bx, Fo, Gy	6
urcharged 'STT-VUJNA' for use in Trieste Zone B (different colours)	Mo	4
FDC spec. cancell.	Aq, Ath, Ca, Fo, Sho, Ski, Ta	8
FDC spec. cancell.	Gy	4

Country	No.	Year	Date	Reason for Issue
Afghanistan	2	1960	. 6	National Sport *buzcashi*
	3	1960	.12	17th Olympic Games (surcharge on *buzca*s stamp)
Albania	2	1959	20.11	1st National Spartacist Games
Argentina	2	1959	5. 9	3rd Pan American Games in Chicago
Australia	4	1960	12.10	100th Melbourne Cup Race
Austria	10	1959	20. 6	World Handball Outdoor Championships Vienna
	11	1959	17. 7	Austrian Workers' Games at Linz
Belgium	4	1960	13. 6	Belgian Parachuting Club
	5	1960	30. 6	Shot-putting (Congo Independence issue)
Belgian Congo	1	1960	2. 6	17th Olympic Games
Brazil	15	1959	20. 1	Victory in the World Football Championshi 1958
	16	1959	30. 5	Victory in the World Basketball Champio ships 1959
	17	1959	13. 6	9th Children's Games
	18	1959	20. 9	11th Spring Games
	19	1959	22.10	World 'Snipe' Championships in Porto Aleg
	20	1960	18.10	12th Spring Games
	21	1960	11.11	World Volley Ball Championships
	22	1960	15.12	Victories of Maria Bueno at Wimbledon 1959–60
Bulgaria	19	1959	25. 3	Youth Football Tournament in Sofia
	20	1959	28. 3	40th Ski-ing Anniversary
	21	1959	8. 9	Youth Festival and Spartacist Games
	22	1959	10.10	50th Football Anniversary
	23	1959	15.12	3rd Parachuting Congress
	24	1960	15. 4	Winter Olympic Games in U.S.A.
	25	1960	3. 6	7th European Women's Basketball Champio ships in Sofia
	26	1960	8. 7	5th World Parachuting Championships
	27	1960	. 8	Olympic Games in Rome
	28	1960	22. 9	10th Bulgarian Cycle Race
Central African Republic	1	1960	15.12	Olympic Games (surcharge on ordinary stam
China (Communist)	4	1959	30. 8	Victory in World Table Tennis Champio ships in Dortmund
	5	1959	10.11	Girl skating (10th Anniversary Pioneer Movement)
	6	1959	28.12	1st National Games in Peking
Congo (Fr.)	1	1960	15.12	Olympic Games (surcharge on ordinary stamp
Costa Rica	5	1960	7. 3	3rd Pan American Football Championshi in San José

Observations	*Events (for abbreviations see table 3)*	*No. of Stamps*
o imperf.	Na	2
	OG, Na	1
	Ath, Bk, Fo, Spo	4
	Aq, Ath, Bk, Bx, Ro	5
	Eq	1
	Ha	1
	Ath	1
	Fl	6
	Ath	1
DC	OG, Ath, Fo	5
ec. cancell	Fo	1
ec. cancell.	Bk	1
ec. cancell.	Eq	1
ec. cancell.	Ath	1
ec. cancell.	Ya	1
ec. cancell.	Spo	1
	Vo	1
	Te	1
	Fo	1
	Ski	1
	Gy	2
e stamp imperf.	Fo	2
	Fl	1
o imperf.	OG, Ski	1
	Bk	1
	Fl	2
rf. and imperf. in different colours	OG, Ath, Ca, Fo, Gy, We, Wr	12
	Cy	1
	OG	1
	Ta	2
	Ska	1
	Aq, Ath, Bk, Cy, Eq, Fl, Fo, Gy, Mo, Na, Ro, Sho, Ta, We, Spo	16
	OG	1
o including one sheet	Fo	7

Country	No.	Year	Date	Reason for Issue
Costa Rica (cont.)	6	1960	14.12	Olympic Games in Rome
Cuba	3	1960	22. 9	Olympic Games in Rome
Czechoslovakia	22	1959	14. 2	Sports issue (World Ice Hockey Champi ships in Prague)
	23	1960	20. 1	2nd National Spartacist Games (I)
	24	1960	27. 2	8th Winter Olympic Games in Squaw Vall
	25	1960	15. 6	2nd National Spartacist Games (II)
	26	1960	15. 6	17th Olympic Games in Rome
	27	1960	28. 8	1st World Aerobatics Championship Bratislava
Dominican Republic	6	1959	15. 5	Polo match: Dominican Republic *v.* Jamai
	7	1959	27. 8	3rd Pan American Games—Trujillo Stadiu
	8	1959	10. 9	3rd Pan American Games
	9	1960	14. 9	Olympic Victors 1956 (IV)
Finland	10	1959	14.11	Women's Gymnastics (Centenary of birth Kallio)
Formosa (Nationalist China)	2	1960	25.10	15th National Games of Taiwan
France	12	1960	11. 7	Olympic Games in Rome (J. Bouin)
Gabon	1	1960	15.12	Olympic Games (surcharge on ordinary stam
Germany (East)	47	1959	10. 8	3rd German Sports and Gymnastics Festiv in Leipzig
—, East	48	1959	23.10	Central Stadium in Leipzig (10th Anniversa of G.D.R.)
—, East	49	1960	27. 1	Olympic Games, 1960
—, East	50	1960	3. 8	World Road Cycling Championships Leipzig
—, West	51	1960	8. 8	Olympic Games in Rome
Ghana	1	1959	15.10	West African Football Championships
	2	1960	15. 8	Olympic Games in Rome
Greece	8	1960	12. 8	Olympic Games in Rome
Guinea	1	1960	12. 9	Olympic Games in Rome (surcharge ordinary stamps)
Haiti	3	1959	27. 8	3rd Pan American Games in Chicago
	4	1959	20.10	As above and Chicago Memorial set especia surcharged
	5	1960	29. 2	Winter Olympic Games in California (a above with special surcharge)
	6	1960	18. 8	Olympic Games in Rome (I)
	7	1960	9. 9	Olympic Games in Rome (II) (25c. surchar
Hungary	14	1959	11. 7	World Fencing Championships in Budapes
	15	1959	15. 7	Yachting (Balaton Tourist set)
	16	1960	29. 2	8th Winter Olympic Games
	17	1960	21. 8	17th Olympic Games in Rome
Ifni	2	1959	23.11	Sports issue—Day of the Stamp

Observations	*Events (for abbreviations see table 3)*	*No. of Stamps*
o one sheet (perf. and imperf.)	OG, Aq, Ath, Ba, Bk, Bx, Cy, Fo, Sho, Te, We	11
c. sheet (imperf. in diff. colour)	OG, Ath, Bx, Sho, Ya	5
	Ath, Ih, Ro	6
	Bk, Gy, Ski	3
	OG, Ih, Ska	2
	Gy	3
	OG, Ath, Gy, Ro	3
OC	Fl	1
	Eq	4
	Spo	1
perf.—surcharge on series 2 (1957)	Ath	8
c. sheets	OG, Aq, Ath, Bx, Fe, Wr	8
	Gy	1
	Aq, Ath, Bk, Fo	6
OC	OG, Ath	1
	OG	1
c. cancell.	Ath, Gy, Spo	5
	Spo	1
c. cancell.	OG, Ath, Bx, Ski, Ya	4
c. cancell.	Cy	2
	OG, Ath, Wr	4
	Fo	5
	OG, Ath	4
OC	OG, Ath	11
	OG	5
	Ath	2
	Ath, Spo	6
	OG, Ath	4
o sheets	OG, Ath, Spo	7
o sheets	OG, Ath, Spo	4
OC spec. cancell. (also imperf.)	Fe	8
o imperf.	Ya	1
o imperf.	OG, Ih, Ska, Ski	7
hest value in sheet (set also imperf.)	OG, Aq, Ar, Ath, Bx, Eq, Fe, Ro, Wr	12
	Ath, Fo	3

Country	No.	Year	Date	Reason for Issue
Iran	5	1959	1.10	World Free Style Wrestling Championship Teheran
	6	1960	9. 6	Olympic Games in Rome
Italy	11	1959	23. 6	17th Olympic Games in Rome
	12	1960	25. 6	17th Olympic Games in Rome
Japan	25	1959	25.10	14th National Games in Tokyo
	26	1960	23.10	15th National Games in Kumakoto
Korea (South)	4	1959	3.10	40th National Games
	5	1960	25. 8	17th Olympic Games in Rome
Lebanon	5	1959	9.10	3rd Mediterranean Games in Beirut
	6	1960	7.12	Olympic Games
Liberia	3	1960	6. 9	17th Olympic Games in Rome
Malagasy	1	1960	13. 4	1st Sports Games in Tananarivo
Malaya	1	1959–1960		*Bersilat* (ordinary pictorial issues as befo
Maldives	1	1960	20. 8	Olympic Games in Rome
Monaco	9	1959	16. 5	28th Monte Carlo Rally
	10	1960	1. 6	29th Monte Carlo Rally
	11	1960	1. 6	Olympic Games 1960
Mongolia	2	1959	6. 6	Sports issue
	3	1960	1. 8	Olympic Games in Rome
Morocco	1	1960	25. 9	Olympic Games in Rome
North Korea	1	1959	2.11	3rd National Games
	2	1960	5.10	15th Anniversary of the Republic, Inaugur tion of Stadium of Pyongyang
North Korea	3	1960	15.12	Sports and pastime issue
North Viet-Nam	2	1958	4.12	Inauguration of Hanoi Stadium
	3	1959	1. 9	Sports issue
Panama	4	1959	26. 9	3rd Pan American Games in Chicago
	5	1960	22. 9	Olympic Games in Rome
Paraguay	1	1960	5. 3	Olympic Games 1960
Philippines	3	1960	30.11	Olympic Games in Rome
Poland	31	1959	3. 1	Sports issue
	32	1960	15. 6	17th Olympic Games in Rome
Portugal	4	1960	2. 5	50th Anniversary of Aero Club
Riu Kiu Islands	1	1960	6.11	8th National Games of Kyushu and Okinav
Roumania	31	1959	12. 9	8th Balkan Games in Bucharest (silver su charge on No. 30)
	32	1959	20. 9	'28th August' Stadium (700th Anniversary Bucharest issue)
	33	1959	5.10	Sports issue

Observations	*Events (for abbreviations see table 3)*	*No. of Stamps*
	Wr	1
	OG, Ar, Eq	2
FDC spec. cancell.	OG	5
FDC spec. cancell.	OG, Ath, Bx, Wr, Spo	9
FDC spec. cancell.	Ath, Fe	2
FDC spec. cancell.	Gy, Na	2
FDC spec. cancell. (also sheet)	Ath	1
FDC spec. cancell. (also sheet)	OG, We	2
	Ath, We, Spo	3
airmail stamps also in sheet (imperf.)	OG, Aq, Ath, Bx, Cy, Fe, Wr	6
highest value in sheet	OG, Ath, Ro, We	5
FDC	Spo	1
issues for Johore (1960), Kedah (new Sultan 1959), Malacca (new coat-of-arms 1960) and Penang (new coat-of-arms 1960)	Na	4
	OG, Bk, Cy	8
	Mo	1
	Mo	1
	OG, Aq, Ath, Eq, Ska, Ski	6
	Ar, Eq, Na, Wr, Spo	8
	OG, Aq, Ath, Eq, Gy, Wr	8
	OG, Ath, Bx, Cy, Fe, Gy, We, Wr, Ya	8
	Spo	1
	Aq, Ath, Cy, Fo, Gy, We, Spo	7
also 'play' motifs	Ar, Wr (Na)	2
	Fo	4
	Aq, So, Wr (Na)	3
	Aq, Ath, Ba, Bk, Bx, Fo	6
two highest values also in sheet	OG, Ath, Bk, Cy, Fe, Fo	6
highest value printed in a sheet is a forgery. FDC	OG, Bk, Fo	7
	OG, Aq, Ath, Bk, Sho	4
spec. cancell.	Ar, Eq, Fo, Ya	4
the stamps were printed together in sheets of four, FDC	OG, Ath, Bx, Cy, Eq	8
also one stamp showing aeroplane	Fl	3
	Ath, Spo	2
spec. cancell.	Ath	1
	Spo	1
	Bx, Eq, Fo, Ha, Ih, Mo, Ru, Te	9

Country	No.	Year	Date	Reason for Issue
Roumania (cont.)	34	1960	5. 6	Olympic Games in Rome (I)
	35	1960	15. 6	Olympic Games in Rome (similar designs as above plus two stamps in souvenir sheets)
	36	1960	15. 6	Parachuting issue—Aviation Day
	37	1960	3. 7	Sprinter (ordinary issue)
Ruanda Urundi	1	1960	2. 5	Olympic Games in Rome
Russia	29	1959	5. 2	Women's World Speed Skating Championships in Sverdlovsk
	30	1959	12. 2	'Victory' in the World Basketball Championships in Chile
	31	1959	7. 8	2nd National Spartacist Games
	32	1959	28.10	Military Sports issue
	33	1960	18. 2	8th Winter Olympic Games in Squaw Valley
	34	1960	8. 8	17th Olympic Games in Rome
St. Pierre and Miquelon	1	1959	25. 9	Sports issue
San Marino	8	1959	19. 5	Famous I.O.C. members (joining by San Marino of the I.O.C.)
	9	1959	29. 8	World University Games in Turin
	10	1960	23. 5	Olympic Games in Rome
	11	1960	27. 8	Olympic Games in Rome (same design as above in three imperf. sheets)
Siam (*see* Thailand)				
Somalia	2	1960	24.11	Olympic Games
Spain	1	1960	26. 3	1st Philatelic Congress in Barcelona
	2	1960	31.10	Sports issue
Spanish Guinea	4	1959	23.11	Sports issue—Day of Stamp
Sudan	2	1960	25. 8	Olympic Games in Rome
Surinam	2	1960	10. 8	Olympic Games in Rome
Sweden	8	1960	30. 6	Centenary of the Voluntary Shooting Movement
Tchad	1	1960	15.12	Olympic Games (surcharge on ordinary stamp)
Thailand	1	1959	15.10	S.E.A.P. Games in Bangkok
Togo	1	1960	27. 3	Olympic Games 1960
Tunisia	1	1960	25. 8	1st Tunisian participation in the Olympic Games
Turkey	7	1959	21. 5	European Basketball Championships in Istanbul
	8	1960	25. 8	Olympic Games in Rome
U.A.R. (Egypt)	2	1960	23. 7	8th Anniversary of the Revolution
U.A.R. (Syria)	3	1960	27.12	Olympic Games
U.S.A.	5	1959	27. 8	Pan American Games in Chicago
	6	1960	18. 2	8th Winter Olympic Games in Squaw Valley

Observations	Events (*for abbreviations see table 3*)	No. of Stamps
erf. and imperf. printed together so as to form the Olympic rings. FDC	OG, Aq, Ath, Bx, Ca, Gy	5
erf. and imperf. FDC	OG, Aq, Ath, Bx, Ca, Fo, Gy	8
lso stamps showing pioneer airmen	Fl	1
	Ath	1
ame design as Belgian Congo but for different colours. FDC	OG, Ath, Fo	5
	Ska	2
asketball stamp of 1954 (surcharged)	Bk	1
pec. cancell.	Aq, Ath, Gy, Spo	4
	Aq, Fl, Mo	4
DC spec. cancell.	OG, Ih, Ska, Ski	5
DC spec. cancell.	OG, Aq, Ath, Bk, Bx, Ca, Eq, Fe, Gy, We, Wr	10
	Ih	1
DC spec. cancell.	OG	7
DC spec. cancell.	Ath	1
DC spec. cancell.	OG, Aq, Ath, Bk, Bx, Cy, Eq, Fe, Fo, Gy, Ho, Ro, Sho	14
DC spec. cancell.	OG, Aq, Ath, Bk, Bx, Cy, Eq, Fe, Fo, Gy, Ho, Ro, Sho	3
	OG, Ath	4
	Pe	4
	Ath, Cy, Eq, Fo, Gy, Pe, Rs	14
	Cy	2
	OG, Fo	3
DC	OG, Aq, Ath, Bk, Fo	5
lso one stamp showing volunteer riflemen of 1860. FDC spec. cancell.	Sho	1
	OG	1
	Ar, Spo	4
	OG, Ath, Bb, Bx, Cy, Ih, Ski	7
	OG, Ath, Bk, Cy, Te	5
	Bk	1
	OG, Ath, Bk, Eq, Fo, Wr	5
ighest value in sheet FDC	Aq, Bk, Eq, Fe, Fo, Ro, We, Spo	8
	OG, Aq, Bk, Eq, Fe	4
DC spec. cancell.	Ath	1
DC spec. cancell.	OG	1

Country	No.	Year	Date	Reason for Issue
Venezuela	3	1959	10. 3	8th Central American Games in Caracas
	4	1959	10. 3	8th Central American Games in Carac (airmail)
Yemen	1	1960	.12	Olympic Games
Yugoslavia	20	1959	26. 6	Partisan Games
	21	1960	25. 4	Olympic Games 1960

Observations	Events (*for abbreviations see table 3*)	No. of Stamps
	Spo	5
	Spo	5
also one sheet (imperf.)	OG	5
spec. cancell.	Aq, Ath, Gy, Ha, Na, Spo	8
	OG, Aq, Ath, Cy, Eq, Fe, Ski, Wr, Ya	8

TABLE 2

SPORTS STAMPS—Sets in Chronological Order 1896–1960

Italics denote first sports stamp issue

Year	*Country*	*Set No.*
1896	*Greece*	1
1906	Greece	2
1907	*Peru*	1
1920	*Belgium*	1
1924	*France*	1
	Uruguay	1
	Costa Rica	1
1925	*Hungary*	1
	Czechoslovakia	1
1926	Czechoslovakia	2
1928	*Netherlands*	1
	Portugal	1
	Uruguay	2
1930	*Cuba*	1
1931	*Bulgaria*	1
1932	*U.S.A.*	1
	Czechoslovakia	3
	U.S.A.	2
	Yugoslavia	1
	Italy	1
	Switzerland	1
1933	*Austria*	1
	Bulgaria	2
	Poland	1
	Italy	2
	Italy	3
	Yugoslavia	2
1934	*Philippines*	1
	Tripolitania	1
	Italy	4
	Yugoslavia	3
	Yugoslavia	4
	Italian Colonies	1
	Eire	1
	Poland	2
	Greece	3
1935	*Colombia*	1
	Salvador	1
	Salvador	2
	Russia	1
	Italy	5
	Canada	1
	Bulgaria	3
	Bulgaria	4
	Austria	2
	Germany	1
1936	Austria	3
	Tannu-Tuva	1
	Germany	2
	Bermuda	1
	(also 1938 and 1940)	
	Germany	3
	Poland	3
	Lebanon	1
1937	Colombia	2
	Colombia	3
	France	2
	Denmark	1
	Roumania	1
	France	3
	Nicaragua	1
	Germany	4
	Dominican Republic	1
	Roumania	2
	Greece	4
1938	*Finland*	1
	Bermuda	1
	(also 1936 and 1940)	
	Czechoslovakia	4
	Panama	1
	France	4
	Czechoslovakia	5
	Germany	5
	Lithuania	1
	Germany	6
	Yugoslavia	5
	Yugoslavia	6
	Russia	2
	Danzig	1
	Russia	3
	Russia	4
1939	Poland	4
	Germany	7
	Sweden	1

Year	Country	Set No.
1939	*Ecuador*	1
	Ecuador	2
	Monaco	1
	Germany	8
	Lithuania	2
	U.S.A.	3
	Germany	9
	Bulgaria	5
	Germany	10
	Monaco	2
	Yugoslavia	7
	Germany	1
	Greece	5
	Haiti	1
1940	Germany	12
	Germany	13
	Russia	5
	Greece	6
	Turkey	1
	Bermuda	1
	(also 1936 and 1938)	
1941	Russia	6
	Hungary	2
	Costa Rica	2
	Costa Rica	3
	Germany	14
	Germany	15
	Germany	16
	Mexico	1
	Germany	17
1942	*Croatia*	1
	Germany	18
	Germany	19
	Germany	20
1943	France	5
	Hungary	3
	Sweden	2
	Germany	21
	Germany	22
	Roumania	3
	Turkey	2
1944	Roumania	4
	Slovakia	1
	Switzerland	2
	Indo-China	1
	Germany	23
	Germany	24
	Germany	25
	Germany	26
	Venezuela	1
1945	Finland	2
	Roumania	5
1946	Switzerland	3
	Roumania	6
	Roumania	7
	Costa Rica	4
	Finland	3
	Bulgaria	6
	Russia	7
	Albania	1
	Algeria	1
	Austria	4
	Colombia	4
1947	Poland	5
	Finland	4
	Yugoslavia	8
	Austria	5
	Nicaragua	2
	Yugoslavia	9
	Roumania	8
	Bulgaria	7
	Japan	1
1948	Switzerland	4
	Austria	6
	Roumania	9
	Russia	8
	Czechoslovakia	6
	Poland	6
	Israel	1
	Korea	1
	Japan	2
	Czechoslovakia	7
	Poland	7
	Monaco	3
	Peru	2
	Roumania	10
	Great Britain	1
	Guatemala	1
	Japan	3
	Russia	9
	Russia	10
	Japan	4
	Bahamas	1
	Yugoslavia	10
	Bolivia	1
	U.S.A.	4

Year	Country	Set No.
1948	Roumania	11
1949	*Burma*	1
	(also 1952 and 1954)	
	Württemberg	1
	Japan	5
	Japan	6
	Yugoslavia	11
	Switzerland	5
	Netherlands	2
	Russia	11
	Germany (WZ)	27
	Turkey	3
	Nicaragua	3
	Nicaragua	4
	(also 1952)	
	Sweden	3
	Russia	12
	Bulgaria	8
	Japan	7
	Honduras	1
	Saar	1
	Russia	13
	Japan	8
	Argentina	1
1950	Czechoslovakia	8
	Hungary	4
	Germany (E)	28
	Guatemala	2
	Switzerland	6
	Brazil	1
	Belgium	2
	Yugoslavia	12
	Bulgaria	9
	Israel	2
	Japan	9
	Roumania	12
	Hungary	5
	Yugoslavia	13
	Panama	2
	(also 1951 and 1952)	
1951	*Indonesia*	1
	Roumania	13
	Germany (E)	29
	Japan	10
	Uruguay	3
	India	1
	Italy	6
	Belgium	3
	Czechoslovakia	9
	Yugoslavia	14
	Roumania	14
	Bolivia	2
	Panama	2
	(also 1950 and 1952)	
	Switzerland	7
	Yugoslavia	15
	Italy	7
	Sudan	1
	Poland	8
	Fiji	1
	Norway	1
	Egypt	1
	Russia	14
	Brazil	2
	Indonesia	2
	Japan	11
	New Zealand	1
	Finland	5
1952	Panama	2
	(also 1950 and 1951)	
	Germany (E)	30
	Venezuela	2
	Austria	7
	Finland	6
	Russia	15
	Italy	8
	Saar	2
	Trieste B	1
	Poland	9
	Germany (E)	31
	Hungary	6
	Germany (WB)	32
	China C	1
	Poland	10
	Portugal	2
	Poland	11
	Panama	2
	(also 1950 and 1951)	
	Yugoslavia	16
	Brazil	3
	Czechoslovakia	10
	Luxemburg	1
	Poland	12
	Burma	1
	(also 149 and 1957)	
	Roumania	15

Year	Country	Set No.
1952	Panama (also 1950 and 1951)	2
	Germany (E)	33
	Japan	12
	Roumania	16
	Portugal	3
	Nicaragua (also 1949)	3
1953	Monaco	4
	Roumania	4
	Hungary (also later)	7
	Italy	9
	San Marino	1
	Czechoslovakia	11
	Poland	13
	Germany (E)	34
	Yugoslavia	17
	Poland	14
	Roumania	18
	Sweden	4
	Hungary (also earlier and later)	7
	France	6
	Roumania	19
	Germany (E)	35
	Hungary	8
	Surinam	1
	Germany (WB)	36
	Czechoslovakia	12
	Israel	3
	India	2
	Gibraltar	1
	Roumania	20
	Japan	13
	Iran	1
	Bermuda	2
	France	7
	Hungary (also earlier)	7
	Guatemala	3
	Poland	15
1954	Bahamas	2
	Colombia	5
	Burma (also 1949 and 1952)	1
	Japan	14
	Sweden	5
	Finland	7
	Mexico	2
	Formosa	1
	Switzerland	8
	Greece	7
	Czechoslovakia	13
	Poland	16
	Germany (E)	37
	Luxemburg	2
	Liechtenstein	1
	Japan	15
	Russia	16
	Philippines	2
	Spanish Sahara	1
	Hungary	10
	Poland	17
	Poland	18
	Colombia	6
	Japan	16
	San Marino	2
	Bulgaria	10
	Turkey	4
	Brazil	4
	Brazil	5
	Australia	1
	Bulgaria	11
	Pakistan	1
1955	Monaco	5
	Czechoslovakia	14
	Liberia	1
	Hungary	11
	Saar	3
	San Marino	3
	Mexico	3
	Lebanon	2
	Poland	19
	Germany (E)	38
	Brazil	6
	Liechtenstein	2
	Roumania	21
	Czechoslovakia	15
	San Marino	4
	Spanish Guinea (also 1956)	1
	Poland	20
	Poland	21
	Iceland	1
	San Marino	5

Year	Country	Set No.
1955	Roumania	22
	Czechoslovakia	16
	Turkey	5
	Roumania	23
	Korea (S)	2
	Guatemala (also 1956)	4
	Japan	17
	Brazil	7
	Iran	2
	Australia	2
	San Marino	6
1956	Russia	17
	Russia	18
	Canada	2
	Italy	10
	Poland	22
	Japan	18
	Monaco	6
	Monaco	7
	Sweden	6
	Spanish Guinea (also 1955)	1
	Guatemala (also 1955)	4
	Poland	23
	Czechoslovakia	17
	Brazil	8
	Germany (E)	39
	Japan	19
	Iran	3
	Germany (W)	40
	Liechtenstein	3
	Bermuda	3
	Finland	8
	France	8
	Saar	4
	Germany (E)	41
	Egypt	2
	Honduras	2
	Russia	19
	Russia	20
	San Marino	7
	Netherlands	3
	Czechoslovakia	18
	Brazil	9
	Hungary	12
	Germany (E)	42
	Bulgaria	12
	Ecuador	3
	Bulgaria	13
	Yugoslavia	18
	Japan	20
	Roumania	24
	Australia	3
	Poland	24
	Japan	21
	Liberia	2
	France	9
	Korea (S)	3
	Peru	3
	Turkey	6
	Poland	25
1957	Poland	26
	Dominican Republic	2
	Russia	21
	Canada	3
	Bulgaria	14
	China	2
	Poland	27
	Iceland	2
	Poland	28
	Brazil	10
	Germany (E)	43
	Czechoslovakia	19
	Poland	29
	Roumania	25
	Liechtenstein	4
	Cuba	2
	Roumania	26
	Bulgaria	15
	Russia	22
	Yugoslavia	19
	Czechoslovakia	20
	Colombia	7
	Russia	23
	Dominican Republic	3
	Russia	24
	Austria	8
	Russia	25
	Lebanon	3
	Dutch Antilles	1
	Malaya (also 1959 and 1960)	1
	France	10
	Roumania	27

Year	Country	Set No.
1957	Spanish Guinea	2
	Brazil	11
	Lebanon	4
	Brazil	12
	Japan	22
	Panama	3
	Iran	4
	Syria	1
	Dominican Republic	4
	Colombia	8
	Afghanistan	1
1958	Egypt	3
	Uruguay	4
	Israel	4
	Czechoslovakia	21
	Austria	9
	Finland	9
	Mongolia	1
	North Viet-Nam	1
	Liechtenstein	5
	Roumania	28
	Spanish Guinea	3
	Roumania	29
	Brazil	13
	France	11
	Somalia	1
	Sweden	7
	Monaco	8
	Japan	23
	Russia	26
	Ifni	1
	Russia	27
	Poland	30
	Bulgaria	16
	Russia	28
	Great Britain	2
	Germany (W & S)	44
	Germany (E)	45
	Indonesia	3
	Haiti	2
	Hungary	13
	Malaya	2
	Ecuador	4
	Brazil	14
	Germany (E)	46
	Bulgaria	17
	Japan	24
	Dominican Republic	5
	Indonesia	4
	Bulgaria	18
	Roumania	30
	U.A.R. (S)	1
	China (C)	3
	North Viet-Nam	2
1959	Poland	31
	Brazil	15
	Russia	29
	Russia	30
	Czechoslovakia	22
	Venezuela	3
	Venezuela	4
	Bulgaria	19
	Bulgaria	20
	Mongolia	2
	Dominican Republic	6
	Monaco	9
	San Marino	8
	Turkey	7
	Brazil	16
	Brazil	17
	Austria	10
	Italy	11
	Yugoslavia	20
	Malaya (also 1957 and 1960)	1
	Hungary	14
	Hungary	15
	Austria	11
	Russia	31
	Germany (E)	47
	U.S.A.	5
	Haiti	3
	Dominican Republic	7
	San Marino	9
	China (C)	4
	North Viet-Nam	3
	Argentina	2
	Bulgaria	21
	Dominican Republic	8
	St. Pierre and Miquelon	1
	Roumania	31
	Brazil	18
	Panama	4
	Iran	5
	Korea (S)	4
	Roumania	32

Year	Country	Set No.
1959	Bulgaria	22
	Lebanon	5
	Ghana	1
	Thailand	1
	Haiti	4
	Brazil	19
	Germany (E)	48
	Japan	25
	Russia	32
	Roumania	33
	North Korea	1
	China (C)	5
	Finland	10
	Albania	2
	Spanish Guinea	4
	Ifni	2
	Bulgaria	23
	China (C)	6
1960	Czechoslovakia	23
	Germany (E)	49
	U.S.A.	6
	Russia	33
	Czechoslovakia	24
	Hungary	16
	Haiti	5
	Paraguay	1
	Togo	1
	Costa Rica	5
	Malaya (also 1957 and 1959)	1
	Spain	1
	Malagasy	1
	Bulgaria	24
	Yugoslavia	21
	Portugal	4
	Belgian Congo	1
	Ruanda Urundi	1
	San Marino	10
	Monaco	10
	Monaco	11
	Bulgaria	25
	Roumania	34
	Iran	6
	Belgium	4
	Czechoslovakia	25
	Czechoslovakia	26
	Poland	32
	Roumania	35

Year	Country	Set No
	Roumania	36
	Italy	12
	Belgium	5
	Sweden	8
	Afghanistan	2
	Roumania	37
	France	12
	U.A.R. (E)	2
	Russia	34
	Mongolia	3
	Germany (E)	50
	Bulgaria	26
	Germany (W)	51
	Surinam	2
	Greece	8
	Ghana	2
	Haiti	6
	Maldives	1
	Hungary	17
	Turkey	8
	Korea (S)	5
	Sudan	2
	Tunisia	1
	San Marino	11
	Czechoslovakia	27
	Bulgaria	27
	Liberia	3
	Haiti	7
	Guinea	1
	Dominican Republic	9
	Cuba	3
	Bulgaria	28
	Panama	5
	Morocco	1
	North Korea	2
	Australia	4
	Brazil	20
	Japan	26
	Formosa	2
	Spain	2
	Riu Kiu Islands	1
	Brazil	21
	Somalia	2
	Philippines	3
	Lebanon	6
	Malaya (also 1957)	1
	Costa Rica	6

Year	Country	Set No.	Year	Country	Set No.
	Central African Republic	1		North Korea	1
	Congo (French)	1		*Yemen*	1
	Gabon	1		*Afghanistan*	3
	Tchad	1		U.A.R. (S)	3
	Brazil	22			

	Afghanistan	Albania	Algeria	Argentina	Australia	Austria	Bahamas	Belgium	Belgian Congo	Bermuda	Bolivia	Brazil	Bulgaria	Burma	Canada	Central African Rep.	China (Communist)
OG Olympic Games[x]	1				6	2		3	5				19			1	
Aq Aquatic Events				1							1		3		1		1
Ar Archery												1					
Ath Athletics		8		1		1		8	4		3	5	15				4
Bm Badminton																	
Ba Baseball (softball)																	
Bk Basketball		1		1							1	3	4				
Bb Bobsleigh																	
Bx Boxing				1							1		1				
Ca Canoeing													2				
Cy Cycling											1		7				2
Eq Equestrian sports					1	6					1	1	3				1
Fe Fencing											1		2				
Fl Flying								7				1	6				4
Fo Football (Association)		1							1		1	4	15				2
Gy Gymnastics												2	15				41
Ha Handball						1											
Ho Hockey																	
Ih Ice-hockey															1		
Iy Ice-yachting																	
Ju Judo																	
Mp Modern pentathlon																	
Mo Motor sports											2		1				1
Mt Mountaineering						1											
Na National sports	4													3			1
Pe Pelota											1						
Rs Roller skating																	
Ro Rowing				1													1
Ru Rugby																	
Sho Shooting				1													1
Ska Skating																	1
Ski Ski-ing						9					1		3		1		
Ta Table tennis																	3
Te Tennis											1	1					
Vo Volleyball												2	3				
We Weight lifting													5				2
Wr Wrestling													5				
Ya Yachting					1	2				6		1			1		
Spo Other sports stamps		1	1								1	3	5				1
	4	11	1	6	7	21	2	16	5	6	16	24	95	3	4	1	67

[x] Olympic stamps showing actual events are also included under their respective sports, and therefore only counted once in the final total.

Colombia	Congo (Fr.)	Costa Rica	Croatia	Cuba	Czechoslovakia	Danzig	Denmark	Dominican Republic	Dutch Antilles	Ecuador	Egypt	Eire (Ireland)	Fiji	Finland	Formosa (Nat. China)	France	Gabon	Germany	Ghana	Gibraltar	Great Britain	Greece	Guatemala	Guinea
	1	11		5	10			40						4		6	1	25	4		4	37		5
1		1		1	1			5		1				1	1	1		1					1	
					1											1								
5		2		6	11			32		2				3	5	3		10	2			19	2	
					/																			
1		1		1																				
		1			2					4					1	1								
																		2						
		1		2	1			1		1								1				2		
					2											1								
2		1			5			1			1					1		15					1	
					1			5		1						1		22					1	
2								2								1		1						
			4		2													3						
2		29			2				4					1	1	1		2	5				11	
					29									5				12						
								1																
					4																			
								1																
					3													7						
					2											1								
												1				2								
																1								
					2											1		1						
													1			1								
		1		1				1										2						
					2			1										2						
					5			1						6		1		6						
1		1								1													1	
					2																			
		1																						
								3		1				1		1		1				2		
1				1		1	1	1										1		1				
16		2			3			1		2	5			2		2		10			3	3	1	
31	1	42	4	13	83	1	1	56	4	13	6	1	1	19	8	26	1	105	9	1	7	45	18	5

		Haiti	Honduras	Hungary	Iceland	Ifni	India	Indo-China	Indonesia	Iran	Israel	Italy	Italian colonies	Japan	Korea (South)	Lebanon	Liberia	Liechtenstein
OG	Olympic Games[x]	18		33						3		18			6	6	12	
Aq	Aquatic Events			8	2									4		1	1	1
Ar	Archery			1						3				1				
Ath	Athletics	16		9		1					2	1		12	4	3	5	4
Bm	Badminton								3					1				
Ba	Baseball (softball)													1			1	
Bk	Basketball			2		2								1				
Bb	Bobsleigh																	
Bx	Boxing			2								1		1		1	1	
Ca	Canoeing			1														
Cy	Cycling			1		2			3			1		1		1		1
Eq	Equestrian sports			2						2				2				
Fe	Fencing			12										1		2		1
Fl	Flying			9														
Fo	Football (Association)			5		2						9	12	1		1	1	4
Gy	Gymnastics			5						1		3		4				4
Ha	Handball																	
Ho	Hockey													1				
Ih	Ice-hockey			2														
Iy	Ice-yachting			1														
Ju	Judo													2				
Mp	Modern pentathlon																	
Mo	Motor sports			1								1						
Mt	Mountaineering			1			2			1				2				2
Na	National sports													1				
Pe	Pelota																	
Rs	Roller skating																	
Ro	Rowing			1													1	
Ru	Rugby													1				
Sho	Shooting																	
Ska	Skating			5										2				
Ski	Ski-ing			7										3		14		2
Ta	Table tennis			2										2				
Te	Tennis													1			1	1
Vo	Volleyball			2										1		1		
We	Weight lifting			1						1				1	1			
Wr	Wrestling			4	2					2		1		2		1		
Ya	Yachting			1										1				
Spo	Other sports stamps	6	2	6			2	2	10		2	18		2		2	1	
		33	2	96	4	7	4	2	16	11	4	42	12	52	9	27	18	20

Lithuania	Luxemburg	Malagasy	Malaya	Maldives	Mexico	Monaco	Mongolia	Morocco	Netherlands	New Zealand	Nicaragua	North Korea	North Vietnam	Norway	Pakistan	Panama	Paraguay	Peru	Philippines	Poland	Portugal	Riukiu Islands	Ruanda Urundi	Roumania	Russia
				8		27	8	8	13					3		6	7	8	4	15	2		5	18	23
1	1					2	1		1		2	1	1			2			2	2				7	10
1							2					1								1					
2	1				1	6	4	1	3		2	1				4		2	2	11	1	1	4	24	16
											8					2			1						
3				3		2					2					3	3	2	2	1					4
																								1	
	1							1	1		2					2			1	5				3	3
																								3	2
	1			5		1		1			2	1				1				17				3	5
						1	6		1											2				2	5
	2					1		1	1							1				5				1	2
																				14	3			8	15
	1					1			1		2	1	4			3	4			2			1	5	8
						1	1	1				1	2							3				8	8
																								1	
									1																
																				2				2	5
						5														2				2	3
															1									1	2
			14																						
																					2				
						1			1											2				4	2
																								2	
						1							1					2	1					1	
						1								1						2				1	6
						2								1						12				6	9
											2													2	
						1					2								1					1	3
																								4	1
								1				1													3
							3	1				1	1												2
						2		1	3	2	2									2				1	2
		1	1		6	7					5	2				5		1		3	1	1		22	15
7	7	1	15	8	7	38	17	8	14	2	31	10	9	3	1	23	7	9	10	90	8	2	5	118	131

		Saar	St Pierre & Miquelon	Salvador	San Marino	Slovakia	Somalia	Spain	Spanish Guinea	Spanish Sahara	Sudan	Surinam	Sweden	Switzerland	Syria	Tannu-Tuva	Tchad
OG	Olympic Games[x]	4			36		4				3	5	3	7			1
Aq	Aquatic Events				1	1						1					
Ar	Archery						1									1	
Ath	Athletics			10	11	1	7	2	5	4		2	1	3			
Bm	Badminton																
Ba	Baseball (softball)																
Bk	Basketball				1		1		2			1					
Bb	Bobsleigh				2												
Bx	Boxing				2		1		2								
Ca	Canoeing																
Cy	Cycling	1			2		1	2	2								
Eq	Equestrian sports	2			1			2					3			2	
Fe	Fencing				2		1										
Fl	Flying				1									2	3		
Fo	Football (Association)				2	1	1	2	5		3	1	3	1			
Gy	Gymnastics				4			2					4				
Ha	Handball																
Ho	Hockey				1												
Ih	Ice-hockey		1		2								1	1			
Iy	Ice-yachting																
Ju	Judo																
Mp	Modern pentathlon																
Mo	Motor sports				2		1										
Mt	Mountaineering																
Na	National sports													1			
Pe	Pelota							6									
Rs	Roller skating				1			2									
Ro	Rowing				1												
Ru	Rugby																
Sho	Shooting				2								3	1			
Ska	Skating				2												
Ski	Ski-ing				5	1							3	1			
Ta	Table tennis																
Te	Tennis				1												
Vo	Volleyball																
We	Weight lifting																
Wr	Wrestling				1						1		1	2		2	
Ya	Yachting				2												
Spo	Other sports stamps											3		2			
		7	1	10	59	4	14	18	16	4	4	8	19	19	3	5	1

Thailand	Togo	Trieste Zone B	Tripolitania	Tunisia	Turkey	U.A.R.	U.S.A.	Uruguay	Venezuela	Württemberg	Yemen	Yugoslavia		
	7			5	7	4	4	6			5	22	564 (131)[xx]	OG
		1				2		2				5	85	Aq
1													16	Ar
	2			1	5		3					13	364	Ath
													4	Bm
							1		9				26	Ba
				1	2	2							59	Bk
	1												6	Bb
	1											1	44	Bx
												1	12	Ca
	1	1		1								1	96	Cy
					1	2						1	81	Eq
						2						1	45	Fe
			7		2	2						5	98	Fl
		1			4	1		8				2	185	Fo
							1					21	178	Gy
												1	3	Ha
													4	Ho
	1												22	Ih
													1	Iy
													2	Ju
													1	Mp
												8	39	Mo
												3	19	Mt
												1	28	Na
													8	Pe
													5	Rs
		1				1						6	27	Ro
													5	Ru
												1	20	Sho
													26	Ska
	1						1			2		4	108	Ski
												1	12	Ta
				1									19	Te
		1											16	Vo
						1							20	We
					7							1	49	Wr
		1										2	40	Ya
3					1	1			14			2	211	Spo
4	7	6	7	5	22	14	7	10	23	2	5	81	2115	

[xx]Olympic stamps unconnected with any specific sporting event.